1980

SPANISH-AMERICAN LITERATURE

in Translation

VOLUME I

A SELECTION OF PROSE, POETRY, AND DRAMA BEFORE 1888

Edited by WILLIS KNAPP JONES

FREDERICK UNGAR PUBLISHING CO.
New York

COPYRIGHT ACKNOWLEDGMENTS

The editor and the publishers are grateful for the cooperation
of those individuals and publishers who granted permission for
the use of their copyrighted material and original translations.
Every effort has been made to trace and to acknowledge properly all copyright owners. If any acknowledgment has been in-
advertently omitted, the publishers will be pleased to make the
necessary correction in the next printing.

Hispanic Society of America. From the *Hispanic Anthology* (1920):
Bello, "To the Agriculture in the Torrid Zone"; Heredia, "Ode to Ni-
agara"; and Pombo, "At Niagara." From *Translations from Hispanic
Poets* (1938): Beatrice Gilman Proske's translation of "Sonnet of Sor
Juana."

University of Oklahoma Press. *Popol Vuh*, translated by Delia Goetz and
Sylvanus G. Morley.

Bulletin of Pan American Union. Vol. 68 (1934): Juan Montalvo, "On
Pichincha," and Vol. 75 (1941): Amarilis, "Amarilis to Belardo."

West Indian Review, IV (1938): Padilla, "Funeral Dirge for Gautier
Benítez."

Carnegie Endowment for International Peace. *Inter-America* IV (1920):
Obligado,"Santos Verga," and V (1922): Mitre, "To America" and
"To Santos Vega."

Read Bain. *La Araucana* and Luaces, "Leaving the Coffee Plantation."

Elijah J. Hill. "Atlantida" in *Colorado College Publication*, II (1915),
and "Ollanta" in *Hispanic Studies* (American Association of Teachers
of Spanish, 1929).

Chesley M. Hutchings. Gómez de Avellaneda, "To Washington."

C. N. Lancaster and P. T. Manchester (trs.). Pedro de Oña. *Arauco
Tamed* (Arauco domado) (Albuquerqué: University of New Mexico
Press, 1948).

Agnes Blake Poor. Olmedo, "To General Flores," Ramallo, "Impressions
at Illimani," and Varela, "May 25, 1838 in Buenos Aires," from *Pan
American Poets* (Boston: Gorham, 1918).

Walter Owen. *Martín Fierro* (and to Holt, Rinehart, and Winston, publishers of the American edition); *Faust* (1943) and *La Araucana* (1945), both privately printed.

To Miami University advanced Spanish students: George Karnezis, Matto de Turner's *Birds Without Nests*; Susan Shelby, Inca Poets; Francis Stearns, Fernández de Lizardi's *Itching Parrot*; and Connie Wick, Núñez de Pineda's *Happy Captivity*.

TO ISAAC GOLDBERG
and EDMUND R. BROWN
editors who early encouraged my translating
by publishing the results

PREFACE

The beginning of Spain's Golden Age in literature is often dated at 1554 with the publication of *Lazarillo de Tormes*. In 1888, with the publication in Chile of Rubén Darío's *Azul*, a collection of verse and prose, the curtain went up on the New World's modernist period with all the exuberance it ushered in. The output of literature since then has exceeded that of the previous four centuries, as can be judged by a comparison of the two volumes of this work, *Spanish-American Literature since 1888* and this volume.

That there is a greater mass of literary production after 1888 does not mean that the period before 1888 was devoid of interesting writings. The New World early influenced all forms of literature. Discoverers and explorers, beginning with Columbus, wrote of their travels and experiences. Priests, slogging through swamps and jungles, told of what they did and saw in accounts, often embellished through imagination, that were as thrilling as mysteries. Europeans and mestizos with European blood set down for posterity the poetry and legends of the original inhabitants of America.

Later, patriots like Bolívar and Morazán put their political philosophy onto paper, and even poets and fiction writers used their crafts to fight Spanish domination. With the increased leisure that followed political independence from Spain, more writers appeared, although often they remained bound literarily to the Mother Country. Drama before 1888 also reflected the New World surroundings and a Spanish heritage, as can be observed in the legendary plays about Indian rulers and the priestly dramatizations of biblical stories, used to help Christianize the Indians. Other plays were imitations of Spain's Golden Age, and many showed French influence. Then as Romanticism developed and merged into the beginnings of the popular theater, gauchos and gringos began to appear on the stage.

Thus, long before 1888, the New World atmosphere had its effect on local writers, and original and contemporary themes and scenes, along with local types, appeared in New World literature. All the phases found in the literature compiled in this volume, *Spanish-American Literature before 1888*, are the seeds sown to flower in Volume II, *Spanish-American Literature since 1888*.

In preparing this volume, the editor had the enthusiastic and unselfish help of many people, whose contributions are acknowledged in another section. But special mention should be made of Walter Owen, who devoted free evenings and weekends to turn Spanish-American literary works into inspired poetry in English; also of a number of my advanced students in Spanish at Miami University who took their first flights into literature by turning Spanish prose into English. My professorial friends, Chesley Hutchings and Paul T. Manchester, willingly allowed their literary labors to be reprinted. And to the editorial staff of Frederick Ungar Publishing Co., especially to Miss Ruth Selden, my gratitude is due for counseling and checking. Many have collaborated to provide whatever merit the volume possesses. To all, my thanks.

W. K. J.

Miami University
Oxford, Ohio

CONTENTS

II. POETRY

JUAN CRUZ VARELA — *Argentina* 218
May 25, 1838 in Buenos Aires 218

OLEGARIO VICTOR ANDRADE — *Argentina* 221
Poem to Atlantis 221

ESTEBAN ECHEVERRÍA — *Argentina* 224
The Captive Woman 225

GAUCHO POETRY — *Argentina* 229
Gaucho Poetry 229

BARTOLOMÉ MITRE — *Argentina* 229
To America 230
To Santos Vega (Argentine Minstrel) 231

JOSÉ HERNÁNDEZ — *Argentina* 233
Martin Fierro 234

ESTANISLAO DEL CAMPO — *Argentina* 243
Faust 244

RAFAEL OBLIGADO — *Argentina* 248
Santos Vega 248

JOSÉ MARÍA HEREDIA — *Cuba* 252
Ode to Niagara 252

GERTRUDIS GÓMEZ DE AVELLANEDA —
Cuba 255
On Leaving 255
To Washington 255

SALVADOR SANFUENTES — *Chile* 256
The Bell Tower 256

MARIANO RAMALLO — *Bolivia* 259
Impressions at the Foot of Illimani 260

RAFAEL POMBO — *Colombia* 263
At Niagara 263

III. DRAMA

CONTENTS

INTRODUCTION

If literature can be defined as the written word preserved for re-reading, then there was no literature in the New World before the arrival of Europeans. Pre-Columbian Indians had no form of writing; the Aztecs used a system of pictography, while the Incas had only the *quipu* with its knots in many-colored yarns to assist the memory.

America's first literary men, consequently, were the explorers, the colonizers, and the missionaries, to whom writing was important chiefly as a means of acquainting the people at home with their achievements and the wonders of their new environment. Perhaps that is why the Spanish word *peregrino* means not only a "pilgrim" and a "traveler," but also a "tall story."

First came Columbus (1451-1506). Though the log of his first voyage has been lost, Padre de las Casas (1474-1565) copied part of it and paraphrased the rest in his *Historia de las Indias* (History of the Indies), started in 1527 and continued almost until his death. Horrified by the cruel treatment Spanish officials inflicted upon the Indians, the priest also included in his book such biting protests of his own that they created the "Black Legend" that has plagued Spain ever since.

Hernando Cortés (1485-1547) sent Emperor Charles V a series of five "Cartas" (1519-1526), or letters, from New Spain with the dual purpose of describing Spain's new possessions to his liege, and of making himself appear worthy of reward for the part he had taken in their conquest.

A different account of Cortés' deeds, and one of the greatest chronicles, was provided by an uneducated, unheroic adventurer, Bernal Díaz del Castillo (1492-1584), whose *Historia verdadera de la conquista de la Nueva España* (True History of the Conquest of New Spain, 1560) was written from the viewpoint of a common soldier. Though formless and lacking in style, with the trivial and the important given equal space, it is full of vitality and reveals the personality of its indignant author, protesting in his old age the inaccuracies of earlier historians.

After the conquest of the hemisphere came its exploration by men who were still essentially medieval-minded, but urged on by the spirit of the Renaissance. The excitement aroused by their deeds and the romance of their environment produced vivid and intense literature, whether their accounts were jotted down on the spot or recalled later in retirement.

Núñez Cabeza de Vaca (1490-1560), shipwrecked in the Gulf of Mexico and forced to wander for nine years across the northern part of New Spain (present-day New Mexico and Arizona), wrote interestingly in his *Naufragios* (The Shipwrecks, 1542) about the Indians who had been both his captors and his friends. And Fray Toribio de Benavente (1500?-1569), who adopted the humiliating name of Motolinía (impoverished), devoted his long life to writing about the history and the languages of his Mexican parishioners.

Other parts of the Western Hemisphere also had their chroniclers. With even greater bravery and under heavier hardships than the armed conquistadors, friars tramped the deserts and the jungles in their sandals, their robes flapping, intent on Christianizing the Indians. They, too, wrote their reports for transmission to Europe. It is no wonder that, for them, a pope removed the requirements for fasting and abstinence from eating meat on Fridays, a dispensation still enjoyed in some parts of the hemisphere.

Fray Gaspar de Carvajal (1504-1584) was the official historian and geographer of Orellana's search for cinnamon that ended with the discovery of the Amazon River, and Pedro Cieza de León (1520?-1554?) gave in his *Crónica del Perú* (Chronicle of Peru) the best account of Inca history until fifty years later when the half-Inca Garcilaso de la Vega (1539-1616) wrote *Comentarios reales de los Incas* (Royal Commentaries of the Incas, 1609-1617), based on what he had learned from his mother's people. Padre Ovalle (1601-1651), a master of style, became Chile's interpreter abroad in *Histórica relación del reino del Chile* (Historic Account of the Realm of Chile, 1646). In Paraguay, Ruiz Díaz de Guzmán (1558-1629), the first American-born historian, combined fact and fancy in his *La Argentina manuscrita* (The Argentine Manuscript, 1612), most of which has been lost.

Other missionary writers, like Padre de las Casas, took a broader view of the New World and its inhabitants. Padre José de Acosta (1539-1616) revealed his Jesuitic training by logical questioning in the writing of his *Historia natural y moral de las Indias* (Natural and Moral History of the Indies, 1590). Its first four parts concern physical and natural sciences; they include thoughts about the origins of the Indians and speculations on why, if all animals came out of Noah's Ark, the New World animals were different from those in Europe. The final three parts deal with "moral" problems of Indian religion, education, and politics.

At least two pre-Columbian prose works have been preserved. After the Indians had learned to read and write, an anonymous Guatemalan wrote *Popol Vuh*, (Book of the People), a collection of precepts and ancient legends in the Nahuatl language. Another unknown author of the sixteenth century translated into Spanish *The Book of Chilam Balam*, a collection of writings by Mayan priests, ranging in subject from religion and history to medicine and astronomy. It confirms the high level of intelligence of the Indians that Padre Acosta claimed.

And so New World prose became a mixture of many cultures; Spanish and Portuguese patterns from Europe, which themselves had been evolved from half a dozen civilizations, merged with Aztec, Mayan, and Inca cultures to produce a literature very different from that of Anglo-Saxon heritage.

In the early 1530's, the Church disapproved of fiction, and Charles V forbade the shipment to America of *Amadis of Gaul* "and other such mendacious histories." On September 7, 1558, the death penalty was decreed for printing, selling, or owning any book banned by the Inquisition, a law that was to remain in force for 210 years.

For a long time there was no writing or printing in the New World. Spaniards in America lacked leisure for writing and had no printing presses. A mother country that discouraged shipments of grapevines to America for fear of destroying the market for Spanish wines could not be expected to permit American printers to compete with printers in Spain, where book production could be more easily controlled by the authorities. Printing presses were first brought to the New World by religious orders, to New Spain in 1539 and to Peru in 1579. Religious books, not secular volumes, were printed. In the seventeenth century, a few more printing presses reached western shores, but they were not imported in any quantity until after 1700. The first newspaper appeared in Bogotá in 1591, followed by one in Lima in 1594, and though they occasionally published poetry, they did not have enough space for fiction.

That does not mean that chroniclers did not occasionally fictionalize the truth in the period after 1598, when bonds between Spain and its colonies began to weaken. Even while protesting the historical accuracy of their accounts, the artist's desire to embellish reality sometimes made them lapse into retrospective wishful thinking.

Son of a wealthy conquistador, Juan Suárez de Peralta (1540?-1595?), though acknowledging his lack of education, wrote of daily life in sixteenth-century Mexico in *Tratado del descubrimiento de las Indias* (Treatise on the Discovery of the Indies, 1589), in forty-four chapters. Though partially based on earlier chronicles, it is interesting because it sheds light on the thinking of the author's contemporaries on Cortés' conquest and the conspiracy involving his son.

Another chronicler, Juan Rodríguez Freile (1566-1640?), frankly claimed the same right as the painter's to interpret his material, and in his *El carnero* (The Sheep, 1636-1638) he combines truth and fiction, anecdote and moralizing, love and witchcraft, in a colorful picture of Bogotá. He began the work at the age of seventy. Another author, writing twenty years after the events he described, and attempting to glorify his father and to establish his own reputation as a soldier and a Christian, was Francisco Núñez de Pineda (1607-1682). He had been captured in 1629 while fighting to put down an Araucanian rebellion in southern Chile and remained prisoner for seven months. His account of this experience, *El cautiverio feliz* (The Happy Captivity) had not only a plot, but a moral, the ennobling influence of Christianity on the savages.

Carlos de Sigüenza y Góngora (1645-1700) of Mexico also claimed to be writing history in his *Los infortunios que Alonso Ramírez padeció en poder de ingleses piratas* (Misfortunes Suffered by Alonso Ramírez Among the Piratical English), an adventure yarn with a belated anti-English flavor. Another belated work was a satirical travel book from Peru named after a Spanish *picaro*, which appeared in 1554, *Lazarillo de ciegos caminantes* (The Guide of Blind Travelers). It was ascribed to Alonso Carrío de la Vandera and signed Calixto Bustamante Carlos Inca, alias Concolorcorvo (Crow-Colored). It narrates a journey from Montevideo to Lima by way of Buenos Aires and other Argentine and Peruvian towns. Its pages abound with partly fictionalized accounts of graft and corrupted officials.

The first book in Spanish America to be called a novel outright was *El Periquillo Sarniento* (The Itching Parrot, 1816) by the Mexican Fernández de Lizardi (1776-1827). Even then, censorship delayed the release of the final volume until after his death. It is another belated picaresque novel, intended not only to depict local customs but to urge their correction. Actually its neo-Classic author had to resort to writing novels when government censorship clamped down on the radical journal he had been publishing.

Lizardi had no immediate followers. Eventually, in 1845, a Realist, Manuel Payno (1810-1894), followed his technique in a fantastic satire of customs, *El fistol del diablo* (The Devil's Stickpin), but then went on to write his Realistic masterpiece *Los bandidos de Río Frío* (The Bandits of Rio Frio, 1889). Altamirano (1834-1893), a full-blooded Mexican Indian, mitigated his crude and emotional realism with elements of Romanticism in *El Zarco* (The Blue-Eyed Bandit), completed before 1888, but not published until 1901.

By now the New World had found its voice, though the tune changed according to the cultural background of its different regions. Following independence there was at first a complete break with Spain and a turning to France for artistic inspiration. French influence blended with native sources resulted in a literary genre that could almost be classified as folklore literature.

Romanticism was in the air. The Argentine Esteban Echeverría (1805-1851) returned from Paris to urge his fellow writers to turn their attention to their own speech and local color. But while Romantics in their poetry, most of them turned Realists in their prose. Echeverría himself could be classified as a Naturalist in 1837 when he attacked the dictator Rosas in the continent's first short story, "El matadero" (The Slaughterhouse). Rosas was also the target of what has been called Spanish America's first novel of real merit, *Amalia* (1851) by José Mármol (1817-1871).

Alejandro Margariños Cervantes (1825-1893), a native of Uruguay, first experimented with *La estrella del Sur* (Star of the South, 1845) before following Echeverría's advice. He wrote the first novel about gaucho life, *Caramurú*, published serially in 1848, and highly regarded when published in full in 1865. His long poem *Celiar* (1852) was practically another gaucho novel.

However, the real spokesman for the gauchos was Eduardo Acevedo Díaz (1851-1921). As a revolutionist and a political exile, he wrote feelingly about civil war in *Brenda* (1876), and about the War of Independence in a trilogy of semi-historical stories that made him Uruguay's greatest novelist. The trilogy's theme was the futility of establishing a civilization based on lawlessness and murder, and his chief character was a hard-riding, hard-living, hard-dying cowboy. *Ismael* (1888) was followed by *Nativa* (The Native, 1890), and *El grito de gloria* (The Shout of Glory, 1893).

If Romanticism tinged the novels of Acevedo Díaz, Realism filled the pages of another River Plate author, Eugenio Cambaceres (1843-1895) who, in his *Potpourri: silbido de un vago* (A Vagabond's Whistle, 1882), was the first novelist to reveal touches of Naturalism. His best-known stories, "Sin rumbo" (Aimless, 1885) and "En la sangre" (In the Blood, 1887), are even more deeply involved in the sordid aspects of life among the lower classes, anticipating the work of Manuel Gálvez (1881-1951), author of *Nacha Regules*.

Farther north, in Cuba, Cirilio Villaverde (1812-1894), though an admirer of Walter Scott, dealt realistically with the customs of contemporary Havana in *Cecilia Valdés* (1839), a novel about a mulatto girl.

Alberto Blest Gana (1830-1920) of Chile started his long career as a novelist in 1853 with "Una escena social" (An Episode in Chilean Society), in which the influence of Balzac is evident. In 1860, when the University of Chile sought to encourage novel-writing by a competition, Blest Gana's first novel, *Aritmética en el amor* (Arithmetic in Love) got the award and was praised for its high moral tone.

Chile was a religious and moral country. That was probably why, when Gana was influenced by another Frenchman, Octave Feuillet, to write a civil war historical novel, whose spirit is thoroughly Chilean, the cover of *Martín Rivas* (1862) declared [it] "offends neither moral nor poetic laws." This novel, in which the middle class revolts against the aristocracy, marked the transition from Romanticism to Realism. Blest Gana was also the author of *Durante la Reconquista* (During the Reconquest, 1897), one of the finest accounts of Chile's struggle for independence (though the country's greatest historical novel is *Pipiolos y pelucones* (Creoles and Spaniards, 1875) by Daniel Barros Grez (1834-1904), a story of the civil war in Portales' time). With a score of books, Gana established himself as Chile's greatest novelist.

Yet a few novelists maintained their status as Romanticists, even in prose. There were three outstanding Romantic novels. One was the idyllic *María* (1867) by the Colombian Jorge Isaacs (1837-1895). He followed the path marked out by Colombia's first novelist, Eugenio Díaz (1804-1865), in *Manuela* (1864), a story about country life. *María* was the first South American novel widely read not only in South America, but throughout the world. The two other important Romantic novels were the Indian novel *Cumandá* (1871) by the Ecuador-

8 SPANISH-AMERICAN LITERATURE

ean Juan León Mera (1832-1894), and the sentimental *Tránsito* by Colombia's Luis Segundo de Silvestre (1838-1887).

The Puerto Rican educator and legal authority Eugenio María de Hostos (1839-1903) is hard to classify among Latin American prose writers. He holds a place among novelists because of his poetic novel *La peregrinación de Baoyán* (The Wanderings of Baoyan), written in 1863 during Hostos' stay in Spain. It is a romantic diary in lyrical prose reflecting the author's philosophy on duty and justice, and stating his political belief that the hope of the Caribbean area lay in unity. Hostos wrote no other fiction, for he was more interested in education than in literature, but he was still considered one of Latin America's important writers.

The Bolivian Nataniel Aguirre (1843-1888) deserves mention for the variety of his novels, ranging from *La bellisima Floriana* (Lovely Floriana, 1874) to his great historical novel *Juan de la Rosa* (1885), intended as the first of a four-volume description of Bolivia's struggle for independence.

From Peru, where one of the first official acts of the independent republic was to create, in 1822, a national library with 1,200 volumes (at that time the largest collection of books in South America), came *La quena* (The Indian Flute, 1845) by Juana Manuela Gorriti (1818-1892). Born in Argentina, she fled with her father to Peru at the age of twelve. She married a half-Indian general who was assassinated while President of Bolivia. In Lima, she wrote a number of novels, chiefly historical. Her obsession with the plight of the Indians, which she voiced in the course of literary gatherings, inspired the Peruvian wife of an English doctor, Clorinda Matto de Turner (1854-1909), to write *Aves sin nido* (Birds Without Nests). It was published serially in a newspaper in 1881, and can be considered the best early statement of the Indian problem. The Indians are pictured as exploited by church and government, a theme that was to be more fully developed later by the Indianists, after the coming of Modernism.

The Dean of Peruvian Letters was Ricardo Palma (1833-1919), head of the National Library and innovator, in 1872, of

Tradiciones, gay anecdotes including a grain of history and a touch of humor. In the next forty years he turned out nine series of them, covering his country's history from the days of the Incas to his own period. Many writers in other countries tried to imitate the form: the Bolivian Vicente G. Quesada (1830-1895?); the Guatemalan José Milla y Vidaurre (1822-1882); and the Mexican General Vicente Riva Palacio (1832-1896), but none quite achieved Palma's success. However this interest in customs, geography, history, and folklore characterized the work of most of the prose writers of Latin America during the four centuries following 1492, and the keynote, even of the Romanticists, was Realism.

Another prose form, the essay, that was to be developed to great heights in the twentieth century, had its start in this early period. Some of the chroniclers would include in their accounts, paragraphs and even chapters on customs, morality, and other subjects. After wealthy literary aspirants began founding their magazines—most of which died after a few issues—opportunities for the publication of essays were greater and more were written, chiefly political. The Mexican Fernández de Lizardi (1776-1827), in his journal of protest, *El Pensador Mejicano* (1812), wrote essays against the Church, the government, and the vices of his fellow countrymen. The Venezuelan Andrés Bello (1781-1865), supplied essays for *El Araucano* of Chile.

Simón Bolívar (1783-1830) of Venezuela expounded his ideas of philosophy and political science in the form of letters. The Ecuadorian Juan Montalvo (1832-1889) boasted that the essays he penned were powerful enough to overthrow tyrants. He also set down his thoughts in essays like "Wáshington y Bolívar," "Elogio de la pobreza," (Eulogy of Poverty) and others, collected in his *Siete tratados* (Seven Treatises, 1882). His imitation of *Don Quijote*, an extended essay, *Capítulos que se le olvidaron a Cervantes* (Chapters That Cervantes Forgot), was published posthumously.

On the shores of the River Plate, Domingo Faustino Sarmiento (1811-1888) and Bartolomé Mitre (1821-1906) wrote patriotic and political essays. Sarmiento's *Facundo* (1845) comprises a series of essays on geography, sociology, and the gaucho and his customs before it finally introduces the figure whose biography it was intended to be.

Eugenio María Hostos (1839-1903) of Puerto Rico is another essayist who comes within the scope of this volume for his writings on education and social problems in *Moral social* (1888). After Modernism, essayists appeared in increasing numbers. José Enrique Rodó (1871-1917) wrote about philosophy, as in "Rumbos nuevos" (New Paths), in his *El mundo de Próspero* (1910). His thoughts about materialism and modern culture are expressed in his lengthy essay *Ariel* (1900). Many other thinkers turned to the essay, especially for literary analysis, but also for sociology and history. Luis Alberto Sánchez (1900 —) of Peru, Germán Arciniegas (1900 —) of Colombia, and Mariano Picón-Salas (1901-1965) of Venezuela are outstanding.

Listed by their countries, others born at the turn of the century are, Argentina: Bernal Canal Feijoo (1897 —), Luis Emilio Soto (1902 —), and Carlos Roberto Erro (1903 —); Bolivia: Guillermo Francovich (1901 —); Chile: Arturo Torres-Rioseco (1897 —); Colombia: Jorge Zalamea (1905 —); Cuba: Jorge Mañach (1898 —), Juan Marinello (1898 —), and Francisco Ichaso (1900 —); Ecuador: Benjamin Carrión (1898 —); Guatemala: Luis Cardoza y Aragón (1904 —); Mexico: Daniel Cosío Villegas (1900 —); Peru: Héctor Velarde (1898 —); and Puerto Rico: Antonio S. Pedreira (1899-1939), Tomás Blanco (1900 —), and Concha Meléndez (1904 —).

Succeeding generations have produced many other contributors to this genre that has assumed such importance in Spanish American literature.

POETRY

Scratch a Latin and you will find a poet, as the saying goes, and it was as true in the early days of Latin America as it is now. Of course the New World produced poets before the arrival of the white man, though their versification technique was different from that of Europe. Repetition and rhythm seem to have been the basis of the Indian songs, judging by the samples preserved and set down in Spanish spelling by the earliest Europeans. Mexican priests recorded Nahuatl poetry, and Felipe Guamán Poma de Ayala (1526?-1615?) and Garcilaso de la Vega (1540-1616) transcribed and preserved some Quechua poetry.

The white men were also moved by the wonder and excitement of the New World to compose their own poems. Despite the scarcity of paper, many verses were committed to writing. There were even poetry contests. The Spaniard Gutierre de Cetina (1517?-1554?), who gained immortality with a madrigal of ten lines beginning "Ojos claros, serenos" (Clear, serene eyes), took part in such a contest during a visit to Mexico in 1585. And it was in one of these competitions that Ruiz de Alarcón gained his only success in his native country. In one contest, more than 2,000 poems were entered.

Another Spaniard who came to the New World in his youth to make his permanent home was Juan de Castellanos (1522-1607). He must have spent much of his time writing poetry because his 150,000-line *Elegías de varones ilustres de Indias* (Elegies of Famous Men of the Indies, 1589) is the longest poem in Spanish and perhaps in world literature. Starting with Columbus, who received from Castellanos his first poetic tribute, this humanist wrote *octavas* (eight-line stanzas) about famous and lowly people: pearl fishermen, English pirates, and rebellious Indians of all parts of the hemisphere. Though it reaches heights of lyric power, it remained unpublished until the nineteenth century.

More famous among the earliest visitors who broke into verse was the young courtier Alonso de Ercilla (1533-1594) who, while helping the courtship of a Spanish prince in England, had learned of the slaughter of Pedro de Valdivia by the Indians of Chile. He volunteered for the punitive army, and wrote a long epic about the expedition, a few stanzas a day, on bits of leather or parchment, that were read around the campfire at night. However, admiration for the valor of the Indians and enmity toward his Spanish commander turned his *La Araucana* into an epic of praise for the people of Chile, when rewritten in 1569 and later. This is the world's only great epic about a modern nation.

La Araucana inspired many other attempts at epic poetry all over the continent, including *Espejo de paciencia* (Mirror of Patience, 1608), about Cuba, by Silvestre de Balboa; *Armas antárticas* (Antarctic Arms) by Juan de Miramontes y Zuázola; *Argentina* (1612) by Martín del Barco Centenera; and *La Christiada*, a baroque religious epic in twelve books, by a Dominican monk of Lima, Diego de Hojeda (1522-1607). But the only long poem to approach the quality of their common inspiration was the unfinished *Arauco domado* (Arauco Tamed, 1596), an account of Araucanian warfare by the native Chilean Pedro de Oña (1570-1643). He is more the lyric poet and his work is richer in striking metaphors than his model, but he was also more under the influence of Góngora.

Another mestizo, the son of one of Cortés' companions, was Francisco de Terranzas (1525?-1600?), probably the first native-born Spanish-American poet, whose tastes ran to courtly, rather than martial, verse. Bernardo de Balbuena (1562-1627) was another early poet, writing while a priest in Mexico, before he became Bishop of Puerto Rico. He imitated Góngora in *La grandeza mexicana* (1604), and was influenced by Ariosto in his epic *Bernardo* (1624), a baroque version of the Chronicle of Roland.

For lack of means, little of the early poetry of Latin America was preserved, and the names of the poets vanished with their works through the centuries. One exception is the seventeenth-century Peruvian poetess who immortalized at least her pen name, "Amarilis," by corresponding with Lope de Vega. Then came a century of near sterility, from which few names emerge.

In the nineteenth century, the rise of a spirit of revolt inspired many writers, especially poets, and by that time literary works stood a better chance of being preserved. Mariano Ramallo (1817-1865) of Bolivia reminisced about the battles of the revolution. José Joaquín de Olmedo (1780-1847) hymned the leaders of Ecuador and urged his fellow Ecuadoreans to make good use of the peace they had achieved. In London, homesick for his Venezuela, Andrés Bello (1781-1865) imitated classic Latin poets in his ode "A la agricultura de la Zona Tórrida" (To Agriculture in the Torrid Zone, 1826), appealing for reconstruction and a back-to-the-soil movement after the revolution.

The arrival of Romanticism from Europe turned many middle-class writers into subjective poets and seekers of freedom. The Spanish Romanticist, Campoamor, had more imitators in Spanish America than in Spain. Many poets followed Echeverría's plea to explore their own environment. Salvador Sanfuentes (1817-1860) used some of the legends of Chile as sources for his ballads. In Argentina, environmental exploration was amply illustrated in a stream of poems about the pampas and its gaucho inhabitants. The legendary cowboy minstrel Santos Vega appeared in many of them, both crude and cultured. Hilario Ascasubi (1809-1875) of Argentina wrote one of the most famous, *Santos Vega* (1872). Estanislao del Campo (1834-1880), though a city man, ably interpreted the reactions of a gaucho in *Fausto*. However it was José Hernández (1834-1886) who became the authentic voice of the cowboy of Argentina's pampas. His *Martín Fierro* appeared in two volumes, in 1872 and 1879, to be universally acknowledged as the classic portrait of the gaucho confronted by savage Indians and betrayed by "The Law." The other side of the picture, the tragedy of the Indians deprived of freedom and hounded by the white man, was recounted by the pitying Uruguayan, Zorrilla de San Martín (1855-1931), in his tragic poem *Tabaré* (1888).

José Eusebio Caro (1817-1853), a cultured Colombian poet, extended his coverage to all free and fearless men, and published his verse in *La Estrella Nacional*, which he founded in 1836. In Venezuela, José Antonio Maitín (1814-1874) showed his Romanticist tendencies in *Canto fúnebre* (Funeral Song) written following his wife's death; this elegy is equaled only by the dirge of the Cuban poetess, Luisa Pérez de Zambrana (1835-1922). Another early Venezuelan romanticist, Juan Antonio Pérez Bonalde (1846-1892), though best remembered for his melodic translation of Poe's "The Raven," also wrote elegies, including

Vuelta a la patria (Home to My Country) and Flor. His feeling
for unbridled nature is revealed in Niágara.

The best known Niágara, however, was written in 1824 by
one of the greatest Romanticists of the north, a poet of independence along with Olmedo and Bello, the Cuban José María
Heredia (1803-1839). To this perpetual exile from his native
Cuba, dreaming of the Aztecs, nature was a state of the soul,
and his spontaneous poetry was intended to stir feelings of protest against the domination of Spain. His tribute to Niagara
Falls became the first translated Latin American poem to be
published in the United States when William Cullen Bryant
printed his version of it in 1827.

Heredia's fellow islander, the quadroon "Plácido" (Gabriel
de la Concepción Valdés, 1809-1844) and José Jacinto Milanés
(1814-1863), were also Romantic radicals. Plácido was shot as a
rebel. Padilla (1829-1896) and Gautier Benítez (1851-1880)
represented the Romantic movement in Puerto Rico. Mexico's
Manuel Acuña (1849-1873), a Romantic in his life as well as in
his verse, committed suicide, a victim of his struggle with the
materialistic doctrines of science.

As the last quarter of the century began, changes could be
observed in poetry. Realism started about 1867. The forerunners
of Modernism, many of whom were cosmopolitan-minded,
sought universality in their writing. José Asunción Silva (1865-
1896) of Colombia represented the transition along with José
Martí (1853-1895), the poet-martyr of Cuba. All these poets
blazed the path to be followed by Rubén Darío (1867-1916) and
the other Modernists with whom Volume II of this anthology
begins.

DRAMA

Authorities differ about the status of drama in Latin America at
the time of Columbus' arrival. In Spain, the first recorded modern dramatic production took place on December 24, 1492,
when Juan del Encina performed a shepherd play in Salamanca,

in the house of the Duke of Alba. In South America at the same time, the Indians were already performing ritual dances appealing to their Gods for rain or good crops. Their pageants and spectacles, staging the deeds of their ancestors, are mentioned by the earliest Spanish colonists, along with farcical performances in which the actors pretended to be lame and blind. But no plotted drama has been found, unless one counts the Guatemalan *Rabinal Achí* (The Rabinal Champion) which was not discovered by white Spanish Americans until the nineteenth century, when it was declared to be an old legendary dance. Certainly the execution of the war chief at the end of the play is not a European element. *Ollanta*, long considered an authentic Inca play, is now known to be the work of some eighteenth-century European who was familiar with Spanish Golden Age drama as well as with Peruvian legends.

For the Europeans in South America, drama served several purposes: entertainment, education, and celebration. Probably few sixteenth-century plays had entertainment as their main purpose. Students in the seminaries occasionally amused themselves with dramatic skits. The first play recorded in Colombia, in 1580, was performed to amuse the guests of Archbishop Zapata. Cristóbal de Llerena (1545?-1610), a choirmaster in Santo Domingo, wrote what he intended to be a humorous prose entertainment, but the performance of his *entremés* (interlude) in 1588, which satirized the local administration, earned him temporary exile.

A few wealthy citizens and several governors built stages and theaters in their homes for private entertainment. Friends of one of Peru's Viceroys even translated foreign plays or provided original scripts for presentation in the viceregal palace in Lima. Pedro de Peralta Barnuevo (1663-1743) not only learned neo-Classicism from the French, but imitated Molière and translated Corneille's *Rodogune* for his patron's little theater. He also wrote original plays, a mythological *zarzuela* following Italian practices, *Triunfo de amor y poder* (Triumph of Love and Power, 1711?) and *Afectos vencen finezas* (Love is Stronger than Politeness, 1720) about Grecian princes, but he might have been utterly forgotten had he not also composed, in 1719, a delightful untitled *entremés* for performance between the acts of his translation. It has been judged the play of the period that would best pass the test of a performance today, dealing as it does with four typically Peruvian beauties of the author's time, and their sweethearts. Also involving contemporary Peruvians in a universal situation is the brief *El amor duende* (The Love Elf, 1725) written by another courtier, Jerónimo de Monforte y Vera (1680?-1740?).

Most plays, however, were performed to make the teachings of the Church more vivid to the Indian spectators. The priests who accompanied Cortés to Mexico in 1519 either brought along or set down from memory the dialogue of *Los Pastores* (The Shepherds), a Nativity play that is still performed annually in Mexico and the southwestern United States. Those among the clergy who were conversant in Indian dialects were soon able to provide versions of religious plays in the languages of their Indian parishioners. Fernán González de Eslava (1534-1601), a Spanish priest in Mexico, produced a series of religious allegories that give an excellent idea of local customs and language. Called *Coloquios espirituales y sacramentales* (Sacred and Spiritual Dialogues), sixteen of them were published in 1610. Another volume of his more worldly plays, if ever published, has been lost.

The first native-born Mexican playwright was Juan Pérez Ramírez (1545-1595?), whose *Desposorio espiritual entre el Pastor Pedro y la Iglesia Mexicana* (Spiritual Marriage of Shepherd Pedro and the Mexican Church) was performed in 1574 to welcome Mexico's new archbishop, Pedro Moya de Contreras. So he gave impetus to the use of plays for the celebration of any special event. Frequently the occasion was a loyal ceremony of allegiance after the coronation of a new king in Spain. A mass in the morning would be followed by a review of the troops or a bull fight. Then, in the afternoon, a play would be performed on a temporary stage in the plaza. One such celebration in Buenos Aires in 1746 included two plays to honor the coronation of Ferdinand VI. Another, in 1760, offered a pro-

gram of six plays. Besides a change in the monarchy, the departure or arrival of a governor or a bishop would often provide the
excuse for the production of a drama by some of the amateur
actors.

However, most of the plays were products of Spain's Golden
Age (1554-1681), both on the theory that imported drama was
superior, and because it was a way of acknowledging bonds with
the motherland. Latin America lost its only chance to claim a
great playwright for its own when the twenty-year-old Juan Ruiz
de Alarcón (1581-1639) left Mexico to complete his education
in Spain. Though patriotic Mexicans try to find evidence that
Alarcón wrote some of his twenty-three plays in the New World
or showed American tendencies, the internal evidence makes
them as Spanish as anything by Lope de Vega.

America came closest to a Golden Age playwright in the brilliant New World woman, Sor Juana Inés de la Cruz (1648-
1695). At the age of eight she wrote her first *loa*, or brief introduction to a dramatic performance. After taking Holy Orders,
she composed a number of *autos sacramentales* for Corpus
Christi performances. She also wrote several long plays, complete
with prefatory *loa* and *entremeses* for between-the-acts entertainment. One of them, *El Divino Narciso* (The Divine Narcissus), had a religious theme; another, *Los empeños de una casa*
(A House Plagued by Love), was an imitation of Lope de Vega.
In collaboration with her confessor, Padre Juan de Guevara, she
wrote *Amor es más laberinto* (Love is a Labyrinth). She could
not compete with Spain's great quartet of experienced Golden
Age playwrights, but then, obviously, she lacked their opportunity for practice, their professional actors, the directors clamoring
for their manuscripts, and their eager audiences willing to pay
for the performance.

For most local playwrights throughout the hemisphere, the
only works that stood a chance of being performed on the stage
were the *entremeses*, the short skits sandwiched between the
acts of imported plays. In Chile, however, the arrival of a new
Captain General in 1690, who had come to inspect his southern
frontiers, provided the opportunity for some anonymous "ge-

nius" to write for local amateurs the full-length play *El Hércules chileno* (The Chilean Hercules), dealing with the Araucanian Indians whom the governor would have to control.

In the eighteenth century, the number of locally written plays increased. In Argentina, a local legend about two Indian chiefs in love with a white woman was dramatized by Juan Manuel Lavardén (1754-1809) in *Siripo* (1789). Gauchos got into the act in *El amor de la estanciera* (The Ranch Girl's Love, about 1785) and *Las bodas de Chivico y Pancha* (The Marriage of Chivico and Pancha, about 1823). Their use of cowboy dialect marked the final step towards a completely national theater.

Classicism also had its partisans all over the continent, and numerous, frequently dull, tragedies were written and sometimes performed. In 1817 the Society of Good Taste was founded in Buenos Aires to regulate drama, and one of its members, the Chilean priest Camilo Henríquez (1769-1825) wrote *La Camila o La patriota de Sud America* (Camila or the Patriot of South America). A number of five act dramas about Indians were written. The president of the United Provinces of Venezuela and Granada, Dr. José Fernández Madrid (1789-1830) was the author of *Guatimocín* (1825), with Cortés as its chief character, and *Atala* (1824), a play about the daughter of a North American chief. Another Classicist, the Mexican Manuel Gorostiza (1789-1851) is remembered for his *Indulgencia para todos* (Indulgence for All, 1818) and especially for his comedy *Contigo pan y cebolla* (Bread and Onions with You, 1833).

But it was Romanticism that brought real life to the Latin American stage. The first Romantic play was *Don Pedro de Castilla* (1836), by Francisco Xavier Foxá (1816-1865) of Santo Domingo. Although its premiere at El Tacón Theatre in Havana was a memorable night (there were fist-fights, and one spectator died), it was not the first play to have been staged there. One month earlier, *Guillermo* had been performed, the work of a Spaniard, José María de Andueza (1795?-1850), who had come to Havana in 1825.

Other Romantic plays soon followed. *Muñoz, visitador de México* (Muñoz, Royal Inspector to Mexico, 1838) by Ignacio

Rodríguez Galván (1816-1842) was Mexico's first good Romantic play. A year later, in his native Zapotecas, Fernando Calderón (1809-1845) performed his romantic play *El torneo* (The Tourney). However, the country's greatest Romanticist was the prolific José Peón Contreras (1843-1907) who unfortunately began writing plays after the momentum of the movement had slackened. Despite his excellent verse and his thrilling plots, many of his plays remain unpublished and a few were never produced.

The Romantic period was the heyday of the Bolivian theater, where sixty works were published in forty years. The Chilean theater, too, got its start during the Romantic era. Carlos Bello (1815-1854), son of the Venezuelan Humanist Andrés Bello (1781-1865), inaugurated the Santiago University Theatre with his *Amores del poeta* (Loves of a Poet) in 1842. And Cuba's Gertrudis Gómez de Avellaneda (1814-1873) made her reputation with the Biblical tragedy *Baltasar* (1858).

By 1846, Spain was witnessing the decline of Romanticism, but the swing of the pendulum toward *costumbrismo* and Realism in the theater came later in Latin America. In Argentina, it was Nemesio Trejo (1850-1916) who was the first to abandon Old World themes in favor of local people and their problems. In the Chilean theatre, it was Luis Rodríguez y Velasco (1838-1919) and Román Vial y Ureta (1833-1896), along with Juan Rafael Allende (1850-1909). Daniel Barros Grez (1834-1904), a Chilean Bretón de los Herreros, was the author of a number of comedies of local customs, like *Cada oveja con su pareja* (Sheep Flock Together, 1879) and his masterpiece, *Como en Santiago* (Just Like Santiago, 1873), successfully revived in 1947 and 1952.

Peru's first important playwright was Felipe Pardo y Aliaga (1806-1868), author of three witty, ironic comedies beginning with *Los frutos de la educación* (The Fruits of Education, 1829). More prolific and technically more competent was Manuel Ascensio Segura (1805-1871), who made his first appearance in the literary world with *El sargento Canuto* in 1839. Though the quality of his verse was poor, he proved a keen ob-

server of his country's weaknesses in a dozen plays, including
La saya y el manto (Skirt and Shawl, 1842) and *Ña Catita*
(Missy Katey, 1845), concerning craftiness in courtship.

These were the various seeds that were to blossom into the
theatrical flowering of the early twentieth century. Pablo
Echagüe, in writing of them, rightly named his book *Theatre in
Formation*, but, once formed, this theater was to produce Florencio Sánchez and many other modern dramatists, first in Argentina, and later in the other Spanish-American nations.

I

PROSE

SPANISH-AMERICAN LITERATURE

ANONYMOUS: POPOL VUH
Sixteenth Century   Guatemala

Before it was conquered by the Spaniards in 1524, the Kingdom of Quiché occupied part of present-day Guatemala. One of its citizens set down the history and legends of its people, probably in paintings or picture writing, but his original work has been lost. However, after the Spanish introduced phonetic transcriptions, the account was transcribed by memory into Spanish script, about 1550. It starts: *"Aré u xe oher tzih Quiché u bi"* (This is the beginning of the old traditions of the place called Quiché).

After a long disappearance, the transcription was discovered about 1702 by Padre Francisco Ximenes (1666-1729) and translated into Spanish under the title *Popol-Vuh* (Book of the People), also called The Sacred (or National) Book of the Quiché. It covers the period from 1040–1550.

The translators of the English version call it "the most vigorous, literary, and significant effort achieved by the American Indian in the field of mythology and history, and expressed in a highly developed language that lends itself to clarity, elegance of style and fluency in narration."

POPOL VUH

Part I. Chapter 4

It was cloudy and twilight then on the face of the earth. There was no sun yet. Nevertheless there was a being called Vucub-Caquix (seven Macaws) who was very proud of himself. The sky and the earth existed, but the face of the sun and the moon were covered.

And Vucub-Caquix said: "Truly they are clear examples of

those people who were drowned, (being monkeys who look like man and descendants of a generation of men that were created and made but were only wooden figures), and their nature is that of supernatural beings.

"I shall now be great above all the beings created and formed. I am the sun, the light, the moon," he exclaimed. "Great is my splendor. Because of me men shall walk and conquer. For my eyes are of silver, bright, resplendent as precious stones, as emeralds; my teeth shine like perfect stones, like the face of the sky. My nose shines afar like the moon, my throne is of silver, and the face of the earth is lighted when I pass before my throne. So then I am the sun; I am the moon, for all mankind. So shall it be because I can see very far."

So Vucub-Caquix spoke. But he was not really the sun; he was only vainglorious of his feathers and his riches. And he could see only as far as the horizon, and he could not see over all the world.

The face of the sun had not yet appeared, nor that of the moon, nor the stars, and it had not dawned. Therefore Vucub-Caquix became as vain as though he were the sun and the moon, because the light of the sun and the moon had not yet shown itself. His only ambition was to exalt himself and to dominate. And all this happened when the flood came because of the wooden people.

Now we shall tell how Vucub Caquix was overthrown and died, and how man was made by the Creator and the Maker.

Part II. Chapter 3

This is the story of a maiden, the daughter of a lord named Cuchumaquic (i.e., "gathered blood").

A maiden then, daughter of a lord, heard this story. The name of the father was Cuchumaquic and that of the maiden was Xquic (i.e., "little blood," or "blood of a woman"). When she heard her father tell the story (of a tree that had never born fruit till the heads of two brothers were buried in it), she was amazed to hear it.

"Why can I not go to see this tree which they tell about?" the girl exclaimed. "Surely the fruit of which I hear tell must be very good." Finally she went alone and arrived at the foot of the tree that was planted in Pucbal-Chal.

"Ah!" she exclaimed. "What fruit is this which this tree bears? Is it not wonderful to see how it is covered with fruit? Must I die, shall I be lost, if I pick one of this fruit?" said the maiden.

Then the skull which was among the branches of the tree spoke up and said: "What is it you wish? Those round objects which cover the branches of the tree are nothing but skulls." So spoke the head of Hun-Hunahpú turning to the maiden. "Do you, perchance, want them?" it added.

"Yes, I want them," the maiden answered.

"Very well," said the skull. "Stretch your right hand up here."

"Very well," said the maiden and with her right hand reached toward the skull.

In that instant the skull let a few drops of spittle fall directly into the maiden's palm. She looked quickly and intently at the palm of her hand, but the spittle of the skull was not there.

"In my spittle and my saliva I have given you my descendants," said the voice in the tree. "Now my head has nothing on it any more. It is nothing but a skull without flesh. So are the heads of the great princes; the flesh is all that gives them a handsome appearance. And when they die, men are frightened by their bones. So, too, is the nature of the sons, which are like saliva and spittle; they may be the sons of a lord, of a wise man, or of an orator. They do not lose their substance when they go, but they bequeath it; The image of the lord, of the wise man, or of the orator does not disappear, nor is it lost, but he leaves it to the daughters and to the sons which he begets. I have done the same with you. Go up, then, to the surface of the earth that you may not die."

After this talking, the maiden returned directly to her home, having immediately conceived the sons in her belly by virtue of the spittle only. And thus Hunahpú and Xbalanqué were begotten. But after six months had passed, her father, who was called Cuchumaquic, noticed her condition. At once the maiden's secret was discovered by her father when he observed that she was pregnant.

Then the lords, Hun-Camé and Vucub-Camé held council with Cuchumaquic.

"My daughter is pregnant, Sirs; she has been disgraced," exclaimed Cuchumaquic when he appeared before the lords.

"Very well," they said. "Command her to tell the truth and if she refuses to speak, punish her; let her be taken far from here and sacrifice her."

"Very well, Honorable Lords," he answered. Then he questioned his daughter. "Whose are the children that you carry, my daughter?"

And she answered, "I have no child, my father, for I have not yet known a youth."

"Very well," he replied. "You are really a whore. Take her and sacrifice her, Ahpop Achih; bring me her heart in a gourd and return this very day before the lords," he said to the two owls.

The four messengers took the gourd and set out carrying the young girl in their arms, and also taking the knife of flint with which to sacrifice her. But she said to them: "It cannot be that you will kill me, O messengers, because what I bear in my belly is no disgrace, but was begotten when I went to marvel at the head of Hun-Hunahpú which was in Pucbal-Chah. So then you must not sacrifice me, messengers."

"And what shall we put in place of your heart? Your father told us: 'Bring the heart, return before the lords, do your duty, and put the heart in the bottom of the gourd.' Perchance did he not speak to us so? What shall we put in the gourd? We wish, too, that you should not die," said the messengers.

"Very well, but my heart does not belong to them. Neither is your home here, nor need you let them force you to kill men. Later, in truth, the real criminals will be at your mercy and I will overcome Hun-Camé and Vucub-Camé. So then the blood and only the blood shall be theirs and shall be given to them. Nei-

ANONYMOUS

27

ther shall my heart be burned before them. Gather the product
of this tree," said the maiden.

The red sap gushing forth from the tree fell into the gourd
and with it they made a ball that glistened and took the shape of
a heart. The tree gave forth sap similar to blood, with the appearance of real blood. Then the blood, or that is to say, the sap
of the red tree, clotted and formed a very bright coating inside
the gourd, like clotted blood; meanwhile the tree glowed at the
work of the maiden. It was called "the red tree of cochineal,"
but since then it has taken the name of Blood Tree because its
sap is called Blood.

"There on earth shall you be beloved and you shall have all
that belongs to you," said the maiden to the owls.

"Very well, girl. We shall go there, we go up to serve you;
you continue on your way while we go to present the sap instead
of your heart, to the lords," said the messengers.

When they arrived in the presence of the lords, all were
waiting.

"You have finished?" asked Hun-Camé.

"All is finished, my lords. Here in the bottom of the gourd is
the heart."

"Very well. Let me see," exclaimed Hun-Camé. And grasp-
ing it with his fingers, as he raised it, the shell broke and the
blood flowed bright red in color.

"Stir up the fire and put it on the coals," said Hun-Camé.

As soon as they threw it on the fire, the men of Xibalba
began to sniff and drawing near to it, they found the fragrance
of the heart very sweet. And as they sat deep in thought, the
owls, the maiden's servants, left and flew like a flock of birds
from the abyss toward earth, and the four became her servants.

In this manner the Lords of Xibalba were defeated. All were
tricked by the maiden.

Part III. Chapter 2

These are the names of the first men who were created and
formed: the first man was Balam-Quitzé, the second, Balam-

Acab, the third, Mahucutah, and the fourth was Iqui-Balam. These are the names of our first mothers and fathers.

It is said that they only were made and formed, they had no mother, and they had no father. They were only called men (i.e., they had no family name). They were not born of woman, nor were they begotten by the Creator nor by the Maker, nor by the Forefathers. Only by a miracle, by means of incantation were they created and made by the Creator, the Maker, the Forefathers, Tepeu and Gucumatz. And as they had the appearance of men, they were men; they talked, conversed, saw and heard, walked, grasped things; they were good and handsome men, and their figure was the figure of a man.

They were endowed with intelligence; they saw and instantly they could see far, they succeeded in seeing, they succeeded in knowing all that there is in the world. When they looked, instantly they saw all around them and they contemplated in turn the arch of heaven and the round face of the earth. The things hidden in the distance they saw all, without first having to move; at once they saw the world, and so, too, from where they were, they saw it.

Great was their wisdom; their sight reached to the forests, the rocks, the lakes, the seas, the mountains, and the valleys. In truth, they were admirable men, Balam-Quitzé, Balam-Acab, Muhucutah, and Iqui-Balam.

Then the Creator and the Maker asked them: "What do you think of your condition? Do you not see? Do you not hear? Are not your speech and manner of walking good? Look, then! Contemplate the world, look and see if the mountains and the valleys appear! Try, then, to see!" they said to the first four men.

And immediately the first four men began to see all that was in the world. Then they gave thanks to the Creator and the Maker: "We really give you thanks, two and three times! We have been created, we have been given a mouth and a face. We speak, we hear, we think, and walk; we feel perfectly, and we know what is far and what is near. We also see the large and the small in the sky and the earth. We give you thanks, then, for having created us, O Creator and Maker! For having given us being, O our grandmother! O our grandfather!" they said, giving thanks for their creation and formation.

They were able to know all, and they examined the four corners, the four points of the arch of the sky and the round face of the earth.

But the Creator and the Maker did not hear this with pleasure. "It is not well what our creations, our works, say. They know all, the large and the small," they said. And so the Forefathers held council again. "What shall we do with them now? Let their sight reach only to that which is near; let them see only a little of the face of the earth! It is not well what they say. Perchance are they not by nature simple creatures of our making? Must they also be gods? And if they do not reproduce and multiply when it will dawn, when the sun rises? And what if they do not multiply?" So they spoke.

"Let us check a little of their desires, because it is not well what we see. Must they perchance be the equals of ourselves, their Makers who can see afar, who know all and see all?"

Thus spoke the Heart of Heaven, Huracán, Chipi-Caculhá. Raxa-Caculhá, Tepeu, Gucumatz, the Forefathers, the Creator and the Maker. Thus they spoke and immediately they changed the nature of their works, of their creatures.

Then the Heart of Heaven blew mist into their eyes, which clouded their sight as when a mirror is breathed upon. Their eyes were covered, and they could see only what was close, only what was clear to them. In this way, the wisdom and all the knowledge of the first four men, the origin and the beginning of the Quiché race, were destroyed.

In this way were created and formed our grandfathers, our fathers, by the Heart of Heaven, the Heart of Earth.

Delia Goetz and Sylvanus G. Morley
From *Popol Vuh, the Sacred Book of the Ancient Quiché Maya* (Univ. of Oklahoma Press, 1950)

CHRISTOPHER COLUMBUS
1451-1506   Italy

In 1477, Cristóbal Colón, as he signed his name, settled
in Lisbon and married the daughter of one of Prince
Henry's navigators. As a sugar buyer for a Genoese mer-
chant in the Azores, he met other pilots and navigators
who believed that land existed to the west, across the
Atlantic. First Columbus attempted to secure the assist-
ance of King John II of Portugal to explore it. Then
he turned to Ferdinand of Spain and spent eight years
trying to obtain his patronage. As is well known, eventually he was outfitted for the expedition; he left Spain
and reached the island of San Salvador, off the American coast, in 1492. The detailed log that Columbus kept
of the journey has been lost, but the missionary and historian Padre Bartolomé de las Casas (1494-1566) had
access to it and copied some of its pages and sum-
marized the rest for his *Historia de las Indias* (History
of the Indies).

The following selection is translated partly from las
Casas' manuscript and partly from Columbus' original
log; the introductory passage was written by Columbus
himself, while the account of his discovery of America
is taken from both las Casas' summary and the Admiral's original account.

THE LOG OF COLUMBUS

"I left the city of Granada on Saturday, the twelfth day of May,
1492, and proceeded to Palos, a seaport, where I armed three
vessels very fit for such an enterprise, and having provided myself with abundance of stores and seamen, I set sail from the
port, on Friday, the third of August, half an hour before sunrise,
and steered for the Canary Islands of Your Highnesses which
are in the said ocean, thence to take my departure and proceed
till I arrived at the Indies, and perform the embassy of your

Highnesses to the Princes there, and discharge the orders given me. For this purpose I determined to keep an account of the voyage, and to write down punctually every thing we performed or saw from day to day, as will hereafter appear. Moreover, Sovereign Princes, besides describing every night the occurrences of the day, and every day those of the preceding night, I intend to draw up a nautical chart, which shall contain the several parts of the ocean and land in their proper situations; and also to compose a book to represent the whole by picture with latitudes and longitudes, on all which accounts it behooves me to abstain from my sleep, and make many trials in navigation, which things will demand much labor."

Here follows las Casas' transcription.

Thursday, October 11th. Steered W.S.W.; and encountered a heavier sea than they had met with before in the whole voyage. Saw *pardelas* and a green rush near the vessel. The crew of the Pinta saw a cane and a log; they also picked up a stick which appeared to have been carved with an iron tool, a piece of cane, a plant which grows on land, and a board. The crew of the Niña saw other signs of land, and a stalk loaded with roseberries. These signs encouraged them, and they all grew cheerful. Sailed this day till sunset, twenty-seven leagues.

After sunset steered their original course W. and sailed twelve miles an hour till two hours after midnight, going ninety miles, which are twenty-two leagues and a half; and as the Pinta was the swiftest sailer, and kept ahead of the Admiral, she discovered land and made the signals which had been ordered. The land was first seen by a sailor called Rodrigo de Triana, although the Admiral at ten o'clock that evening standing on the quarterdeck saw a light, but so small a body that he could not affirm it to be land; calling to Pero Gutiérrez, groom of the King's wardrobe, he told him he saw a light, and bid him look that way, which he did and saw it; he did the same to Rodrigo Sánchez of Segovia, whom the King and Queen had sent with the squadron as comptroller, but he was unable to see it from his situation.

The admiral again perceived it once or twice, appearing like the light of a wax candle moving up and down, which some thought an indication of land. But the Admiral held it for certain that land was near; for which reason, after they had said the Salve which the seamen are accustomed to repeat and chant after their fashion, the Admiral directed them to keep a strict watch upon the forecastle and look out diligently for land, and to him who should first discover it he promised a silken jacket, besides the reward which the King and Queen had offered, which was an annuity of ten thousand maravedis. At two o'clock in the morning the land was discovered at two leagues' distance; they took in sail and remained under the square-sail lying to till day, which was Friday, when they found themselves near a small island, one of the Lucayos, called in the Indian language Guanahani.* Presently they descried people, naked, and the Admiral landed in the boat, which was armed, along with Martin Alonzo Pinzón, and Vincent Yáñez his brother, captain of the Niña. Arrived on shore, they saw trees very green, many streams of water, and diverse sorts of fruits. Numbers of the people of the island straightway collected together. *Here follow the precise words of the Admiral.* "As I saw that they were very friendly to us, and perceived that they could be much more easily converted to our holy faith by gentle means than by force, I presented them with some red caps, and strings of beads to wear upon the neck, and many other trifles of small value, wherewith they were much delighted, and became wonderfully attached to us. Afterwards they came swimming to the boats, bringing parrots, balls of cotton thread, javelins and many other things which they exchanged for articles we gave them, such as glass beads, and hawk's bells; which trade was carried on with the utmost good will. But they seemed on the whole to me, to be a very poor people. They all go completely naked, even the women, though I saw but one girl. All whom I saw were young, not above thirty years of age, well made, with fine shapes and faces; their hair short, and coarse like that of a horse's tail, combed toward the

* Now thought, because of the Admiral's description, to be Turk's Island.

forehead, except a small portion which they suffer to hang down behind, and never cut. Some paint themselves with black, which makes them appear like those of the Canaries, neither black nor white; others with white, others with red, and others with such colors as they can find. Some paint the face, and some the whole body; others only the eyes, and others the nose. Weapons they have none, nor are acquainted with them, for I showed them swords which they grasped by the blades, and cut themselves through ignorance. They have no iron, their javelins being without it, and nothing more than sticks, though some have fish-bones or other things at the ends. They are all of a good size and stature, and handsomely formed. I saw some with scars of wounds upon their bodies, and demanded by signs the cause of them; they answered me in the same way, that there came people from the other islands in the neighborhood who endeavored to make prisoners of them, and they defended themselves. I thought then, and still believe, that these were from the continent. It appears to me, that the people are ingenious, and would be good servants; and I am of opinion that they would very readily become Christians, as they appear to have no religion. They very quickly learn such words as are spoken to them. If it please our Lord, I intend at my return to carry home six of them to Your Highnesses, that they may learn our language. I saw no beasts in the island, nor any sort of animals except parrots." These are the words of the Admiral.

HERNANDO CORTÉS
1485-1547   Mexico

Cortés, son of a poor family of Extremadura, was dismissed from the University of Salamanca because of poor scholarship and, in 1504, he decided to go west to make his fortune. He was second in command to Diego Velasquez in the conquest of Cuba in 1511, and was appointed by him to head an expedition to invade Mexico in 1519. Once the conquest was achieved, Cortés resigned his commission and claimed allegiance to Emperor Charles V alone. In a series of five "Cartas" (Letters) he reported his activities between 1518 and 1526, exaggerating his tribulations in order to appeal to imperial generosity. Back in Spain in 1528, he was kindly received; the king made him Marqués del Valle and appointed him Captain General of Mexico. But Cortés never made his fortune. In 1544, in his last letter to Charles V, he complained, "I am old, poor, and 20,000 ducats in debt, having spent the 100,000 I acquired." The letter still exists, with the following comment added in pencil, "No hay que responder" (there is no need to reply). He died in poverty.

The five dispatches run from 10,000 to 40,000 words. The first disappeared and has been reconstructed by a scribe who probably saw and copied the original. The second, perhaps the most interesting, is dated 1520. Full of wonder and horror, it describes the burning of the boats, the march into enemy territory, and the capture of Montezuma, the Aztec Emperor whom Cortés calls Muteczuma. The cruelty and rivalry of the white people disillusioned the Indians who rose against them in the "Noche Triste" of June 30, 1520, and drove them out of the city. The letter was published in Seville in 1522 by a German printer, Krombreger, and immediately translated into Latin and Italian, to be sold throughout Europe.

The third letter, dated 1522, deals with the recapture of the Mexican capital and the conquest of the land. The fourth (1524) concerns political organization, and the fifth (1526), which was not recovered until many years later, described Cortés' expedition to Honduras and his return to the capital in June of 1526, where he was greeted by the Indians with tears of joy. This English version is taken from a translation by George Folsom, published in 1843.

THE DISPATCHES OF
HERNANDO CORTÉS

Letter II. Chapter VII

As soon as it was daylight, the enemy renewed the combat with still greater vigor than the day before, for the number of them was so immense that there was no need of levelling the guns, but only to direct them against the mass of Indians. And although the firearms did much injury, for we played off thirteen arquebuses besides muskets and crossbows, they produced so little impression that their effect scarcely seemed to be felt; since where a discharge cut down ten or twelve men, the ranks were instantly closed up by additional numbers, and no apparent loss was perceived . . . Our men were compelled to fight all day long without cessation, while the enemy were relieved at intervals by fresh forces, and still had a superabundance of men. But we had none of our Spanish force killed on this day, although fifty or sixty were wounded, and we continued the contest till night, when we withdrew wearied into the garrison . . .

Muteczuma, who was still a prisoner (together with his son and many other persons of distinction, who had been secured at the beginning of operations) now came forward and requested to be taken to the terrace of the garrison, that he might speak to the leaders of his people and induce them to discontinue the contest. I caused him to be taken up, and when he reached a battlement projecting from the fortress, and sought an opportunity to address the people who were fighting in that quarter, a stone thrown by one of his own subjects struck him on the head with so much force that he died in three days after. I then gave his dead body to two Indians who were amongst the prisoners, and taking it on their shoulders they bore it away to his people; what afterwards became of it, I know not. The war, however, did not cease, but increased in violence and desperation every day.

On the same day a cry was heard in the quarter where Muteczuma had been wounded, some of the enemy calling to me to approach them, as certain of their captains wished to confer with me. I accordingly did so, and we passed amongst them; when after a long parley I asked them to discontinue their attack, since they had no good reason for it, having received many benefits from me and having always been treated well . . . They replied that they would not cease their attacks until I departed from the city . . .

The next day in the morning I made another sally from our quarters and God again gave us success and victory, although the enemy appeared in great numbers, and defended the bridges protected by strong entrenchments and ditchs which they had formed during the night; we took them all and covered them up; and some of our horsemen followed on the heels of the fugitives in the heat of victory and pursued them to the mainland. While I was employed in repairing the bridges and filling them up, messengers came to me in great haste, reporting that the enemy had attacked the garrison and at the same time had sued for peace, several of their leaders being in waiting to see me. I immediately went with two horsemen to see what they wanted. These men assured me that if I would engage not to punish them for what they had done, they would raise the blockade, replace the bridges that had been destroyed and restore the causeways, and that hereafter they would serve Your Majesty as they had done before. They also requested that I would bring them a priest of theirs whom I had taken prisoner, who was, as it were, the commander-in-chief of their religion. He came and addressed them, and brought about an arrangement between me and them; and it appeared that they immediately dispatched messengers to inform the captains and the people who were in the camp that the attack on the garrison and all other offensive operations should cease. Upon this being done, we took leave of them and I went to the garrison to procure some food.

While I was beginning to take some refreshments, information was brought me in great haste that the Indians had attacked the bridges that I had taken the same day and had killed many Spaniards . . .

Seeing the dangerous situation in which we were now placed and the very serious injury that the Indians were doing us every day; and fearing they would also destroy the remaining causeways, as they had done the others, and when that was effected, death would be our inevitable fate; and moreover having been often entreated by all my companions to abandon the place, the greater part of whom were so badly wounded as to be disabled from fighting, I determined to quit the city that night.

I took all the gold and jewels belonging to Your Majesty that could be removed and placed them in one apartment, where I delivered it in parcels to the officers of Your Highness, whom I had designated for this purpose in the royal name; and I begged and desired the alcaldes, regidores, and all the people to aid me in removing and preserving this treasure; I gave up my mare to carry as much as she could bear; and I selected certain Spaniards, as well my own servants as others, to accompany the gold and the mare, and what remained, the magistrates and myself distributed amongst the Spaniards to be borne by them. Abandoning the garrison, together with much wealth belonging to Your Majesty, the Spaniards, and myself, I went forth as secretly as possible, taking with me the son and two daughters of Muteczuma and Cacamacin, cacique of Aculuacan, with his brother, whom I had appointed in his place, and several other governors of provinces and cities whom I had taken prisoners.

Arriving at the bridges (now broken up) which the Indians had left, the bridge that I carried was thrown over where the first of them had been, without much difficulty, as there was none to offer resistance, except some watchmen who were stationed there, and who uttered so loud cries that before we had arrived at the second bridge, an immense multitude of the enemy assailed us, fighting in every direction, both by land and by water. I sallied across with great speed, followed by five horsemen and a hundred foot with whom I passed all the broken bridges swimming, and reached the mainland. Leaving the people who formed this advance party, I returned to the rear, where I found the troops hotly engaged; it is incalculable how much our people suffered, as well Spaniards as our Indian allies of Tascaltecal, nearly all of whom perished, together with many native Spaniards and horses, besides the loss of the gold, jewels, cotton cloth and many other things we had tried to bring away, including the artillery. Having collected all who were alive, I sent them on before, while with three or four horse and about twenty foot that dared to remain with me, I followed in the rear, incessantly engaged with the Indians until at length we reached a city called Tacuba . . .

In this defeat it was ascertained that one hundred and fifty Spaniards lost their lives, together with forty-five mares and horses, and more than two thousand Indians, our auxiliaries. Amongst the latter were the son and daughters of Muteczuma and other caciques whom we had taken prisoners . . .

I have written to Your Majesty, although in a poor style, the truth as to all that had transpired in these parts, and whatever it was necessary Your Highness should be informed of; and in the other despatch that goes with the present one, I send to beg your royal Excellency to appoint a person of high character to come hither and make inquiry and investigation as to everything for the information of Your Majesty; in this despatch, likewise, I most humbly entreat the same thing, since I shall consider it in the light of a distinguished favor, as a means of imparting entire credit to what I write.

Most noble and most excellent Prince, may God our Lord preserve the life and very royal person and most powerful state of your sacred Majesty, and grant you for a long period the addition of as many greater kingdoms and dominions as your royal heart may desire. Dated at La Villa de la Frontera of this New Spain, the 30th of October, 1520.

From your sacred Majesty's most humble servant and vassal, who kisses the royal feet and hands of Your Highness.

FERNÁN CORTÉS

George Folsom

BERNAL DÍAZ DEL CASTILLO
1492-1584   Mexico

One of the most vivid accounts of Spain's conquest of
the New World was written by an uneducated Spaniard
who had fought no less than 119 battles in Cortés' army.
After the conquest of Mexico, Bernal Díaz del Castillo
spent the rest of his long life in Guatemala. Correcting
some of the exaggerated accounts in earlier chronicles,
especially Gómara's of 1552, he wrote *Historia verdadera de la conquista de la Nueva España* (True History
of the Conquest of New Spain, 1560, published 1632).
In this gossipy and lively report from the common soldier's point of view, he even writes of his comrades'
crimes against the Indians. His style is rambling and
not very grammatical.

THE HISTORY OF THE CONQUEST
OF NEW SPAIN (MEXICO)

Preface by the Author

I have noticed that the majority of chroniclers before starting
their accounts provide prologue and preface, expressed with
lofty rhetoric to lend luster to their words. But being no Latin
scholar, I fear to attempt such prefatory material, since it would
need eloquence beyond my power to provide a preface for our
adventures and the mighty deeds of the conquest of New Spain
in the company of that valiant Captain Hernando Cortés.
What I myself have seen and the fighting in which I had a
share, I shall describe simply, with the help of God, as a true eye
witness without distortion. I am now an old man, more than
eighty-four years of age, and I have lost my sight and hearing,
and unfortunately I have accumulated nothing of value to leave
to my children and heirs, except this true story, and they will
soon discover what a wonderful story it is . . .

*Cortés led an expedition that landed in Mexico, despite
counter-orders by Diego Velásquez. When he started inland, he
burned his ships so that no one could desert and return to Cuba
or Santo Domingo.*

Chapter LVII

Having done this, Cortés ordered all the Indian chiefs of the
uplands, our allies and rebels against the Great Muctezuma, and
told them how they must serve those who remained behind in
Villa Rica and finish constructing the church and the fortifica-
tions and the houses. There, before them all, Cortés took Juan
de Escalante by the hand and proclaimed to them: "This is my
brother." And whatever he ordered, they should obey, and that
if any of them needed any favors or help against Mexican Indians, they should appeal to him, because he would go in person
to help them. And all the chiefs willingly agreed to follow his
orders. I remember that they burned incense before Juan de Escalante then, in spite of his protests. I have said that he was a
person well qualified for any job and a friend of Cortés'; and he
put him in charge of the town and port, confident that if Diego
Velásquez sent any force, there would be stout resistance.

Here is where the Chronicler Gómara says that when Cortés
ordered the ships to be burned, he did not dare let the soldiers
know that he proposed to go to the capital in search of the great
Muctezuma. It didn't happen that way at all, for, what sort of
people are we Spaniards not to be willing to go ahead anywhere
we can find booty and fighting? In addition, Gómara says that
Pedro de Ircio was left in Vera Cruz as commander. He wasn't
well informed. Juan de Escalante was the one left as Captain
and Governor, and Pedro de Ircio received no appointment, not
even as a Squadron Commander . . .

The arrival in Mexico

We proceeded along the causeway that here is eight paces in
width and runs so straight to the City of Mexico that it does not

seem to me to swerve either much or little, but broad as it is, it
was so crowded with people that there was hardly room for
them all, some of them going to, and others returning from
Mexico, besides those who had come out to see us, so that we
were hardly able to pass the crowd. And the towers and the cues
were crowded with Indians, as were the canoes all over the lake.
And it was not surprising, because they had never seen horses or
men like us.

We saw such marvelous sights that we hardly knew whether
what appeared before us was real, because on the land were
many more. The whole lake was covered with canoes, and in
front of us we could see the great city of Mexico— And our
number hardly exceeded four hundred men. Nor had we forgotten the warnings frequently given by the Indians of other regions that we should not enter the City of Mexico because they
would kill us as soon as they had us inside . . .

When we neared the city we saw many chiefs and Caciques
approaching, clad in rich mantles. The Great Muctezuma had
sent them in advance to welcome us, and when they reached
Cortés, they greeted him in their language and as a sign of
peace, they touched their hands against the ground.

Then came the Great Muctezuma, borne in a rich litter and
accompanied by several important Caciques. When he reached
us, he got down from the litter and approached under a canopy
of green feathers, decorated with gold and silver embroidery and
with pearls and precious stones. He was magnificently dressed,
according to his custom, and wore sandals with gold soles and
the upper parts decorated with precious stones. Four nobles
held the canopy over his head while others preceded him,
spreading rugs on the earth so that he should not tread on dirt.

When Cortés saw the great Muctezuma approaching, he
dismounted from his horse. Muctezuma greeted him and our
captain replied through our interpreters. Doña Marina translated his wishes for the Emperor's good health. Then Cortés
brought out a necklace made of glass stones which, as I have
said, are called "Margaritas." They were of various colors and
strung on a cord of gold and perfumed so that they had a sweet

scent. And he put it around the neck of the great Muctezuma, and then was about to embrace him, but the Caciques restrained him by holding his arm, for they considered touching the person of the Emperor an insult.

Then Cortés, through the lips of Doña Marina, said how happy he was to visit so mighty a ruler, and how much he appreciated the honor shown in coming in person to welcome him . . .

They took us to a grand palace that had belonged to the father of Muctezuma. That was where the Emperor had his temple of idols as well as a secret chamber where he kept jewels and gold, treasure that he had inherited from his father Axayaca. They took us to that palace because they regarded us as *teúles* or supernatural beings and so wanted to lodge us near the temple of the idols. There they had prepared extensive quarters for us soldiers and others richly decorated for our captain.

When he arrived, we entered an extensive patio. Here the great Muctezuma took Captain Cortés by the hand and led him to the quarters where he was to live. And he himself gave him a valuable necklace adorned with shrimps of gold that he placed around the neck of Cortés, and Cortés gave him appropriate thanks through his interpreters.

After that, the Emperor went to his palaces that were not very far away and we went to our lodgings. But we kept our guns ready because both the cavalry and the rest of us soldiers had been ordered to keep on the alert.

An elaborate banquet with native dishes was provided for us and we sat down to eat it. This was our fortunate and daring entry into the great city of Tenochtitlan, Mexico, on the 8th day of November in the year of our Lord Jesus Christ, 1519.

W.K.J.

BARTOLOMÉ DE LAS CASAS
1474-1566 Spain

When Padre de las Casas, called "The Apostle to the Indians," reached the New World in 1502, he conceived an idealistic plan to colonize South America and protect the Indians, even suggesting the importation of slaves from Africa to replace them as workers. His writings called the attention of Emperor Charles V to the serf-like position of the Indians in such books as *Brevísima historia de la destruccion de las Indias* (Very Short History of the Destruction of the Indies, 1527; published 1552). Spain's enemies used his works to create the "Black Legend" of Spanish cruelty. Though he was not a professional writer, this Dominican friar expressed himself with deep, if somewhat exaggerated, feeling. As a result of his efforts, Charles V did issue some "New Laws" in 1542, but they were so badly implemented that the Indians' condition was hardly improved.

The translation, *The Tears of the Indians*, signed "J.P." and published in London in 1656, is the source of this selection, comprising one chapter and the final page of that work.

THE TEARS OF THE INDIANS
OF NEW SPAIN (MEXICO)

In the year 1517, New Spain was discovered; after the discovery of which they did nothing first or second, but immediately fell to their old practices of cruelty and slaughter: for in the following year the Spaniards (who call themselves Christians) went thither to rob and kill; though they gave out that they went to people the Country. From that year unto this present year 1542, the violence, injustice and tyrannies of the Spaniards came to their full height; and now quite forgetting their human natures, they laid aside all fear of God or of their King. For the slaughters, massacres, cruelties, devastations of countries, destructions of cities, violences, tyrannies, and rapines of the Spaniards, which they did commit in these so many and so large kingdoms, are so numberless, and strike the mind with such a horror, that those which we have before related, are nothing in respect of these which we are to relate, being all perpetrated in the year 1518 and continued to this very month in a most sad and dreadful manner; so that what we said before holds very true, that the Spaniards still went on from bad to worse, themselves striving to exceed themselves in wickedness.

And thus from the first entry of the Spaniards into New Spain, which happened upon the tenth day of the month of April, continuing from the eighteenth year until the thirtieth, in which space of time are contained twelve years complete, there hath been no end of the bloody massacres and cruel slaughters of the Spaniards, perpetrated in the continent of Mexico and the parts adjoining, which contained four or five large kingdoms, that neither for compass nor fertility gave place to Spain. All this region was more populous than either Toledo, Seville, Valladolid, Augusta Cesarea, or Faventia; nay I may affirm that there is not at this present, neither was there when those places were at the highest of their flourishing estate, so many people as in those parts, which take up the space of above a thousand and eight hundred miles. In these ten or twelve years, what with Men, Women, Youths and Children, above four millions were by the Spaniards consumed, part by fire, part by the sword in these destructive wars; wars more unjust and more condemned both by the Law of God and men, than any invasion of the Turk against the Catholic Religion. Neither do we now reckon on those that died under the intolerable yoke and burdens of their captivity.

There is no language, no art or humane science, that can avail to recite the abominations and bloody actions committed by these enemies not only of Commonwealths, but of all humane societies.

Final Section

I Friar Bartholomew Casaus, of the Order of St. Dominic, who went to these parts through the mercy of God, desiring the salvation of the Indians, that so many precious souls redeemed with the blood of Christ might not perish, but wishing with my whole heart that they might through the knowledge of their Creator live eternally: Because of the care also and compassions which I bear to my Country, which is Castile, fearing lest God should destroy it in his anger for the sins which it hath committed against his divine Majesty, the faith and honor of divers great persons in the Court of Spain, zealously religious, and who abominate these bloody and detestable actions, after many hindrances of business, did at length put an end to this brief Tractate at Valentia the eighth day of December 1542, when the Spaniards (though they were in some places more cruel, in some places less), after the end of all their torments, violences, tyrannies, desolations and oppressions, were at length come to Mexico, which enjoys a gentler usage than other parts; for there is an outside of Justice, which doth somewhat restrain their cruelty, though not at all the immoderate tributes which they lay upon them. And now I have a real hope that Charles the Fifth, our Sovereign Lord and Prince, Emperor and King of Spain, (to whose ears the wickedness and impieties of these tyrants do daily come, which are committed against the will of God in these Countries, for they have hitherto concealed these things from him) not less subtily than maliciously, will extirpate the causes of so many evils, and apply fitting remedies to the calamities of this New World delivered by God to him as to a Lover of Justice and Mercy. Which God we do beseech to grant him happiness in his life and in his Imperial dignity, and to bless his Royal soul with eternal happiness. Amen.

FINIS

"J.P."

"MOTOLINÍA"
1500?-1569   Mexico

Fray Toribio de Benavente came to New Spain in 1524 with a group of other Franciscan missionaries. Their drab clothes, in contrast to the finery of the conquistadors, caused considerable comment among the Indians who kept repeating the word "motolinía." An interpreter, questioned about it by Benavente, translated the word as "poor." The Franciscan exclaimed, "This is the first word I learned in the language I shall need to preach to these people, and I shall take it for my name." And from then on he was known as Padre Motolinía. His preaching took him through New Spain, Guatemala, and Nicaragua, and he was regarded as a chief authority on Indian life and customs. His *Historia de los Indios de Nueva España* (History of the Indians of New Spain, 1560) contains a famous description of a dramatic performance in Tlaxca, New Spain, in 1538. From his comments, it would seem that he was the author of at least one of the plays performed. He also wrote *Doctrina Christiana en lengua mexicana y castellana* (The Christian Doctrine in Indian and Spanish Languages) in dialogue form.

HISTORY OF THE INDIANS
OF NEW SPAIN

In order that you may see the skill of these Indians, I shall tell here what they did and performed, a little later, on the day of St. John the Baptist (June 24, 1538), which was the following Monday. And there were four plays and to write them in prose, which is no less devout than their usual verse form, took all day Friday, and in the next two days, that were Saturday and Sunday, the actors learned their lines and performed them very devoutly.

They performed *Father Zacharias*, that lasted an hour and

ended in an attractive motet. On another stage, actors performed *The Annunciation of the Virgin,* that was very worth seeing and lasted about the same time. Then in the patio of Saint John's Church, to which the procession proceeded, was performed *The Visit of Our Lady to Saint Isabel.*

I have left the most important one for last, and it was the festival celebrated by members of Our Lady of the Incarnation. They had prepared a play to perform near the door of the hospital, and it dealt with *The Fall of Our First Parents,* and in the opinion of all who saw it, it was one of the most notable events yet to take place in this New Spain.

The abode of Adam and Eve was so beautifully decorated that it seemed a Paradise on earth, with many fruit trees and flowering bushes, some with natural flowers and some made of feathers and gold. In the trees was a wide variety of birds, from owls and birds of prey to tiny songsters . . . And there were also birds made of gold and feathers, marvelous to behold. There were also so many rabbits and hares that the place seemed full of them, and a lot of other animals that I had never seen before.

There were also two ocelots tied, and they were very fierce. They are neither cats nor panthers. And once Eve was careless and bumped into one of them, and it courteously got out of her way. This was before her sin, because if it had come later, when she had fallen from Grace, I am afraid she would not have fared so well. And there were other tamer animals, and Adam and Eve played with them. There were four rivers or fountains that came out of Paradise, and the Tree of Life in the midst of the Garden, and near it the Tree of Knowledge of Good and Evil, with fruit made of gold and feathers . . .

After the procession arrived, the show started. It lasted for some time because, before Eve ate and Adam followed her suggestion, Eve went back and forth from the serpent to her husband and from her husband to the serpent, three or four times. And every time, Adam kept resisting and pushing Eve indignantly away. She kept begging him and bothering him and saying it was very evident that he didn't love her and she loved him

much more than he loved her; and sitting in his lap, she impor-
tuned him so much that finally he went with her to the Forbidden Tree and in the presence of Adam, Eve ate of the fruit and
gave some to him, also, and he ate; and upon eating it, they
realized the evil of what they had done; and although they hid
as best they could, they could not escape the view of God; and
He arrived in majesty, accompanied by many angels; and after
He had called Adam, he blamed it on his wife, and she tried to
pass the guilt on to the serpent, while God was cursing them
and announcing to each his punishment.

The angels produced two well-made garments of the skin of
animals, and they dressed Adam and Eve in them. And the most
noteworthy thing was to watch them leave, banished and weeping. Three angels took Adam away and three others had hold of
Eve, and they went away singing the chant *Circomdederunt
Me.* It was so well performed that everybody who witnessed it
was weeping bitterly. And there remained one Cherub guarding
the gates of Paradise with his sword in his hand.

Then there was the world, another land very different from
the one they had left, because it was full of thistles and thorns
and snakes, as well as rabbits and hares. And when the new
dwellers in the world reached there, the angels showed Adam
how he must labor and till the soil, and they gave Eve spindles
to weave and make clothes for her husband and her children;
and after trying to comfort those who remained unconsoled, the
angels went away singing. And their song was a *villancico*, or
peasant song, that went like this:

> Why did Adam and Eve,
> The original pair,
> Eat the forbidden fruit
> In the Garden so fair?
>
> The original pair,
> Eve and her man,
> Into banishment went,
> To accord with God's plan

For eating the fruit
And breaking the ban.

This play was performed by the Indians in their own language, and many of them wept and felt very sorry, especially
when Adam was banished and taken to Earth . . .

W.K.J.

ALVAR NÚÑEZ CABEZA DE VACA
1490-1557   Mexico

Cabeza de Vaca, or "cow's head," was a nickname that
Alvar Núñez inherited from an ancestor, to whom King
Sancho of Navarre had given it for marking the location
of a mountain pass with the skull of a cow at the battle
of Las Navas de Tolosa in 1212. His *Los naufragios*
(The Shipwrecks), covering the years 1528 to 1536, is
a chronicle unequaled in its descriptions of sufferings
and privations.

In 1527, Pánfilo de Narváez left Spain with 600 colonists and soldiers to take possession of his land grant in
eastern New Spain. Through storms, desertions, and
shipwreck on the Florida coast, north of present-day St.
Petersburg, their number was finally reduced to four:
Alvar Núñez of Jerez, the treasurer and first mate; Captain Alonso del Castillo Maldonado of Salamanca; in-
fantry captain Andrés Dorantes of Extremadura; and his
slave, Estévanico. (Buckingham Smith translated the
Spanish *negro* as "black," giving rise to the tradition
that Estévanico was a Negro, but he was probably a
Moor.)

Frequently captured by Indians, they wandered across
the north-western part of New Spain (present-day New
Mexico and Arizona), down the Pacific coast to the gulf
of California, and finally to Mexico City. Besides a joint
report by the survivors, Núñez wrote *Los naufragios*,
first published in Spain in 1542. Reading it, both Coronado and De Soto were tempted to go exploring. It was

translated by Smith in 1851, and by Fanny Bandelier, wife of the well-known explorer of Indian pueblos, in 1905.

THE SHIPWRECKS

Out of six hundred colonists, only four are left. Indians spare their lives because of their ability to cure them. About their methods, Núñez writes:

We all prayed to God our Lord the best we could to send health; for that He knew there was no other means than through Him by which this people would aid us so we could come forth from this unhappy existence. He bestowed it so mercifully that, the morning having come, all the Indians got up well and sound and were as strong as though they never had a disorder. It caused great admiration and inclined us to render many thanks to God our Lord whose goodness we now clearly beheld, giving us firm hopes that he would liberate and bring us to where we might serve Him.

The Spaniards are then separated; they are kept as captives in different tribes which gather only once a year during the tuna (prickly pear) season. The four men take advantage of one of these reunions to escape together.

Chapter 20

The second day after we had moved, we commended ourselves to God and set forth with speed, trusting despite the lateness of the season and that the prickly pears were about ending, that with what food remained in the fields we might still be enabled to travel over a large territory. Hurrying on that day in great dread lest the Indians should overtake us, we saw some smokes, and going in the direction of them we arrived there after vespers, and found an Indian. He ran as he discovered us coming, not being willing to wait for us. We sent Estévanico after him, when he stopped seeing him alone. The negro told him we were seeking the people who made those fires. He answered that their houses were near by and that he would guide us to them. So we followed him. He ran to make known our approach, and at sunset we saw the houses. Before our arrival, at the distance of two crossbow shots from them, we found four Indians who waited for us and received us well. We said in the language of the Mariames that we were coming to look for them. They were evidently pleased with our company and took us to their dwellings. Dorantes and the negro were lodged in the house of a medicine man, Castillo and myself in that of another.

These people speak a different language and are called Avavares. They are the same that carried bows to those with whom we formerly lived, going to traffic with them, and although they are of a different nation and tongue, they understand the other language. They had arrived that day with their lodges at the place where we found them. The community at once brought us a great many prickly pears, having heard of us before, of our cures, and of the wonders our Lord worked by us, which, although there had been no others, were adequate to open ways for us through a country poor like this, to afford us people where oftentimes there were none, and to lead us through immediate dangers, not permitting us to be killed, sustaining us under great want, and putting into these nations the heart of kindness, as we shall relate hereafter . . .

Chapter 22

. . . Of the eight months we were among these people, six we supported in great want, for fish are not to be found where they are. At the expiration of this time (Summer, 1535), the prickly pears began to ripen, and I and the negro went, without these Indians knowing it, to others farther on, a day's journey distant, called Maliacones. At the end of three days I sent him to bring Castillo and Dorantes, and they having arrived, we all set out with the Indians who were going to get the small fruit of certain trees on which they support themselves ten or twelve days whilst the prickly pears are maturing. We underwent great hunger; we ate daily not more than two handfuls of the prickly pears which were green and so milky that they burned our mouths. As there was lack of water, those who ate suffered great thirst. In our extreme want we bought two dogs, giving in exchange some nets with other things and a skin I used to cover myself.

I have already stated that throughout this country we went naked, and as we were unaccustomed to being so, twice a year we cast our skins like serpents. The sun and air produced great sores on our breasts and shoulders, giving us sharp pain; and the large loads we had, being heavy, caused the cords to cut into our arms. The country is so broken and thickset that often after getting our wood in the forest, the blood flowed from us in many places, caused by the obstruction of thorns and shrubs that tore our flesh wherever we went. At times, when my turn came to get wood, after it had cost me so much blood, I could not bring it on my back but by dragging. In these labors my only solace and relief were in thinking of the sufferings of our Redeemer and in the blood He shed for me, in considering how much greater must have been the torment He sustained from the thorns than that I there received.

The first evidence of the presence of white men is given by the buckle of a sword-belt hanging from the neck of an Indian. He reports the arrival of "certain men like us who had come from Heaven and arrived at that river bringing horses, lances, and swords, and that they had lanced two Indians. They had then gone to sea."

Núñez tells the Indians he will go in search of these people and order them not to kill or enslave the Indians.

Chapter 32

. . . We passed through many territories and found them all vacant; their inhabitants wandered fleeing among the mountains, without daring to have houses or to till the earth for fear of Christians. The sight of one village was an infinite pain to us, a land very fertile and beautiful, abounding in springs and streams, the hamlets deserted and burned, the people thin and weak, all fleeing or in concealment. As they could not plant, they appeased their keen hunger by eating roots and the bark of trees. We bore a share in the famine along the whole way; for poorly could these unfortunates provide for us, themselves being so reduced they looked as though they would willingly die. They brought shawls from those concealed because of the Christians, and presented them to us; and they related how the Christians at other times had come through the land, destroying and burning the towns, carrying away half the men and all the women and boys, while those who had been able to escape were wandering about as fugitives. We found them so alarmed they dared not remain anywhere. Yet when God was pleased to bring us here, they began to respect us as the other Indians had done, and sometimes even more. Thence it may be seen that to bring all these people to be Christians and to the obedience of the Imperial Majesty, they must be won by kindness which is a way certain, and no other is.

Buckingham Smith

FRAY BERNARDINO DE SAHAGÚN
1499?-1590   Mexico

The long-lived Spanish Franciscan friar Sahagún reached New Spain in 1529 with a score of companions, and he devoted the rest of his life to educating his parishioners. He also studied and wrote about the Indian languages. To collect data on early Mexican history, he consulted elderly Indians and set down their words in one of the New World's most valuable documents, *La historia general de las cosas de Nueva España* (General History of the Affairs of New Spain). Part of it was history and part was pedagogy, as can be seen in the following selection.

GENERAL HISTORY OF THE
AFFAIRS OF NEW SPAIN

Book VI. Chapter 22: Which contains the counsels that the chief father or lord gave his son on decorum in everyday activities: eating, sleeping, drinking, speaking, listening, looking, and dressing.

My son, I have told you many things essential for your education and upbringing, so that you may live in this world as a gentleman, descendant of illustrious and upstanding people, and it remains for me to tell you other things worthy of being known and remembered, which have come down from our ancestors, and which should be told you unless I want to do you wrong.

First of all, you must be careful to awaken and watch and not sleep all night, so that people will not say of you that you are lazy and a sleepy head. Be careful to get up at midnight to pray and call on the name of our Lord who is everywhere, though invisible and impalpable, and take care to dust the places where the images stand and to burn incense before them.

Second: Be careful when in the street or on the highway to proceed sedately, neither too fast nor too slow, but with modesty and maturity. Do not go along bobbing your head from side to side, lest they say you are stupid or foolish and badly brought up, or that you walk like a child.

The third thing that you must note, my son, concerns your way of speaking. It behooves you to speak calmly, and not rapidly nor with anxiety, and do not speak loud, lest they call you loud-mouth or tone-deaf, or fool or madman or rustic; have a moderate tone, neither high nor low, and let your words be soft and gentle.

The fourth thing you should observe is that in the things you hear or see, especially if they are evil, keep silent and pretend that you have not heard them; and do not stare with curiosity at the face of people, nor notice the finery that they wear, nor the manner of their disposition, especially women, because the proverb has it: To stare at a woman is to rape her with your glance.

Fifth, be careful to avoid listening to things that do not concern you (above all if they are bad), especially details about other people. Let others say what they want, but pay no attention to it; pretend not to hear, and if you cannot get out of earshot when such affairs are discussed or when people are listening to them, do not answer or comment. Listen, but be careful not to speak.

Sixth, my son, you should be warned not to wait for people to call you twice. Answer the first time, and get up and see who is calling you, and if someone wants to send you somewhere, go in a hurry; if they ask you to carry something, take it without delay; be diligent and swift; do not be lazy; be like the wind. As soon as you receive your orders, be off! Do not delay to be summoned twice or told a second time, because to wait to be told twice or called twice is the way of a knave. That is what lazy people do, and vile and worthless people. And that is the reputation you would get, and you would be considered haughty, and for that reason it is a good plan quickly to put into your head or onto your shoulder whatever you are supposed to carry somewhere.

In the seventh place, I counsel you, my son, that your wearing apparel be unobtrusive and modest. Do not go to extremes in your clothing, nor be too fantastic. Do not choose over-embroidered robes, and at the same time, do not wear a dirty or tattered garb, for that is the sign of poverty or a low taste. Do not wear your gown dragging or too long, or you will trip over it, and do not tie it under your armpits so that it is too short. Although you see others doing these things, do not imitate them. Take care, my son, not to attract attention either because of your gown or your sandals.

My eighth advice, my son, is to consider the way you eat and drink. Be careful not to eat too much, morning or night. Be temperate when you dine, but if you toil, you should take food before you start. Good manners in eating means that when you dine, you do not eat too rapidly or too carelessly. You should not take too big bites of bread or put too much food into your mouth, lest you choke. Do not swallow like a dog. You will eat slowly and calmly, and when you drink, drink temperately. Do not make crumbs of your bread or snatch food from the plate. Eat calmly so that others at the table do not laugh at you. If you choke on your food or display bad manners, your table companions may feed you bountifully so that they may mock you and call you a glutton or a drunkard. Before you dine, wash your hands and lips. When you eat with others, never just sit down, but take the water and pitcher and pour water for them to wash, and after the meal, do the same and provide wash water for the rest. Then pick up the food that fell onto the floor and sweep the dining space; finally wash your hands and mouth and clean your teeth.

I have spoken these few words to you, my son, although there is much more I could say about decorum, that is necessary when one would live modestly, much of which the ancients declared, but you would not be able to remember it all. One thing I do want to say, and you will do well to remember it, because things taken from the treasures and coffers of our ancestors deserve to be remembered, was thus phrased by them: "The safe road along which to travel through this world is high and steep. If we deviate from it, we cannot help falling from a great height into a deep gully." By this I mean that it is necessary in all that we do and say to be guided by Providence.

Now you have heard everything that I have to say; in all things keep to the middle path.

W.K.J.

DIEGO DE LANDA
1524-1579   Mexico

Archbishop de Landa of Yucatán, who first arrived in New Spain in 1549, is remembered for two reasons. In 1562 he ordered all first-hand Mayan documents to be seized and burned as "works of the devil" in the public square of Mani. The documents consisted of picture writings set down on paper made out of pounded bark, joined together to form large, oblong books. Only three of them are believed to have escaped the flames. And, in 1566, de Landa wrote *Relación de las cosas de Yucatán* (Account of Things in Yucatán), with drawings and explanations of Mayan hieroglyphics, and observations on the native customs and culture of the last days of Mayan independence.

Lost for three centuries, de Landa's manuscript was discovered and given to the Royal Academy of History in Madrid in 1863, where it served to teach scholars how to interpret the inscriptions found on Mayan monuments and decipher their remarkable calendar. De Landa's style is not noteworthy. He strings many of his sentences together and mixes present and past tenses in a confusing way, but his work is one of the most valuable of early Spanish American documents.

ACCOUNT OF THINGS
IN YUCATÁN

XV. Cruelties of the Spaniards toward
the Indians

The Indians received rebelliously the Spanish yoke of servitude, but the Spaniards had well distributed the towns covering the territory. Still there were among the natives a few who stirred them up, on which account they inflicted very severe punishments that caused a diminution in the population. They burned alive several chief men of the Province of Cupul and hanged others. Charges were brought against the inhabitants of Yobain, a town of the Cheles, and the chief citizens were seized and put in stocks in one building that was then set on fire, burning them alive with the greatest inhumanity in the world. And Diego de Landa hereby says that he saw a gigantic tree in whose branches a captain hanged many Indian women with their children at their feet. And in the same village and in one two leagues away, called Verey, they hanged two Indian women, one a young girl and the other recently married whose only crime was that they were beautiful and might upset the Spanish soldiers. This act was to make the Indians realize that the Spaniards were not interested in their women; and the memory of these two has endured a long time among both Indians and Spaniards because of their extreme beauty and the cruel way in which they were killed . . .

The Spaniards gave as excuse the fact that, being so few in number, they would have been unable to control so many people without frightening them by terrible punishments, and they offer as an example the history of the Hebrews in The Promised Land, where because of God's commands they committed extreme cruelties. On the other hand, the Indians were right in defending their liberty and trusting to the most valiant among them, and they thought they would be brave against the Spaniards . . .

XXXI. Clothing and adornment of Yucatán's Indian women

(I say) that the Indian women of Yucatán are in general of better appearance than Spanish women and larger and well-built and without the big buttocks of Negresses. Those who are pretty are proud of it and, as a matter of fact, they are not unattractive; they are not light, but dark-skinned, more because of the sun and their continual bathing than by nature. They do not powder their faces as our women do, because they consider it immodest. Customarily they filed their teeth like saw-teeth because they consider that elegant, and the old women performed the task with certain stones and water.

They also pierced the septum of their noses in order to fill the hole with an amber stone, and they consider it pretty. They also pierced the ears for ear rings like their husbands; they tattooed the body from the waist up—except the breasts, because of nursing—using patterns more dainty and beautiful than those of the men. They bathed very frequently in cold water, like the men, with no thought of modesty, because they were accustomed to strip naked in the places from which they took drinking water. Sometimes they would bathe in water heated by fire, but not very often, and more because of health than to get clean.

Like their husbands, they would anoint themselves with red salve, and if possible would also use a certain product of sticky, perfumed gum, which I believe is liquid amber, though they call it *iztah-te*. This they applied by means of a brick-like soap which was gaily decorated, and with it they would grease their breasts, arms and shoulders, and then they thought they were very attractive. Depending on the quality of the ointment, it often lasted for them a long time.

They wore their hair very long and they used to,—and still do,—arrange it attractively in two sections, and they would braid it as another sort of hair-do. The mothers took a great deal of care in arranging the hair of marriageable girls, and I have seen many Indian girls with as elaborate coiffures as any of the most husband-conscious Spanish women. Until they grow up, the little girls wear their hair in two or four pigtails, which is very becoming.

The Indian women of the coast, of the Provinces of Bacalar and Campeche, are very modest in their attire because in addition to the skirt from the waist to the ankles, they covered their breasts, tying a doubled shawl under their armpits. The only garment of the other Indians was a long, wide bag, open at both sides, and it reached to their thighs, and they fastened it by the ends. In addition they carried the blanket with which they always sleep, and which they folded and rolled up when they were on the road.

XLI. Cycle of the Mayas. Their writing

Not only did the Indians keep account of the year and the months, as I recorded previously, but they had a way of counting time and affairs by epochs composed of twenty year periods, reckoning thirteen twenties, named with one of the twenty let-

ters of their days that they call Ahau, not in order, but reckoned
backward as can be seen in my illustration.

In their language they call these periods Katunes, and by
means of them it is remarkably easy to keep track of their
epochs, and so it was not difficult for the old man whom I mentioned in the first chapter to speak of events that had happened
three hundred years earlier.

I do not know who devised this count by Katunes. If it was
the Demon, he did what honors him, and if it was a man, he
must have been a great idolater because he added all the deceits,
omens, and trickery with which these people walked in their
misery, completely deceived; and so this was the science to
which they gave most belief and most greatly esteemed and
which even the priests could not completely figure out. The way
they had of reckoning their affairs and making their divinations
was that in their temples they had two idols dedicated to two of
these characters. To the first one, according to the cross above
my circular plan, they offered their worship and sacrifices to escape plagues during a twenty year epoch. But after the first ten
of the twenty had passed, they did nothing but burn incense
and revere it. And when the twenty years of the first idol was
completed, they began to follow the fortunes of the second, and
sacrifice to it, and they would get rid of the first idol and set up
the second to be worshipped for ten years . . .

LII. Conclusion

The Indians have not lost, but rather have gained with the coming of the Spaniards, even in small matters; but it is no wonder,
because in spite of the fact that at first the changes were forced
upon them, they have begun to enjoy and make use of them.
Now they have many fine horses and mules and machos. Asses
do not thrive and I believe it is wrong to provide them, because
they are bad-tempered and destructive. There are many fine
cows, pigs, sheep, goats, and such dogs as are useful, and these
are the things that can be counted among the beneficial contributions to the Indies. Cats are useful and necessary, and the

Indians are fond of them. Chickens and doves, oranges, limes, citrons, grapes, pomegranates, and many vegetables. But only the melons and calabashes provide more seeds; for the rest, seed from Mexico is necessary. Silk of very good quality is also produced.

The Indians also have iron tools and the use of mechanical devices that have profited them. The use of money and many other things from Spain, things without which the Indians previously got along all right, allow them to live more like human beings, helped in their physical activities and in their growth according to the precepts of philosophy, art, and nature.

Not only has God given them through the Spanish nation this increase in material things so necessary to man, so that whatever they give in repayment to the Spaniards is little, but there have also come to them what cannot be bought or deserved: justice and Christianity and the peace in which they live, which makes them still further indebted to Spain and the Spaniards, and especially to the very Catholic Monarchs who with continued care and lofty Christianity have provided and continue to provide these two benefits—much more than their original founders, those evil parents who begat them in sin and as children of wrath, while Christianity creates them in grace for the enjoyment of eternal life . . .

W.K.J.

PEDRO CIEZA DE LEÓN
1520-1554   Peru

When Francisco Pizarro moved southward into Peru in 1522, missionary writers followed him. One outstanding chronicler among them was Cieza de León, whose *Señorió de los Incas* (Kingdom of the Incas) is a detailed account of Indian customs, while his *Crónica del Perú* (The Chronicle of Peru) concerns the rivalry among the Spanish leaders trying to take possession of the territory. Cieza de León wrote in long sentences linked by semicolons, and his chapters contain few paragraphs. Addi-

tional punctuation and paragraphs have been provided
in the translation that follows.

THE CHRONICLE OF PERU

Chapter II: Concerning the founding of Panama
and why I write about that before anything else

Before I begin writing of the affairs of the Kingdom of Peru, I
would like to report what I know about the origin and beginnings of the inhabitants of these Indies of the New World, especially of the natives of Peru, following the account that they
report having heard from their ancestors, although it is actually
a mystery whose truth only God knows. However since my chief
purpose, in the first part of my chronicle, is to describe the land
of Peru and tell of the founding of the cities in it, along with the
rites and ceremonies of the Indians of the kingdom, I shall leave
their origin and beginning (I mean what they say about it and
what we can presume) for the second part, where I shall deal
fully with it. And since, as I say, in this part, I am to describe
the founding of many cities, I believe that if, in ancient times
Dido founded Carthage and gave it a name and government,
and Romulus founded Rome, and Alexander, Alexandria, and
because of that, achieved eternal memory and fame, even more
and with greater reason shall the glory and fame of His Majesty
be perpetuated throughout the centuries. In his royal name have
been founded in the great Kingdom of Peru so many and such
rich cities where His Majesty has given laws to the natives that
they may live quietly and in peace. And since, before the cities
were founded and settled in Peru, the city of Panama was
founded and settled, in the Province of Tierra-Firme called Castilla del Oro, I am beginning with it, even though there are
other cities of superior qualities in the kingdom. But I am doing
so because at the time of the conquest, it was from here that the
captains sailed for the discovery of Peru and from here came the
horses and arms and everything else for the conquest.

Therefore I start with this city and then I shall enter the port of Uraba in the Province of Cartagena, not far from the great River of Darien, where I shall give account of the Indian villages, and the Spanish towns from there to the town of Plata and the site of Potosí that are the southern limits of Peru where, according to my figuring, there are more than twelve hundred leagues of road. I traversed most of them and I dealt with, saw, and got acquainted with the things that I mention in this history; and I have observed carefully and diligently all of them so that I can write as truthfully as I should in this history without including any improper things.

I say, therefore, that the city of Panama was founded near the South Sea and eighteen leagues from Nombre de Dios, which is a settlement beside the North Sea. It is limited in area on account of a swamp or lagoon that hems it in on one side. And on account of the vapors that come from it, it is considered to be unhealthy. It is laid out and built on an east-west axis in such a way that when the sun comes out, people cannot walk in its streets because there is absolutely no shade. And this is especially felt because the climate is very hot and because the sun is so lethal that if a man were to remain out in it, even for only a few hours, it would so effect him that he would die. And this has happened to many people. Half a league inland there were attractive and healthy locations where they could originally have built the city. But today since the houses are now very valuable on account of the cost of building, even though everyone realizes the obvious dangers of living in so unsanitary a location, the city has never been relocated; and chiefly because the old conquistadores are all dead and the present citizens are businessmen who intend to remain only long enough to make themselves rich; and so, some come and others go, and nobody has any regard for the public good.

Near this city runs a river that originates in the mountains. It also has much nearby land and many other rivers on some of which the Spaniards have estates and farms, and have planted much brought from Spain, like orange, citron, and fig trees. In addition there are many native fruit trees, fragrant pineapples and bananas, an abundance of excellent guayabas, star apples, aguacates, and other fruit common to the land. In the fields can be seen large herds of cattle because the land is well adapted to their production. The rivers are full of gold, and so, as soon as the city was founded, a large quantity was extracted.

The city is easily provisioned since supplies come from both oceans. When I say both, I mean the North Sea, across which ships come from Spain to Nombre de Dios, and the South Sea with navigation from Panama to all the Peruvian ports. In the confines of the city neither wheat nor barley is grown. The owners of the estates raise a quantity of corn, and from Peru and Spain flour can always be obtained. There is fish in all of the rivers and there is excellent fishing in the ocean, although different from the kinds found in the waters around Spain; along the coast, near the houses of the city, in the sand can be found some very small clams that they call *chucha*, and of which there is a great quantity, and I believe that at the moment of settling, it was on account of these clams that the city was located in this spot, because with them around the Spaniards could be assured they would not suffer from hunger.

In the rivers there are many alligators so large and fierce that they make a remarkable sight. In the Cenu River I have seen many of a monstrous size and I have eaten many of the eggs that they lay on the shore. One of these alligators we found high and dry along what they call the San Jorge River, when I went exploring with Capt. Alonso de Cáceres in the Province of Urute, so huge and ungainly that it measured more than twenty-five feet long. And we killed it with our lances, and its ferocity was something to see, and after killing it, we ate it, since we were starving. The meat is bad and with an annoying odor. These alligators or crocodiles have eaten many Spaniards and horses and Indians who were crossing rivers, traveling from one place to another.

Within the boundaries of this city few natives are to be found, since all have been destroyed by the harsh treatment they received from the Spaniards, and from the diseases they contracted. The major part of the city is populated, as I have said, by many honored merchants coming from everywhere; they do business here and in Nombre de Dios, and business is so great that it is almost comparable to that of the city of Venice because ships arrive frequently in this city from ports in the South Sea to unload their cargos of gold and silver, and the number of ships sailing across the North Sea to Nombre de Dios is very great, and a great deal of the merchandise reaches this region by boats up the Chagre River, which is five leagues from Panama, from where it is transported by many large trains of pack animals that the merchants have for this purpose. Near the city, the river makes an *ancón*, or open bay, where the ships come, and at high tide they can enter the port, which is excellent for small ships.

Pedrarias de Ávila, former governor of Tierra-Firme, founded and settled this city of Panama in the name of the invincible monarch, Carlos Augustus, King of Spain, our Lord, in the year 1520; and it is eight degrees north of the Equator. It has a good port, where the ships can enter and beach at ebb tide. The high and low tides in the sea differ so much that more than a half league of beach is left dry at low tide, only to be covered again at high tide. As a result, there is a problem of anchorage, I believe, because at low tide the ships find bottom at three fathoms, but when the tide is high, it is at seven fathoms. And since in this chapter I have dealt with the city of Panama and its location, in the next I shall tell of the ports and rivers that there are along the coast as far as Chile. In this way, my work will have great clarity.

W.K.J.

GARCILASO INCA DE LA VEGA
1539-1616   Peru

Of all the historians of Inca civilization, Garcilaso de la Vega was best qualified for the task. Son of a Spanish conquistador and the granddaughter of Tupac Inca Yupanqui, and related to the famous Spanish poet of the

same name, Garcilaso was born in Cuzco, and spent his
childhood among the Indians. At the age of twenty he
was sent to Spain to study. He fought in several wars,
and then returned to Córdoba where he wrote *La Florida del Inca* (Wanderings of Hernando de Soto, 1605).
Four years later, he completed the first volume of *Comentarios reales* (Royal Commentaries), about the ancient history and customs of his mother's people, and
one of Latin America's great works of literature.

The second volume, published in Córdoba in 1617,
concerns the Spanish conquest. In his attempts to defend his Indian ancestors, Garcilaso lapses into pane-
gyrics and frequently exaggerates their qualities and
riches in his appeal to the imagination of the Spaniards
for whom he was writing. But his work, based on first-
hand knowledge, is entertaining literature and has been
of incalculable value to all subsequent historians.

Sir Paul Rycaut made a faulty translation during the
reign of James II, published first in 1688, and it was also
translated in the compilation by Samuel Purchas, *Purchas His Pilgrimes* (1625), from which three excerpts
are reprinted here.

ROYAL COMMENTARIES

Part I

Blasco Nunnez de Balboa, An. 1513, discovered the South Sea,
& was thereof made Adelantado, and the conquest of those Regions granted him by the Catholike Kings. He made three or
foure Ships for discovery, one of which passed the line to the
South, sailing along the coast; and seeing an Indian Fisherman
at the mouth of a River, foure of the Spaniards went ashore
farre from the place where he was, being good runners and
swimmers to take him.

The Indian marvailing what kinde of creature the Ship under saile might be, was taken in the midst of his muse and carried a shipboard. They asked him by signes and words (being

somewhat refreshed after that dreadful surprize and bearded sight) what Countrie that was, and how called. The Indian not understanding what they demanded, answered and told them his proper name, saying Beru, and added another word, saying Pelu: as if he should have said, if yee aske me what I am, my name is Beru, and if you aske me whence, I was in the River, Pelu being the common name of a River in that language. The Christians conceived that hee had understood them, and answered to the purpose; and from that time Anno 1515, or 1516. they called by the name of Peru that great and rich Empire, corrupting both names, as they use in Indian words. Some later authors call it Piru. After the discovery of the Incas Kingdome the name still continued, howsoever the Natives to this day (seventie two years since the conquest) will not take it in their mouthes, although they speake with Spaniards and understand them: neither have they one generall name for all those Provinces, as Spaine, Italy, France with us, but call each by its proper name; and the whole Kingdome they call Tavantinsuyu, that is to say, the fourth part of the World. That River also where they tooke the Indian, was after by the Spaniards called Peru. Yucatán received the name from like accident, the first discoverers asking the place the Indian answering tectetán, tectetán, that is, "I understand you not," which they understood of the proper appellation and corruptly called the place Yucatán.

Later Garcilaso writes about the rulers of the Indians.

Touching the originall of the Incas Kings of Peru, this author affirmeth, that when hee was a childe, his mother residing in Cusco her Countrie, every weeke there came to visite her some of her kindred which had escaped the tyrannies of Atau-huallpa, at which time their ordinary discourse was alway of the originall of their Kings, of their Majestie and great Empire, Conquests, and Government: such discourses the Incas and Pallas hold in their visitations, bewailing their losses. Whiles I was a boy I rejoyced to heare them as children delight to heare tales, but being growne to sixteene or seventeene yeares of age,

when they were one day at my Mother's in this discourse, I spake
to the ancientest (my Mother's Uncle) desiring him to tell me
what he knew of their first Kings, seeing they kept not memory
of their antiquities, as the Spaniards use in writing, which by
their Bookes can tell all their antiquities and changes which
have happened since God made the World. I desired him to tell
me what traditionary memorials he had of their Originals. He
willing to satisfie my request, recounted to me in manner following, advising mee to lay up these sayings in my heart.

In old times all this region was untilled and over-growne
with bushes, and the people of those times lived as wilde beasts,
without religion or policie, without towne or house, without till-
ing or sowing the ground, without raiment, for they knew not
how to worke Cotton or Weoll to make them garments. They
lived by two and two, or three and three, in caves and holes of
the ground, eating grasse like beasts, and rootes of trees, and
wilde fruits, and man's flesh. They covered themselves with
leaves, and barkes of trees, and skins of Beasts, and others in
leather. Once, they lived as wilde beasts, and their women were
in common and brutish. Our Father the Sunne (this was the
Incas manner of speech, because they derived their pedegree
from the Sunne; and for any besides the Incas to say so, was
blasphemie, and incurred stoning) seeing men live in this fashion, tooke pittie on them, and sent from heaven a Sonne and a
Daughter of his owne, to instruct men in the knowledge of our
Father the Sunne, and to worship him for their God; to give
them lawes also and precepts of humane and reasonable course
of life in civill fashion, to dwell in houses and townes, to husband the earth, to sowe and set, to breede cattle. With these
ordenances our father the Sunne placed these his two children
in the lake Titicaca, eightie leagues from Cusco; and gave them
a barre of Gold two fingers thicke, and halfe a yard long, for a
signe that where that barre should melt with one blow on the
ground, there they should place their residence and Court.
Lastly, hee commanded that when they had reduced the people
to serve him, they should uphold them in justice with clemencie
and gentlenesse, behaving themselves as a pittifull Father deal-

eth with his tender and beloved children, like as he himselfe
gave them example in giving light and heate to all the world,
causing the seedes and grasse to grow, and the trees to fructifie,
the cattle to encrease, the seasons to be faire, and encompassing
the world once every day: that they should imitate him, and
become benefactors to the Nations, being sent to the earth for
that purpose. Hee constituted also and named them Kings and
Lords of all the Nations which they should instruct and civilize.

After these instructions he left them, and they went up from
Titicaca travelling to the North, still as they went striking with
that barre of Gold, which never melted. Thus they entered into
a resting place seven or eight leagues Southwards from this Citie
Cusco, now called Pacarec Tampu, that is, Morning Sleepe, and
there slept till morning, which he afterwards caused to be peo-
pled, and the inhabitants boast greatly of this name, which the
Inca imposed. Thence they travelled to this valley of Cusco,
which was then a wilde wildernesse, and staid first in the hill-
ocke, called Huanacanti, in the midst of the Citie; and there
making proofe, his Golden Barre easily melted at one stroake,
and was no more seene. Then said our Inca to his Sister and
Wife: "In this Valley our Father the Sunne commands us to
make our aboade."

*In Book II, Chapter 27, the author tells of the early litera-
ture of his people:*

The Amautas, who were the Phylosophers, were skilled at
composing Comedies and Tragedies that on solemn feast days
were performed before the rulers and their guests at Court. The
Actors were not base persons but Incas and the Nobilitie and
children of the *Curaras* or Governors, and war leaders even to
the commanders, in order that the dramas might be properly
performed. The Arguments were the acts of their ancestors, of
the deeds and grandeur of dead kings and other heroic men, besides military deeds, triumphs, and victories. The plots of the
Comedies dealt with agriculture and homey and familiar things
. . . They had no base or dishonest parts intermixed, nor vile

or low entremeses; all dealt with serious and honorable affairs.
And those who performed well received jewels and gifts.

They made Verses short and long with measuring the syllables without rimes, I have given an instance: the argument is
(like that of Jupiter and Juno in our Poets) the daughter of a
King had a pitcher full of water to moisten the earth, which her
brother brake, and with the blow caused thunders and light-
nings. They were found in knots and particoloured threads
called *quipus*, being very ancient. The words are thus in Peruan
and English, the syllables also in like number and meeter.

Cumac Nusta	Fairest of Nimphes
Totallay quim	Thine owne Brother,
Puynnuy quita	This thy Pitcher
Paquir Cayan	Now is breaking;
Hina Mantara	Whose hard striking
Cunun numum	Thunder, lightens,
Ylla pantac	And throwes fire-bolts.
Camri Nusta	But thou sweet Nimph,
Unuyn Quita	Thy faire Pitcher
Para Munqui	Pouring, rainest:
May nimpiri	Sometimes also
Chichi munqui	Thou sendst forth haile,
Riti munqui	Thou sendst forth snow.
Pacha rurac	The worlds maker,
Pacha camac	Pachacamac
Vira cocha	Viracocha
Cay hinapac	To this office
Churasunqui	Hath thee placed
Cama sunqui.	And authorised.

Samuel Purchas

RUIZ DÍAZ DE GUZMÁN
1558-1629   Paraguay

America's first native-born historian was a mestizo of
Asunción whose original chronicles of the conquest have
been lost. However, parts of another work by Ruiz,
La Argentina manuscrita (The Argentine Manuscript),
completed about 1612, have been preserved. Its chap-
ters include his story of Lucia Miranda, courted by two
Indian chiefs, which became the basis of *Siripo*, the first
Argentine drama and other later works, and the story of
La Maldonada, a Paraguayan version of Androcles and
the lion.

THE ARGENTINE MANUSCRIPT

Chapter 12. Madame Maldonada and
the lioness

About this time, Buenos Aires was suffering from a terrible famine. Lacking food, the inhabitants were eating frogs, snakes, and
any rotting meat found in the fields. Some even ate the excre-
ment of others, having reached such extremes of hunger as when
Titus and Vespasian besieged Jerusalem and its inhabitants ate
human flesh. This is what happened here, also, because those
who were alive sustained themselves on the flesh of those who
died, even those who were hanged as criminals, of whom nothing was left but bones. And there was one man who kept himself alive on the entrails of his own brother who had died. Finally almost everybody perished, but it happened that one Spanish woman, unable to endure her hunger, decided to leave the
settlement and go to live among the Indians.

Starting up the coast, she got as far as Punta Gorda in the
mountains. Then since night was approaching, she looked for
shelter. Finding a cave in a gorge along the coast, she went inside, only to face a fierce mountain lioness about to give painful

birth to cubs. Frightened almost to death, the woman fainted. When she recovered, she was lying at the feet of the lioness.

The lioness, seeing such prey, was about to tear the woman to pieces, but the natural goodness of the beast made it pity the woman, and ceasing its growling and the fury of its attack, it became more kindly toward her. And the woman, no longer frightened, assisted in the lion-birth and helped produce two little cubs. She remained in the cave for several days, recovering, fed by food brought by the lioness for her cubs. The woman was well-pleased by the treatment she received for her midwifery.

It happened that one day some Indians came upon her as she was going to the river for water, and they took her to their village and one of them made her his woman. And about what happened then, I shall tell you later . . .

Chapter 13

A surprising event occurred and so I'll tell about it. Chance had it that a Spanish captain, exploring the region, found in one village the Spanish woman that I mentioned previously. He brought her back to civilization. When Francisco Ruiz Galán saw her, he ordered her thrown to the wild beasts to be eaten. To carry out his orders, the soldiers took the poor woman and tied her to a tree about a league beyond the settlement where great numbers of wild animals hunted food. Among them came the lioness that this woman had helped deliver of cubs. And when it recognized her, it defended her from the other creatures that wanted to rip her to bits. Remaining at her side, the lioness protected her that night, the next day and night, until the third night when the captain sent out several soldiers to see what had happened to that woman.

Finding her alive and with the lioness and her two cubs at her feet—wild beasts that withdrew without attacking the soldiers, to let the men reach her—the Spaniards were amazed at the instinct and humanity of that wild animal. Untying the woman, they took her with them, with the lioness roaring in a display of feeling and solicitude for its benefactor, at the same

time revealing its royal spirit and gratitude and a humanity not
possessed by men. And so this woman, condemned to death and
exposed to wild animals, became free.

I knew this woman, and her name was Maldonada, that is to
say, "Badly Endowed," when it should have been Biendonado,
because quite evidently she did not deserve her punishment,
since necessity had forced her to leave her people and seek shelter among the Indians. Some attribute this severe punishment
to Captain Alvarado and not to Francisco Ruiz, but whoever
was responsible, it happened as I described it, and it was a display of almost unheard-of cruelty.

W.K.J.

ALONSO DE OVALLE
1601-1651   Chile

Many critics consider the Jesuit priest Ovalle the greatest Chilean master of prose. Born in Santiago, he studied
there and in Córdoba, and became rector of Chile's
Seminary of San Francisco Javier. In 1640 he was called
to Rome where he found such ignorance of his country
that he wrote *Histórica relación del Reino de Chile*
(Historic Account of the Realm of Chile, 1646). More
than a simple history, it deals with customs, describes
people and places, and traces the progress of the Church
in Chile. While the style is uneven, the language is so
pure that the Spanish Royal Academy uses quotations
from it in its dictionary, and lists its author as a *maestro
del idioma* (master of the language). The work was apparently written in Italy. On his way back to Chile,
Ovalle died in Lima of a malignant fever.

HISTORIC ACCOUNT OF THE REALM OF CHILE

Usages and customs of the native inhabitants

The Chilean women are so vigorous that, sometimes when it is necessary and there are no men around, they take up arms as though they were men. And they play Chueca (like Lacrosse) which is the game that best demonstrates the agility and speed of the Indians in the competition, rivalry, and persistence with which each team of from thirty to fifty players tries to get the ball to its goal, the members of one team helping each other against its opponents and playing different positions to be the better able to help their side, striking the ball and advancing it in spite of the resistance of the other side. And when two players converge on it, they dash like deer after the ball, one to knock it along and the other to follow and advance it into enemy territory toward their goal. It is fun to watch, and many people attend the game that often takes all afternoon to decide who get the prizes and sometimes it doesn't end, and they have to finish it the next day.

The strength and courage of the women come from the way they are brought up, unspoiled and unprotected, without regard for sun, cold, or other inclemencies of the weather. In the coldest part of the winter, when even the birds freeze, they wash their heads in cold water and let the wind dry them. And they bathe their children in the river, starting when they are very young, and after childbirth they get out of bed in a very short time and go about the duties of the house, as if it had been some other woman who had suffered the dangers and pains of childbearing.

If women do this, what about the man? It is quite noticeable how little they shun the water, even in the coldest weather; and it is remarkable to see an Indian on the road, with no protection except the simple costume that, as we have said, he usually wears, no hat on his head and no protection from the inclemen-

cies of the sky. I have often seen them walking in severe rain-
storms, with the water pouring down on their heads and running off their feet, looking like ducks, soaked and thoroughly
chilled, yet laughing in disregard of their travail, that for most
people would be intolerable.

I remember, apropos of this, hearing of a remark by a witty
gentleman to one of our priests, recently arrived from Europe
and full of zeal and charity for his neighbor, who was unhappy
at seeing the Indians so naked in the winter (which is severe in
those regions) and so poorly protected from the rain. The priest
started to pity him in his conversation with the gentleman, so
the Chilean asked him a question.

"What protection does Your Reverence have on your face to
protect it from the cold?"

"None, sir," replied the priest.

"Why not? How can you endure such cold, with your face
unprotected against the wind?"

"I'm accustomed to it," the priest told him.

"Well, then," the caballero told him, "think of the Indians
as all face, because from childhood they are accustomed to having their bodies as little covered as we see this Indian, exposed
to cold and rain, and so they are all face. Tell me, Holy Father,
who would feel sympathy for a trout in the water on a chilly
day? Nobody, because it is so natural and they've been brought
up in this element! We can say the same about these Indians
who, like the fish, have spent their lives under these conditions.
So you must not consider it strange."

With such exposure, their skin is so tough and their flesh so
like iron that a blow that would put the stoutest Spaniard into
bed, or a chill he would avoid for fear of catching cold, would be
taken by the Indian in stride, with little attention paid to it. I
have seen their heads split open by a blow with a *Chueca* stick
when someone was fighting them for the ball as they played
Chueca, or a similar blow on the shin or some other part of the
body that left a wound six inches long. And they paid no attention to it, but kept on with their regular duties. And sometimes
I've seen them wash off the blood with cold water and apply

herbs and remedies that seem to be very potent and must be
good for their constitution because they get well quickly and
throw off their attacks and diseases much more easily than the
Spanish do.

Calamities of captivity

It would be a great calamity, as who could doubt, to see Spaniards captured by these barbarians, who in addition to being such,
hate the Spaniards for killing so many of them and destroying
their land, subjecting them to slavery and capturing what no one
else had been able to conquer before the Spaniards arrived. This
feeling kills all sense of pity in the Indians for those they capture, and so they use them with all sorts of severity in the town
and in the field, starving them, keeping them poorly clothed,
disregarding their illnesses, and mistreating them as much as
possible.

But though it is heartbreaking to see such noble people,
brought up in comfort, reduced to so vile and miserable an existence, what exceeds all human endurance is to see delicate ladies who had done everything to escape such inhuman captivity,
subjected to the same treatment; their delicate upbringing and
feminine weakness makes them more susceptible to pain and
more worthy of compassion from those who see them, so far
from their loved ones and captives of those terrible enemies
among whom there may be a few sympathetic toward their trouble, but most pay no attention to it.

I don't know whether the Indians stripped the women of
their clothes, as they do the men, but the most pity they showed
was to look at them rather as their women than as their slaves.
Time itself compelled them to dress as Indians, since their own
clothes would last only a little while and after that they would
have to accommodate themselves to the weather and the customs
of the land, covering themselves with some sad blanket, without
skirts or other clothes to which they were accustomed, their feet
bare on the ground, a few skins for bed, and everything else
connected with eating and living on the lowest and most miser-

able scale possible; because if the Indians spend their lives scorning the conveniences and comforts that the Spanish know, how
could their slaves do anything else? A bit of *mote*, which is corn
boiled in water, was their usual sustenance, beans and herbs and
similar plants made up their fare. This was their bread, mixed
with tears when they set down to eat, not at tables, but on the
ground, remembering the comforts and good food that they had
known and enjoyed in their own homes.

                                                          W.K.J.

FRANCISCO NÚÑEZ DE PINEDA Y BASCUÑÁN
1607-1682   Chile

As the son of the famous conquistador don Alvaro,
Pineda became a prize possession when captured in
the battle of Cangrejeras (1629) by the Araucanian
chief, Maulicán. His life was spared and, during his
seven months of captivity, he was exhibited in various
towns and got to know the Indians. He was then ran-
somed for two hundred pesos in silver. He lived to occupy high posts in the frontier army, to become governor of Valdivia in 1673, and later to become a Peruvian
official.

Twenty years after his captivity, using the literary
training the Jesuits had given him, Pineda wrote *El
cautiverio feliz y razón de las guerras dilatadas de Chile*
(The Happy Captivity and the Reason for the Numerous Wars of Chile). Wars were "numerous," according
to the Indians, "because of Spanish cruelty." Influenced
by Spanish novels, he gave his work a fictional swing,
with dialogue, suspense, and intrigue. As a good Christian, he also included moral precepts and admonitions
concerning righteous living and justice. The manuscript
was not printed until 1863.

The following passages include a chapter of the first
book, in which Pineda is captured following the battle
of Cangrejas, and, from the third book, the description
of a feast and the offer of an Indian wife.

THE HAPPY CAPTIVITY

The beginning of the captivity
Book I. Chapter IX

In the midst of these tribulations and anguish, I found myself three or four times unsaddled and without my horse. I raised my hands and soul to heaven with trust, and when I least expected it, I once more found myself on the horse and firm in the saddle. The force of the current was so swift and strong that I will never know by what luck my horse got to the other bank of the Biobío River. The rest, who were with us, were carried more than 1000 feet down the river from where my companion, the other soldier, and I scrambled out, along with another Indian who was riding a spirited horse.

When I found myself safe from that terrible danger (for even in the bloody battle I had not worried about nor feared death), I did not cease to give infinite thanks to God for having rescued me from the rapid current. Although the Indians had been brought up along its water, two of the men drowned and the rest were swept from their horses.

When the soldier, my companion, estimated that the Indians were more than 1000 feet down the river, he had me lead his horse by the bridle from a great ravine which walled in the banks of the river. He said to me in a determined voice: "Captain, this is a good time for us to escape and avoid greater risks. And since the opportunity has presented itself, there's no reason why we shouldn't take it. These enemies cannot quickly escape from dangers and risks in which they find themselves, so in the meantime we can outdistance them. And even though we have only a small advantage, they will not dare to follow our footsteps, for the fear that they have that our army might come in pursuit of them, right down to these banks; since this is still our land."

After we talked for a quarter of an hour, we saw an Indian coming out of the water, like the rest, without his horse, that

had drowned. We asked him about our captors on the chance
they had been seen to escape from the river. He told us that he
thought my captor (Chief Maulicán) must have drowned, because he saw two dead Indians floating down the current. I was
worried by his words, thinking there might be arguments now
about who was my master, and in the midst of their quarrel I
might be killed as the best way to end any bad feeling between
either side. With these considerations, we went walking down
stream looking for our masters. We met another Indian who
assured us that some had crawled out and that my captor had
taken shelter on a small island, where he was preparing his horse
to swim with him to the mainland. With this information we
started on and soon we sighted him on the island with other
companions who had escaped to the island. Having driven their
horses ahead of them, they were swimming along behind. As
soon as I recognized my captor's horse, with my last bit of
strength I hurried to seize it, and I took it by the bridle, and my
companion had caught his chief's horse in the same way. When
my captor saw me holding his horse by the bridle, he began to
embrace me. He said to me very joyfully: "Captain, I thought
you had already returned to your land. I am happy to see you
since you have returned my soul to my body. Come, embrace me
again and be very sure that if so far I had desired fervently to
save you and look after your life, this act that you have now
performed for me has so won me over that I will see myself dead
rather than allow misfortune to come to you. And I give you my
word of honor that you may return to your land and look again
joyfully on your father and your friends."

A feast
Book III. Chapter XXXI

That night was given over to dancing and festivities with which
they are accustomed to follow their plowing and their planting,
and since the sun had set, my companion remained with us. The
chief, Quilalebo, who was giving the feast, celebrated his arrival
with more than usual ceremony, because he was truly ostenta-

tious and gallant in his actions. After we had feasted splendidly, the old chiefs, the one from Villarrica, and I went to the fire where the dance had already begun. The chiefs begged me to dance with them, and I did so to please them. In the midst of this entertainment, Quilalebo, my new friend, brought his daughter to me, who was among those dancing. He brought her and some of the other girls to where we were watching and told her to take my hand and dance with me because he had given her to me as my wife. The rest of the chiefs chose among those girls who had accompanied Quilalebo's daughter and began dancing hand in hand with them. At the persuasion of her father and the rest of the ancient chiefs, I did the same thing after the girls toasted us. That is what the unmarried girls are accustomed to doing when they want the unmarried men to dance with them, or when they wish to flatter the old chiefs. And in this way they frequently find husbands at these feasts and dances, which they call "gnapitun."

On this occasion the girl's mother came to where we were standing, and engaged in conversation. She offered me a jar of clear, sweet corn liquor from the earthen jugs that Chief Lepumante had sent for me. She treated me as her son-in-law, signifying that she was happy that her husband, Quilalebo, had given her daughter to me. She was one of the principal ladies of Valdivia, and said her child was the granddaughter of one of the ancient conquistadors. At that time she told me his name, but since it did not matter to me that she had been involved with one of those barbarians, I did not try to remember the name. I took advantage of the occasion to tell her about the obstacles which prevented my marrying her daughter. I gave her polite and agreeable reasons, repeating what I had previously told the girl. Since she was an understanding woman, even though primitive in language, dress, and customs, she told me that my reasons seemed just, but nevertheless, her husband had wanted me to entertain and dance hand in hand with his daughter. The old lady took one of her daughter's hands and one of mine, and between the two of them, showing my excitement and happiness, I did what the rest of the people were doing. And although

I was present in body, because I could not help it, in the midst
of these dancers, my spirit and heart remained in God's presence as I sought His help and guidance which He bestows mercifully to those who fear and love Him. For this is the doctrine
of Saint Paul.

Connie Wick

JOSÉ DE ACOSTA
1539-1616   Peru

Jesuit-trained Padre Acosta exemplified the Renaissance
spirit by investigating and reasoning, rather than blindly
accepting dogma. For that reason, his *Historia natural y
moral de las Indias* (Natural and Moral History of the
Indies, 1590) differs from most accounts of the peoples
and geographical regions of the New World. The first
four volumes deal with natural history, and his approach
was scientific to the point of questioning the Bible. The
last three volumes concern the inhabitants of the New
World, their governments and their cultures. Here
again, his enlightened viewpoint differed from the generally held idea that Indians were ignorant people, fit
only to be slaves. Because the book was written after his
return to Spain, "here" in the text refers to Europe and
"there" to South America.

NATURAL AND MORAL HISTORY
OF THE INDIES

Book IV. Chapter 36: How can there be
animals in the Indies such as exist
in no other parts of the world

It is even more difficult to find out the origin of such animals in
the Indies as are not found in this part of the world. Because if
the Creator produced them there, then there is no use talking

about Noah's Ark, nor any need for having saved, back in those days, all the species of the birds and the animals, if they were going to be created again. Nor does it seem that with the six days of creation, God left the world finished and perfect, if other kinds of animals were still unformed, especially perfect animals in no way inferior to those already known. And if we say that all these different kinds of animals were saved in Noah's Ark, and it follows that those animals went to the Indies from this part of the world, then those others, not found in this part of the world must have gone along, too. If this is true, I would like to know how come no examples of them remain around here, but are found only in strange and foreign parts of the world? This is certainly a question that has long perplexed me. I say, for instance, if the Peruvian sheep, that they call *alpacas* and *llamas*, are not found in any other part of the world, then who took them to Peru or how did they go, since there is no trace of them elsewhere? And if they didn't go from some other part of the world, then how were they produced and formed there? Did God perhaps make a second creation of animals? And what I say about the *alpaca* and the *guanaco*, I can say of a thousand different kinds of birds and animals unknown by name or appearance to the Romans or the Greeks or to any of the present European nations. Unless we can say that although all the animals left the Ark by natural instinct or divine Providence, some of them went to other regions where they liked it so well that they did not want to go anywhere else, or if they did leave, they were not preserved, or in time they died out, as happens in many cases. And when you come to think of it, that is not a situation confined to the Indies, but it is true of many places in Asia, Europe, and Africa, in all of which one reads of different animals not found elsewhere, or if they are found, it is known that they were brought from there. Well, since these animals came from the Ark, for instance, elephants that are found only in India, and from there they were taken elsewhere, we might say the same of these animals of Peru and of the rest of the Indies, that cannot be found elsewhere in the world. One ought also to consider whether these animals differ specifically and essentially from all the others, or whether it is an accidental difference that could be caused by various accidents, as among the races of man one finds blacks and whites, giants and dwarfs. Also, for instance, in monkeys one finds some with tails and some without, in sheep, there are some smooth and some woolly, some big and strong and with long necks, like those of Peru, and others smaller, weaker, and with short necks like the sheep of Castile. But to state the only sure thing, anybody who tries by talking of accidental differences to explain the development of the animals of the Indies and relate them to European varieties, will have trouble getting away with it. Because if we are to judge the species of animals by their characteristics, they are so different that to try to match them up with the kinds known in Europe would be to call an egg a chestnut.

Book VI. Chapter 1: That the opinion of those who hold that the Indians are men lacking in understanding is false

Having discussed the religion as practiced by the Indians, I shall try in this book to write about their customs and system of government, for two purposes. One is to change the false opinion generally held of them, that they are crude people, like beasts without understanding or with so little that it scarcely deserves the name. From this error springs much notable harm, since they are used like animals and with complete lack of consideration or respect. That this belief is base and pernicious is well known by anyone who has traveled among them with any thought or attention, observing and learning their secrets and lore, and by so doing realizing how ignorant of them are those who think they know a lot, the people who are usually the most stupid and self-centered.

I see no better way of refuting this prejudicial opinion than to let people know about the order and mode of living of the Indians when they follow their own customs. Though these include some barbarous and unwarranted practices, yet there are also many others worthy of admiration, and on this account it is obvious that by nature they are capable of receiving instruction, and in some respects they are superior to the inhabitants of our countries. One should not be surprised to find grave errors mixed with their admirable qualities because that is not unknown even among the greatest legislators and philosophers, even including Licurgus and Plato. And in the wisest countries, like Rome and Athens, we can discover laughable signs of ignorance, but I am sure that if the Mexican and Inca governments were compared to what existed in the time of the Romans and Greeks, their laws and governments would be greatly admired. But since without knowing anything about this, we charge in, waving our swords, without listening to them or understanding them, the culture of the Indians seems of little importance to us and we consider them savage animals, provided for our service and desires.

The most observant and wise men who have penetrated and sought out their secrets, their practices, and ancient governments, have a very high opinion of them and marvel that there could be such order and reason among them. One of these authors is Father Polo Ondegardo, whom I usually follow when giving details about Peru; and concerning Mexico I am guided by Juan de Tovar, formerly prebendary of the Church of Mexico, and now a member of our Company of Jesus. By order of Viceroy Martín Enríquez, he made diligent and thorough investigation of the ancient history of Mexico. And I have also consulted several other authors who orally or in writing have provided me with abundant information about all that I am saying.

The other purpose that can be achieved by my report of the Indians' laws and customs, as well as their political system, is to help them and let them be self-governed, since in everything not running contrary to the law of Christ and the Holy Church they should be governed according to their own code of *fueros*, that is, their municipal laws; and an ignorance of them has caused grave mistakes, since those who judge and command do not know by what system of laws their subjects should be judged and commanded. Besides being unjust and unreasonable, this method of procedure runs the risk of causing them to hate us, who in good as well as evil have always tried to be both just and reasonable toward them.

Book VI. Chapter 28: Concerning the dances and festivities of the Indians

Since it is the part of good government for a people to enjoy their recreation and pastimes when fitting, it is well that we make mention of these customs of the Indians, especially of the Mexicans. There has never been a race of men yet discovered that does not have its forms of pleasure, including games and dances and pleasant exercises. In Peru I saw a sort of fight, all in fun, that so roused the passions of the teams that their *puella*, as they called it, became very dangerous. I have also seen a thousand different kinds of dances in which various crafts and professions were imitated, like shepherds, laborers, fishermen, and hunters. Usually they were accompanied by music, dance steps, and rhythm, slow and stately. And there were other dances by masqueraders, called "*guacones*," and the dances and actions were demoniacal. I have seen men dancing on the shoulders of others, like the dancers in Portugal who carry their "*pelas*," as they call them. The greater part of these dances involved superstitions and idolatry because in this way they worshipped their idols and the tombs of their ancestors. And that is the reason why priests have tried to suppress such dances, although they still encourage those dances that are chiefly for recreation.

They play various musical instruments for their dances. Some are a sort of flute or reeds, some like drums, some a sort of shell; but the usual music is provided by the human voice, with one or two singing the words and all the other Indians coming in on the chorus. Some of these ballads are artfully done and involve history. Others were full of superstition; a few were plain nonsense. We who have lived among them have tried to set the tenets of our Faith in the form of their songs, and it is fine to see how well the endeavor has turned out, because with their joy in singing, they spend days hearing and repeating them

86 SPANISH-AMERICAN LITERATURE

tirelessly. Also they have composed in their own language and to
their own music, octaves and ballads and redondillas, and it is
marvelous how the Indians have taken to them and how much
they enjoy them. This is certainly a fine and necessary device for
these people. In Peru they usually called these dance ballads
"*taqui*"; in the Antilles they were called "*areytos*"; and in Mexico "*mitotes*."

W.K.J.

CARLOS DE SIGÜENZA Y GÓNGORA
1645-1700   Mexico

A Mexican-born relative of the popularizer of Gon-
gorism, Sigüenza was the foremost humanist of colonial
New Spain. Educated by the Jesuits, he was not only a
poet, a philosopher and an historian, but he also taught
mathematics at the University of Mexico and later became a surveyor in Pensacola, Florida. At one time he
was the chaplain of a hospital where he became the
friend of Sor Juana. As an historian, influenced by
Spanish picaresque novels, he wrote what he claimed
to be the authentic account of the adventures of a
young Puerto Rican, Alonso Ramírez (born in Puerto
Rico in 1662), who came to New Spain in search of a
relative and continued his journey toward the Far East.
He called it *Infortunios que Alonso Ramírez padeció en
poder de ingleses piratas* (Misfortunes of Alonso Ramírez, 1690). The liveliness of this fictionalized history in
seven chapters sets it apart from the many dull accounts
of journeys written in the New World.

MISFORTUNES OF ALONSO RAMÍREZ

*Captured by English pirates, Alonso is set adrift in the Atlantic
with a half-dozen companions. A fearful storm drives their ship
onto an unknown island.*

Chapter VI. Thirst, hunger, infirmities, deaths
with which they were tormented on this coast;
unexpectedly they find Catholic people and
know they are on terra firme in Yucatan
in northern America

There was no tree or anything on the island to protect us against
the wind that blew violently and unrestrained, but making repeated supplications to God Our Lord, and making sure that we
were in a location from which we would not be swept away, we
spent the night.

The wind continued and so the sea did not calm for the next
three days. Nevertheless the next morning, seeing the lay of the
land, we waded through water up to our waists for about a hundred feet and reached the mainland.

Since we were all dying of thirst and unable to find fresh
water anywhere on the land, I decided to forget danger for the
sake of the relief and comfort of my miserable shipmates, and go
aboard the wreck. Commending my soul to the Virgin of Gua-
dalupe, I entered the sea and reached the ship where I got an ax
and everything necessary to make a fire.

Then I made a second trip and by exerting my strength, or
perhaps I should say miraculously, I transported a cask of water
to shore. Since I didn't dare risk a third trip that day, as soon as
we had quenched our thirst, I started the strongest of the men
to work cutting down some of the many palms around there and
we ate the palm hearts. Then lighting a fire, we spent another
night.

At daybreak we discovered several pools of rather salty water
among the palms, and while my companions were congratulat-
ing each other on the discovery, Juan de Casas and I went
aboard the wreck, from which in a small boat we brought back,
(despite the heavy sea and wind) the foretop sail, two foresails,
and the mainsail, in addition to rags from other sails. We were
also able to salvage some guns, powder, and bullets, along with
whatever we thought might come in handy.

Having built a hut large enough to shelter us all, I set out even though I didn't know in what direction to look for inhabitants. For no good reason, I headed south along the coast. Juan de Casas went with me, and after walking that day about twelve miles, we killed a couple of wild pigs. After arguing about whether to waste the meat that the rest needed so badly, we returned with it to our comrades.

We retraced our steps the next day until we reached a river of salt water so wide and deep at its mouth that we could not cross and so, although we came upon some ancient straw huts and were confident that eventually we would find inhabitants, after four days of effort we sadly returned, since we could go ahead no farther.

I found my comrades in even greater trouble than I, because the pools where they got water were gradually drying up and they were all so swollen that they looked like gout sufferers. The day after my return there was no more water, and although for five days our need to find more sent us searching everywhere, the water we found was even more bitter than sea water . . .

The place was not only sterile and parched, but unhealthy as well, but although my companions were aware of it, for fear of dying on the way to some other place, they could not be persuaded by me to leave. But what my words did not accomplish, God was pleased to bring about by the nuisance of the plentiful mosquitoes. By their stinging, they were undoubtedly what partly caused the swellings that I spoke about.

We had spent thirty days in that location living on wild chickens, palm hearts and some shell fish. Before leaving, as a last effort I visited the wreck which had not yet broken up, and loading all the cannons, I fired them twice. I intended with the noise to alert anybody living inland, hoping the gun firing would bring them to investigate and so end our suffering.

Well-stocked with powder and balls—and nothing else—we started north along the shore, leaving the ship behind. (I wish we could have taken it with us, even on our backs, on account of what I shall narrate later.) We proceeded very slowly because of the weakness of all my companions. When we reached a stream of fresh, but reddish, water hardly twelve miles from our first site, we spent two days there.

Juan and I wanted to scout ahead but the others begged piteously for us to stay and help them. We went on together each at the best speed he was capable of. When we had covered about a league, we halted, and although we waited till 9 P.M., Francisco de la Cueva had not appeared. Giving orders to Juan de Casas to start the march at dawn, I returned looking for him. I found him a mile or so back, face down, unconscious, though not yet dead. This Philippine trader in China who had survived a thousand evils, had been conquered by two boils on his chest and another in the middle of his back that extended to his brain. By noon he was dead. I made a deep hole in the sand, and praying to God for the repose of his soul, I buried him and set up a cross made of two pieces of tough wood. Then I returned to my companions.

I found them camped about a league beyond where I had left them. Antonio González, the other Philippine trader, was dying. There was nothing we could do for him, having no medicine to restore him; while I was trying to cheer him, I dropped off to sleep. When my worries awoke me, I found him dead. All of us helped to bury him and I took advantage of the two deaths to urge them to continue walking as far as possible, convinced that it was our only hope of saving our lives.

That day about ten miles were covered, and in the next three days we advanced about fifteen leagues. The increased speed was due to the fact that with the exercise, and the sweating we did, our swellings were reduced and our strength increased. Here we found a very salty river, not wide but extremely deep. A swamp beside it delayed us a whole day because we were unable to find a ford. However with palm logs, a bridge was constructed, and we went on, because I did not permit the fever I was suffering to stop me.

The next day as we left camp with Juan de Casas and me ahead, a deformed bear crossed our path. Though I put a shot into him, he came at me and in spite of the way I defended myself with the stock of my gun, I was so weak and it was so

strong that I would have been killed except for the help of my
companion. We left it lying there and continued on.

*A week later they find a hut, the home of savage Indians,
which makes Alonso think they had reached the Florida coast.
With his fever, he is too ill to care, but his servant Pedro brings
news of the approach of two naked men. Their cries in Spanish
identify them as friends and they tell him he has reached the
Province of Yucatán, New Spain. He thanks God and the Virgin for his safety.*

                                                                W.K.J.

"CONCOLORCORVO"
Eighteenth Century   Peru

The identity of the author of *El Lazarillo de ciegos
caminantes* (The Guide of Blind Travelers) has long
been a mystery, complicated by the fact that, while
clandestinely published in Lima in 1775-76, the book
was falsely dated Guijón, 1773. Relating the story of a
postal commissioner, Alonso Carrió de la Vandera, who
was traveling from Uruguay to Peru, and describing the
customs of people met along the route, it was supposed
to have been written by his dusky Indian companion,
Calixto Bustamante Carlos Inca, nicknamed "Concolorcorvo" (Crow-Colored). Recently, however, the authorship has been fairly well authenticated; Alonso Carrió
de la Vandera was a Spaniard who for some unknown
reason wanted his low opinion of the Indians and the
clergy, as well as his report on the resources of Argentina, to be ascribed to someone else. However the author
of one of the eighteenth century's most readable travel
books deserves recognition.

THE LAZARILLO (GUIDE) OF
BLIND TRAVELERS

Prologue

I am a pure Indian, except for my mother's deceits, for which I am not responsible. Two of my cousins, princesses of royal birth, preserve their virginity, to their regret, in a convent in Cuzco where our king maintains them. I find myself ambitious to obtain the job of dog-catcher in Cuzco's Cathedral, in order to enjoy ecclesiastical immunity, and in securing that appointment, my authorship of this travelog will be useful because, though God and my conscience compel me to acknowledge that I had the help of others in writing it, people who in their leisure moments whispered in my ear, and was aided by a certain monk of San Juan de Dios who supplied the Latin tags, I am largely responsible for padding out in paraphrase what the Inspector Don Alonso Carrió told me in fewer words. Imitating his style, I mixed in some amusing bits in order to entertain the traveller for whom I particularly wrote. I'll see to it that the substance of my trip be reduced to a hundred octavo pages. Into less than a quarter of that amount did the Inspector compress the essential part, as can be seen in the rough draft that is still in my possession, but that sort of brief account does not instruct the public that has not seen those vast countries and therefore cannot understand what may be found there. I keep close to the truth. The great cosmographer, Dr. Cosme Bueno, at the end of his annual report, gave a general idea of the kingdom, dealing individually with each bishopric. This is a work truly useful and necessary to help provide a complete history of this vast viceregency.

If the time and erudition wasted by the great Pedro de Peralto in his *Lima Founded and Spain Vindicated* had been devoted to composing a civil and natural history of Peru, I do not doubt that he would have acquired more fame, besides giving luster and splendor to the whole monarchy, but most men are inclined to prefer events in a far-away country, while completely overlooking what is happening in their own country. I am not implying that Peralta y Barnuevo did not know the history of this kingdom; I only condemn his choice from what I heard mentioned by wise men.

Arriving one afternoon at the countryhouse of a Tucumán gentleman, with the Inspector and the rest of his company, we noticed that the host talked in a very odd manner and asked strange questions. On his table were four very tattered books with worn bindings. One was about the trip to China made by Fernán Méndez Pinto; one was "The Theatre of the Gods," and the third was a short history of Charlemagne and his Twelve Peers of France. The fourth was Pérez de Hita's "Civil Wars of Granada." The Inspector, who was the one leafing through these books and who had read them with great pleasure during his youth, praised his host's library, then asked him if he had read other books. The good gentleman replied that he knew them by heart but in order not to forget their contents, he read them daily because one ought to read only a few books and pick out the best. Observing the extravagance of this good man, the Inspector asked him if he knew the name of the present King of Spain and the Indies; to which the gentleman answered that his name was Charles III, as he well knew because he had heard him mentioned in the Governor's proclamation. He added that he had also heard that he was a fine gentleman, of cape and sword.

"And the name of this fine gentleman's father," the Inspector continued. "What was his name?"

To this the gentleman answered promptly that naturally everybody knew that. The Inspector, remembering the response of a wise Frenchman, persisted in inquiring about the name, and the gentleman answered at once that it was Charles II, actually his great grandfather. He could furnish no details of his own country beyond seven or eight leagues round about, and what he did tell was so imperfect and distorted that it seemed the delirium of dream of a man half asleep.

I was going to continue my Prolog but about this time the

Inspector said he wanted to read it. He told me it was plenty long for the book, and if I made it much longer, people would say this about it:

"The architect is a fool or boor
Whose building's eclipsed by the size of the door."

Or a proverb that says about the same thing:

"A house in the mountains, the work of a nut,
With a fancy façade and behind it, a hut."

"I don't believe, don Alonso," said I, "that my Prolog deserves such a censure because there will be a great big house." To which he replied in Latin:
"Not all that is great is good, but all that is good is great."
I did not pass judgment on his Latin because the Inspector only wanted me to know that he was quoting a sentence from Tacitus, with which I close, putting my finger in my mouth, my pen in my inkwell, and my inkwell in the corner of my room until another trip makes its appearance, unless before then I make my final farewell to my readers.

Patricia M. Henderson

A LOCAL FESTIVAL

It starts with the New Year, since that is when they elect their mayor and other officials. Beforehand, the men and women have prepared their expensive clothes and their beautifully harnessed horses. The delicious sweets and the best fruits of the realm are provided by the leading ladies of the community, as are the drinks, hot and cold. The hot drinks are kept all year in their containers for the disciples of Bacchus, while the cold drinks, that are also plentiful, are chilled with snow brought in the day before.

The festivities consist chiefly of bullfights, lasting from the

94 SPANISH-AMERICAN LITERATURE

first of the year till Lent, except for a few days that are not official holidays. The four chief officials bear the expenses of these bullfights, with the help, I am told, of the royal representative. The cost runs high, because, besides refreshments for all those in the main plaza, cups of sherbet and plates of sweetmeats are distributed to those who cannot come to sit in the balconies in the square. There is always a bull available. As soon as one tires, he is released in one of the side streets for the amusement of the populace. Special bulls are also sent to important people so that they may be entertained and may enjoy the bullfighting from the balconies of their own houses. There are no professional bullfighters. The employees of the farms, riding fast horses, are usually the ones who take part, as well as young men on foot, generally Indians, who correspond to the lower class in Spain.

Sometimes bulls decorated with silks, silver and gold, and with many silver stars fastened lightly to their hides are offered, and that is their misfortune because everybody tries to kill them to get the loot. The nobility of Cuzco appear in the plaza on fine horses beautifully adorned with velvet decorated with gold and silver. The clothing of the horsemen is often made of the choicest fabrics of Lyon, France, as well as locally, but this finery is covered by a cloak that they call a "poncho," striped and woven of alpaca wool. That is certainly shabby material for so brilliant a function.

These horsemen are attendants to the mayor and the alcaldes, who take their positions at street corners to watch the bullfighting and to gallop away when attacked, or to greet the ladies and receive their gifts of fine candies or perfumed water, tossed from the balconies. The kind of gift varies according to the recipient, but usually the ladies have bags of cheap candy to throw to the crowd that throws them back, and those of the lower class pick them up and sell them to the men on horseback.

At the end of the festivities, which comes when the church bells sound for Angelus, a couple of bulls bearing roman candles are released and fireworks are set off, while handkerchiefs and banners are fluttering in the balconies. And there is shouting amid the confusion, sometimes sounding like the cackle of geese in Andalusia, ending in bumps and bruises, but few deaths. At night in the houses of the officials, serenades precede rich banquets until the last night of Carnival. Then everything is tidied up by the dawn of Ash Wednesday.

The Inspector liked my description, though he did not agree with my comparison of the shouting with the cackle of geese, since I used the word *"tiroteo,"* that has other meanings. The bruises that are serious come from the attacks of the bulls but more so from the drunken fights of the Indians . . . The wounded don't feel them till the next day, when they appear by the dozens at the hospital.

There are many other fiestas celebrated in this great city, but now it is time to leave it and visit the next place.

W.K.J.

SIMÓN BOLÍVAR
1783-1830   Venezuela

The liberator of northern South America was also an accomplished and prolific writer, and he left a considerable body of work when he died, neglected by those he had freed. Even his final comment had a literary flavor: "To fight for liberty is to plow the sea."

The two excerpts translated here are the oath he took on the Aventine Hill in Rome in 1803, while traveling with his tutor, the philosopher Simón Rodríguez, and a passage from a letter written in 1815 at a most discouraging period in his career. After the Declaration of Independence in Caracas, 1811, the revolutionists turned against him, and he barely escaped the royalist armies. In Jamaica Bolívar wrote "Carta a un caballero que tomaba gran interés en la causa republicana en la América del Sur" (Letter to a gentleman greatly interested in the republican cause in South America). Its recipient was probably the Duke of Manchester, governor of the island. It discusses the position of the colonies, their poor preparation for self-government, and their chances of success; this thoughtful analysis contained predictions that have come true to a remarkable degree.

OATH

I swear before you, I swear by the God of my Fathers; I swear by my honor and I swear by my country, that I shall not give rest to my arm nor repose to my soul until I have broken the chains that bind us by the will of the power of Spain.

THE JAMAICA LETTER

In so far as our citizens do not possess the talent and political virtues that distinguish our brothers in the United States, instead of being in our favor, I am much afraid it will contribute to our ruin. Unfortunately these qualities seem to be greatly lacking in us to the degree that is required and instead, we are dominated by vices contracted under the control of a nation like Spain, that is outstanding only in fierceness, ambition, vengeance, and covetuousness . . .

I especially want to see formed in America the greatest nation on earth, great not so much for its extent and riches, as for its freedom and glory. Even though I aspire to perfection in government in my country, I cannot persuade myself that the New World is at the moment ripe for one great republic. Since that is impossible, I do not dare desire it, and even less do I crave a universal monarchy in America, because such a project is not only useless, but impossible. The abuses now existing would not be cured, and our regeneration would be fruitless. The American states need the care of paternal governments to cure the sores and wounds of despotism and war. The capital, for instance, would be Mexico; that is the only city that could be so, for its intrinsic power, without which there can be no chief city. Let us imagine, for instance, the seat of power in Panama, a middle point between the extremes of this vast continent. In that case, would the people not continue languidly in their present disorder? In order for a single government to give life and enthusiasm, and set in action the springs of public prosperity, correcting and perfecting the New World, and bringing admiration on itself, it would be necessary to have the faculties of a god, not to mention the knowledge and virtues of all mankind . . .

I am not in favor of a federal system, between the populace and their representatives, because it would require perfection and demand virtues and political talent far beyond our own; and for the same reason, I do not accept the idea of a mixed monarchy of aristocracy and democracy, such as has brought such fortune and splendor to England. Since it would be impossible for us to achieve such perfection and balance between republics and monarchies, let us avoid falling into demagogic anarchy or the absolute rule of a tyrant. Let us seek a mean between these two extremes that would bring us to the same pitfalls, the same unhappiness and dishonor.

I am going to risk setting down the result of my thinking about the future of America, not the best, perhaps, but the most likely of attainment.

Because of the nature of the setting, riches, population and character of the Mexicans, I imagine that at first they will try to establish a representative government in which the Executive Branch will have supreme power, concentrated in an individual who, if he carries out his functions with skill and justice, can almost certainly retain his power for life. If his incapacity or violent administration incites a popular commotion that overthrows him, the Executive Power may be replaced by an assembly. If the most powerful party is military or aristocratic, it will demand a monarchy that at first will be limited and constitutional, but afterward inevitably will sink into absolute control, since we must agree that there is nothing more difficult in political order than the preservation of a mixed monarchy; and it is also necessary to agree that only a people as patriotic as the English is capable of restraining the authority of a king and of maintaining the spirit of liberty under sceptre and crown.

The states of the Isthmus of Panama will perhaps form a federation. Because of their excellent position between two oceans they can in time become the commercial crossroads of the world; their canals can shorten distances, linking in mercantile bonds Europe, America, and Asia, a condition that will bring to this fortunate region, tributes from the four quarters of the globe. Perhaps some day the capital will be established here, as Constantine tried to make Byzantium the capital of the ancient hemisphere . . .

We know little of the opinions prevailing in Buenos Aires, Chile, and Peru. Judging by appearances, there will be a central government in Buenos Aires in which the military will be the most powerful, because of its internal bickering and external wars. This constitution will necessarily degenerate into an oligarchy or a dictatorship with greater or lesser restrictions, whose ultimate form no one can guess. It would be a pity for such a thing to happen, because those people inherit a splendid glory.

The Kingdom of Chile is destined, by the nature of its situation, the innocent and virtuous customs of its inhabitants, and the fierce republicanism of the Araucanian Indians, to enjoy the blessings springing from the just and pleasant laws of a republic. If any republic endures long in America, I would guess it would be Chile. The spirit of liberty has never been extinguished there; the vices of Europe and Asia will come slowly, or never, to corrupt the customs of that extreme of the universe. Its territory is limited; it will always be beyond infectious contact with the rest of mankind; it will not alter its laws, usages, and practices; it will preserve its uniformity in political and religous beliefs. In short, Chile can be free.

W.K.J.

Elsewhere, Bolívar expresses his thoughts on the ultimate fate of the continent as a whole, and some ideas on Pan Americanism. They help make this document one of the most famous in the history of Latin America.

It is even more difficult to foresee the future fate of the New World, to set down its political principles, or to prophesy what

manner of government it will adopt. Every conjecture relative to
America's future is, I feel, pure speculation. When mankind was
in its infancy, steeped in uncertainty, ignorance, and error, was
it possible to foresee what system it would adopt for its preservation? . . . I look upon the present state of America as similar to
that of Rome after its fall. Each part of Rome adopted a political system conforming to its interest and situation or was led by
the ambitions of certain chiefs . . . But this important difference exists: those dispersed parts later re-established their
ancient nations . . . But we scarcely retain a vestige of what
once was; we are, moreover, neither Indian nor European, but a
species midway between the legitimate proprietors of this country and the Spanish usurpers. Though the rebelling colonials in
Latin America are Americans by birth, we derive our rights from
Europe . . . This places us in a most extraordinary and involved
situation . . .

The role of the inhabitants of the Latin American hemisphere has for centuries been purely passive. Politically they were
nonexistent. We are still in a position lower than slavery and
therefore it is more difficult for us to rise to the enjoyment of
freedom . . . So negative was our existence in Politics, com-
merce and administration that I can find nothing comparable in
any other civilized society . . . We were cut off and, as it were,
removed from the world in relation to the science of government and administration of the state. We were never viceroys or
governors, save in the rarest instances; seldom archbishops or
bishops, diplomats never; as military men, only subordinates; as
nobles, without royal privileges.

It is harder, Montesquieu has written, to release a nation
from servitude than to enslave a free nation. South Americans
have made efforts to obtain liberal, even perfect, institutions,
doubtless out of that instinct to aspire to the greatest possible
happiness, which, common to all men, is bound to follow in
civil societies founded on the principles of justice, liberty, and
equality. But are we capable of maintaining in proper balance
the difficult charge of a republic? It is conceivable that a newly
emancipated people can soar to the heights of liberty and, un-

like Icarus, neither have its wings melt nor fall into an abyss? Such a marvel is inconceivable and without precedent. There is no reasonable probability to bolster our hopes . . .

It is a grandiose idea to think of consolidating the New World into a single nation. It is reasoned that as these parts have a common origin, language, customs, and religion, they ought to have a single government. But this is not possible. Actually Latin America is separated by climatic differences, geographic diversity, conflicting interests, and dissimilar characteristics. How beautiful it would be if the Isthmus of Panama could be for us what the Isthmus of Corinth was for the Greeks? Would to God that some day we may have the good fortune to convene there an august assembly of representatives of republics, kingdoms, and empires, to deliberate upon the high interests of peace and war with the nations of the other three quarters of the globe. This type of organization may come to pass in some happier period . . .

Surely unity is what we need to complete our work of regeneration. The division among us, nevertheless, is nothing extraordinary, for it is characteristic of civil wars to form two parties, *conservatives* and *reformers*.

I shall tell you with what we must provide ourselves in order to expel the Spaniards and found a free government. It is *union*, obviously; but such union will come about through sensible planning and well directed actions rather than by divine magic. Latin America stands together because it is abandoned by all other nations . . .

When success is not assured, when the state is weak, and when results are distantly seen, all men hesitate; opinions are divided, passions rage, and the enemy fans these passions in order to win an easy victory because of them. As soon as we are strong and under the guidance of a liberal nation which will lend us her protection, we will achieve accord in cultivating the virtues and talents that lead to glory. Then will we march majestically toward that great prosperity for which South America is destined.

Anon. Life, July 14, 1961

FRANCISCO MORAZÁN
1799-1842   Honduras

Many Latin American military men were as skilled with the pen as with the sword. The great Honduran patriot and liberal, Morazán, was one of these. Son of a French Creole father and a Honduran mother, he was a man of intelligence, decision, and perseverance, who used his military genius to help free Central America from Spain. In 1829 he became president of the federation of the five small Central American countries. He was re-elected when his opponent died on the eve of the next election, but his Conservative enemies gained power, and in 1840 he was exiled to South America.

To defend his reputation, he began to write his *Memorias* (Memoirs) in 1841 from New Granada. Recalled by fellow citizens who were disillusioned by the substitute government, his attempt to unite the region failed, like many later attempts. He was betrayed and shot without trial. His dying remark "Posterity will justify us," has come true.

Here is the beginning of his Memoirs, which cover only part of his public life. Many believe that a second part has been lost.

MEMOIRS OF GENERAL MORAZÁN

To write of the lives of public men who have played their part in peaceful times under a constitutional government, it is enough to know their deeds and the laws and to be impartial and accurate in one's observations. To narrate the lives of those who have figured in times of revolution and anarchy when the only law was the salvation of the nation, it is not enough to be acquainted with the events, to know the ostensible causes, and to weigh the circumstances that were influential upon them; it is also necessary to seek the true spirit that moved them, in the secrets of the human heart, without allowing oneself to be led astray by those who, apparently impartial, constitute themselves interpreters, with the intention of satisfying their base and evil passions.

The same action may be either motivated by common interest or suggested by an atrocious vengeance, and in one case it deserves public commendation and in the other to be considered an unpardonable sin.

The death of Caesar would have been a crime in the eyes of the Romans if they had been unaware of the motive of Brutus in executing him. And no one today would attribute to the British government the desire to shorten the days of Napoleon if it had explained the causes that compelled it to exile him to the unhealthy atmosphere of the Island of St. Elba.

It is no less true that the partisan spirit has often been able to deceive the impartial writer and transmit by this artifice to posterity as true history what was only a work of vengeance or flattery. But this fault is not found alone in those who report to us what happened in ancient times. It can be observed, also, in those who hope to instruct coming generations about what is happening in the modern era, where passion is often aroused by the abuses found in print.

Do not think on this account that I desire to impose a censorship. Whatever is established to destroy a vice that is inherent in man's freedom to express thought, carries within itself the germ that can also destroy this laudable freedom which, if it has upheld moderate monarchical governments, is also, without dispute, the very soul of democratic institutions.

Yes, many times has it been abused to insult me, and I protest to Central Americans against those who attack me, but far from depriving my enemies of their possession of this miserable recourse, I shall try not to pass the limits of moderation and decorum.

I do not write to arouse passions and even less to indicate the flaws or speak ill of those who calumniated me in publications in Jalapa and Mexico. I take up my pen only to vindicate myself. Only this feeling has been able to conquer the reticence I have always had about speaking to the nation even in my own behalf, because not only have I never believed myself equipped for such action, but I also lack the humility that makes a beggar of one who wants to defend himself, since I have always believed that unless one aspires to deceit, he should present himself to the public under his true colors.

During the eight years that I served as Chief Magistrate, many of my enemies accepted public positions without being moved to examine the legality of my election. And others, who heaped injuries upon me, I have always treated with silence, since I did not wish to use to discredit them the advantage given me by my position.

But when I observed that in my misfortune even some of my friends are misjudging me, I decided to make an accounting of my public life.

Unwilling to trust my memory about all the events during fourteen years of revolution, I sent to Central America for the documents. But while they are on the way, time is passing. My enemies give a sinister interpretation to my silence; they hurl new calumnies against me, and most people do not have at hand any report of my public conduct that will reveal their lies. So I see myself obliged to speak, even though briefly, about the principal events of the revolution of 1828 that have been maliciously distorted by some and unjustly criticized by others. I shall try to back them up by trustworthy documents.

W.K.J.

JOSÉ JOAQUÍN FERNÁNDEZ DE LIZARDI
1776-1827   Mexico

The picaresque novel had been dead in Spain for 150 years when Lizardi was born, and its revival in Spanish America is but one example of the liberalizing effects of Neoclassicism. Though Mexico was still a Spanish colony, the intellectuals sought freedom of thought as well as political freedom. By 1811, Lizardi was publishing pamphlets denouncing the restrictions of the church and, until Iturbide's ambitions became clear, advocating political independence.

In 1812, when the Mexican Viceroy finally recognized the 1810 Cadiz decree on the Freedom of the Press, Lizardi established his own journal, *El Pensador Mexicano*, and used its title "The Mexican Thinker" as his pen name. But censorship was reimposed and he was imprisoned for seven months. He then turned to novel-writing and produced the continent's first novel, *El Periquillo Sarniento* (The Itching Parrot), conceived as a four-volume work. By February of 1816, the first six chapters were finished, but the final book was not printed until after his death, in 1830. In the next fifty years, eight editions appeared in Mexico, and for some time a million copies a year were printed by a Barcelona publisher. Its chief character is too timid to be a real picaro; he lives cautiously and manages to die in bed, but most of his friends are killed or hanged. What the author advocates here is pure mediocrity in morals and manners. Though occasionally wordy, *Periquillo* is still read because of its good story, local color, and accurate picture of the life and customs of Mexico's lower classes in the early nineteenth century. Lizardi's several other novels are less important, but this one has been called the novel of the century.

THE ITCHING PARROT

Pedro Sarmiento was supposedly born in 1773 in an aristocratic family. He was nicknamed Periquillo Sarniento (The Itching, or Scabby Parrot) by his schoolmates, a pun on his name that was also associated with his first day at school when he appeared wearing green trousers. Having completed his university education, he tried to find a profession with little work and good pay. Priesthood looked promising but he associated with evil companions. His father's death provided him with an inheritance that he squandered. Then in picaresque fashion, he worked for

a series of masters; barber, apothecary, and in the passage trans-
lated here, for a doctor.

    Part III, Chapter 2: Periquillo relates how he entered Dr.
Purgante's service, what he learned under the doctor's guidance,
the way he robbed him, his flight, and the adventures he experi-
enced in Tula, where he pretended to be a doctor.

    "Let no one say who he is because his works will proclaim
him." This maxim is as old as it is true; everyone is convinced of
its infallibility, and so, why must I weigh my evil actions when
by relating them, they will be weighed? What I would like, my
children, would be that you do not read the story of my life as
you would read a novel, but rather that you will look beyond the
actions themselves and ponder the sad results of my laziness,
uselessness, inconstancy, and the other vices that encumbered
me, analyzing the events of my life that led me astray, discover-
ing their causes, fearing their consequences, and avoiding the
common errors made by me and others, thus absorbing for your
guidance the sound maxims of the correct Christian morality
that my reflexions present to you, and in a word, my desire
would be that you look deeply into the substance of this work,
that you enjoy the ridiculous situations, and that you recognize
the errors and abuses enough so you won't imitate the one or
embrace the other, and that where you find some virtuous act,
you will be attracted by its admirable strength and strive to imitate it. That is to say, my children, that I would like your reading of my life to have three results, two essential ones and one
secondary: a love of virtue, an abhorence of vice, and entertainment. This is my desire, and for these reasons rather than any
others, I embark on the unpleasant task of writing down for you
my most hidden crimes and faults. If I do not achieve my desire,
at least I shall die with the consolation that my intentions were
praiseworthy. Enough of digressions since writing paper is expensive!

    I had previously mentioned that I was going to call on Dr.

Purgante, and indeed I found him after his siesta in his study, seated in an easy chair, with a book propped before him and a snuff box beside him. He was a tall man, with thin face and legs, but a big belly, olive-skinned and with heavy eyebrows, green eyes, a beaked nose and a big mouth that lacked teeth. He was bald and therefore wore a curly wig when he went out. The day I went to see him, he was wearing a long gown down to his ankles, of the kind they call a kimono, with a pattern of flowers and foliage, and he wore a large cotton *birreta* cap stiff with starch and shiny from ironing.

The moment I came in, he recognized me and said:

"Well, Periquillo, my boy, from what far-off horizons have you come to visit my humble abode?"

His style of talk had no effect on me because I already knew that he was pedantic, and so I started to tell him my adventures, intending to lie about anything that put me in a bad light, but the doctor interrupted me.

"Yes, yes! I know about the turbulent catastrophe that ensued with your master in the pharmaceutical emporium. As a matter of fact, Perico, you almost transferred your innocent patient in a twinkling from his couch to his coffin by mistaking arsenic for magnesia. There is no doubt your trembling, reckless hand bears much of the blame, but your pharmaceutical preceptor is little less to blame. I have frequently proved to him that all noxious and poisonous drugs should be incarcerated with the key in the possession of the most adept official, for only with such assiduous diligence will fatal equivocations be eliminated. But in spite of my remonstrances, my only reward is to be considered eccentrically individualistic and divergent from doctrines of the school of pharmacy, for people do not realize that it is proper for a sage to change. *Sapientis est mutare consilium,* as the saying goes, and custom is indicative of another nature, *consuetudo est altera natura.* Well, that is his affair. But tell me, what have you been doing in the interim? Because unless the news that on wings of fame has penetrated auricular recipients was false, some time ago you launched yourself on the career of a second Aesculapius."

"That is true, sir," I told him. "But out of pride I have not sought you, a most regrettable decision, since in these past few days I have sold my cloak, frock and kerchief in order to eat."

"Balderdash!" exclaimed the doctor, "a feeling of pride is excellent, *optime bona,* I might say, when the crime originates from primal causes, but not when there are ameliorating circumstances, because if under those circumstances, *hic te nunc,* the individual knew he was doing wrong, *absque dubio,* he would refrain from committing them. Anyway, my dearest boy, would you like to enter my service and become my *consodal in perpetuum* forever?"

"Yes, sir," I replied.

"Very well. In this *domo,* house, you shall have *in primio,* in the first place, the *panem nostram quotidianum,* our daily bread; and in addition, *alienude,* enough to drink; *tertio* a bed *sic vel sic,* such as it is; *quarto,* the external teguments necessary for your physical well-being; *quinto* you will be assured of good health for here in our diet we observe the six natural things and eschew the six unnatural things prescribed by the most illustrious men in the medical field; *sexto* you will be able to imbibe the science of Apollo, *ex ore meo ex visu tuo et ex bibliotheca nostra,* from my mouth, your eyes, and our library. Finally, *postremo,* you will receive each month for your *surrupios* or *quod cumque velis,* that is to say, for your tobacco or whatever your fancy, five hundred and forty four maravedis, for doing what madame my sister requires of you and taking charge of the health of my mule whom you will serve and wait on as assiduously as you do on me.". . .

"But sir, how much does 544 maravedis amount to in hard cash?" I inquired, "because it does not seem that my work would be worth that much."

"You deserve that sum, *stultissime famule,* you stupid youth, since all those hundreds amount to precisely two pesos."

"Very well, sir," I told him. "But I am especially happy that I shall be in the company of a gentleman as *sapiente* as you are, from whose instructions I shall receive more benefit than from the powders and salves of don Nicolas, my previous master."

"Very true," said Dr. Purgante, "since I shall open to you the palace of Minerva. With my teaching you will preserve your health for years to come and perhaps, perhaps, you will acquire money and esteem."

Frances Stearns

For seven or eight months Perico works as the doctor's servant, reading his medical books and observing his practices; one night, after being scolded and threatened with a beating for not giving the mule her supper, Perico decides to take revenge on the doctor and change his lot at the same time.

Having come to this decision, that very night I gave the mule a double ration of corn and bran, and when the household was deeply asleep, I put on all her harness, not forgetting a single trapping. I made a bundle of fourteen books, some dog-eared, some in Latin, others in Spanish, because I believed that doctors and lawyers need many books to win respect, even if they never use or understand them. In the pack I put the cape and collar of my master, along with an old sisal wig, a collection of prescriptions, and most important of all, his diploma of a Bachelor in Medicine and his certificate of examination. I made these documents refer to me, with the aid of a knife and a bit of lemon juice that helped me erase enough to change names and dates.

I did not forget to supply myself with money, because, although they hadn't paid me a maravedi in wages all the time I had been there, I knew where the doctor's sister kept her moneybox that received all she saved from expenses. Remembering the proverb that he who robs a thief merits a hundred years of grace, I skillfully stole the moneybox. Opening it, I saw with delight nearly forty dollars, though she had almost squeezed them out of shape packing them in.

With these stakes for my journey, I left the house at four thirty in the morning, locking the gate and pushing the key back under the door.

W.K.J.

MANUEL PAYNO
1810-1894   Mexico

An honest politician as well as a diplomat, Payno also
wrote novels recalling past customs. His *El fistol del diablo* (The Devil's Stickpin), published serially in *The
Scientific and Literary Review* in 1845-46, was the first
full-length Mexican novel since the time of Fernández
de Lizardi. It was long indeed; its 1,600 pages filled two
volumes, and a sequel was promised. Even longer was
his *Los Bandidos de Río Frío* (The Bandits of Rio Frio,
1889-1910), a kind of Mexican *War and Peace* set in
the early nineteenth century, which the author called a
story of "customs, crimes, and horrors." Payno's novels
combine Romanticism with realistic details. While not
outstanding as literary works, they are important as historical and folklore documents.

THE DEVIL'S STICKPIN

Volume I, Chapter 1
A mysterious visit

*Arthur, 22 years old and educated in England, returns to Mex-
ico and decides that it is time to experiment with love. A
strange man wearing a diamond stickpin enters his room and
tells him what he is thinking about. He says his name is "The
Man of the Calias Passage," and promises to see him the next
day.*

The next morning, the rays of the sun entering through the
blinds of Aurthur's room, scattered the ideas that had disturbed
his sleep. Calmer now, he rang the bell for the servant to bring
him a cup of tea, and from his night stand he took a novel by
Walter Scott. As he was losing himself in its pages, he felt someone touch him. He turned and found himself staring at the man
with opal eyes.

"I'm glad to see you, sir," Arthur told him, sitting up in bed.

"You see, I kept my promise."

"So I see. But how did you get in? The door is closed and I heard no clicking of the latch."

The stranger replied with an ironic smile.

"I get in through windows, roofs, even cracks. Wherever air can get in, so can I."

Arthur replied with a laugh.

"Sir, you surround yourself with such a mysterious air that I can't help laughing. Forgive me, and sit down."

"You are forgiven, young man," said the stranger, sitting on the edge of the bed. "But tell me, has my scarf pin been shining all night in the darkness of your bedroom?"

"This is too much!" Arthur shouted, sitting up and grabbing a pistol from the table. Without moving, the stranger laughed so ironically that the disconcerted young man replaced the pistol.

"Sir, you're driving me mad! You keep reading my thoughts. If you don't tell me who you are, I'll suspect you."

"Young man, be grateful that I didn't tell you my name last night. I could have told you all about myself, but I was afraid that the darkness and the solitude might have a fatal effect on you."

"What do you mean by that?"

"I mean you might have been more frightened than you are now. Now would you like to hear my history?"

"That's what I want most. Where did you come from?"

The stranger sighed sadly.

"My home land is magnificent, splendid. Misfortune is unknown there, but for many years I have wandered an exile . . ."

"Well," exclaimed Arthur. "Are you the Wandering Jew?"

"I wish I were," sighed the man. "But the Wandering Jew is constantly on the move, never able to pause. To some degree I am more unfortunate, though in another way I have more freedom, since I can stop wherever I please or go from one place to another, wherever my duties call me."

"Are you a salesman, then?" Arthur asked.

"I'll tell you my business. Wherever there is a civil war, I turn up to inflame passions and increase the hatred and political rancor. In diplomatic crises, I mix in government conferences, supplying ideas of deceit and distrust. In love matters, I always take part. Wherever I see a happy couple, I sow discord. If they are young lovers, I inspire jealousy. You see, in spite of my misfortunes there are always ways of enjoying myself. So I forget the country where I lived as happy as an angel, from which I was driven out, never to return."

As he listened, Arthur's face became pale, his arms dropped onto his chest as if unhinged, and his gaze, fixed as though petrified, could not leave the opal eyes and brilliant stickpin of the stranger.

"Apparently you are not feeling like talking," said the man.

"Such evil frightens me, and if I really believed your words, I would order you out of my house instantly. Tell me the truth. Who are you?"

"Arthur, you should have guessed my name by now, but since you are not as clever as I thought, I'll tell you that . . ."

"Well," laughed the young man, "I suppose you are somebody from the other world. So much the better! You can see to it that I have supernatural luck in my love affairs."

"I'll speak seriously. The world is very different from what you think, and you might as well face it. Frivolity can bring regrets."

"Don't speak of that. I know that life has its sorrows and serious moments, but I'm sure you exaggerate . . . You are making fun of me. I'm only a poor student. And you are a rich gentleman who knows the world and are amusing yourself. Since I have ambition, youth, health, and a heart ready for love and adventures, I'd like to be your companion. So I must know what to call you."

"Call me whatever you like. How about Rugiero, the husband of Laura in a play by Martínez de la Rosa? If you are serious about accepting me as a companion, I'll promise to show you the world and make you a success. Tomorrow there is to be a famous dance. I'll introduce you to some beautiful girls, so prepare to start your conquests."

"You seem to have many friends in the city."

"Yes, many. The Mexican women go for us foreigners. They believe I'm a rich Italian nobleman traveling for pleasure. That is not entirely untrue. I am rich and noble, and besides, I want to be your friend. So tomorrow night at nine I'll come for you."

"I'll be ready."

Arthur held out his hand and they shook hands like old friends. Afterward Arthur took a big cup of tea and milk, then lay back on his soft pillow, and slept again, lulled by fantastic and golden dreams.

Chapter 46. The two beggars

Now that our readers have accompanied us, not only to Tampico and Havana, but to witness disagreeable scenes in the slums, we shall take them to the boarding house where Celeste's catastrophe took place. In the same room where she fought against misery, where she shed so many tears, where she suffered the insults of the justice of the peace and his bailiffs, lived two old beggar women. One was called Marta, the other was Agueda.

The room had changed its appearance; the walls were cleansed and whitewashed, the ceilings new and completely washed, and there was a brazier in one corner. In the two corners at the back were two beds, and even though they were only some wooden benches painted green, on top were some soft cushions of wool covered with a slip made of many small squares of chintz of all colors. On the wall, fastened with gilded nails, were a number of pictures, among them the Virgin of Ocotlan, the Captive Child, and others. A big red box decorated with Chinese gold stood between the beds, and a small table of white wood completed the picture.

The lives of kings, magistrates, great merchants, and rich landowners were not any more pleasant than that of these two old women, who got up at six o'clock every morning. They would send a boy out with the orders for breakfast, then set the table and sit down quietly in their places. Their breakfast consisted of milk and delicious chocolate with butter rolls, and when it was over, they used to go to one of the neighboring churches, hearing at least two masses, repeating the Lord's Prayer, the Salves, Credos to various saints, and then they would leave the church to wander about the city, until about two-thirty or three in the afternoon, when they would return to eat. They would then set the table with fresh linen, and after saying grace, they used to sit down to savor their food, which often was delicious.

In the afternoon, one or the other of them used to go out on some errands, but by evening prayers, they were always ready to close the door and check up on their accounts. One of them would set on the tip of her nose a pair of large spectacles, open a leather-bound book, by the famous Padre Parra, and would then start reading moral lessons till eight-thirty or nine. After that, they repeated Magnificats, novenas, and prayers, and finally, following snacks of delicious fried *frijoles* and drinking a glass of foaming *pulque* from one of the best stores in the city, they would go to bed.

W.K.J.

ESTEBAN ECHEVERRÍA
1805-1851   Argentina

One of the most important Argentine Unitarians, as the political opponents of Dictator Rosas were called, Echeverría introduced Romanticism into Argentina on his return from a five years' visit to France. But he was also strongly realistic, almost Naturalistic, in his anti-Rosas "El matadero" (The Slaughterhouse, 1837), in which events taking place in a slaughterhouse symbolize the butchery of the assassins who kept Rosas in power. Written during the author's exile in Montevideo as sketches for a novel rather than a finished short story, the work was published in 1871, after his death. It is

Romantic in its blending of horror and humor, the grotesque and the picturesque, as well as in its rebellious hero and its atmosphere of death, made melodramatic by the sound of guitar music.

THE SLAUGHTERHOUSE

In a slaughterhouse, fifty cattle are being butchered. Because of floods, no meat has been available in Buenos Aires for two weeks, and the poor of the city have been starving. This morning they are sitting around, watching the savage and bloody scene, and waiting for meat. The last animal, a ferocious bull, escapes and gores a child whose blood spurts from his wound. Eventually captured, the bull is brought back and slaughtered against a background of howling dogs, circling vultures, and Negresses fighting for scraps from the animals. Then the butchers, who in their free time are members of the Mazorca that assassinate the Dictator's enemies, see a young man riding past.

Suddenly the rough voice of a butcher shouted: "There goes a Unitarian!" And hearing such a significant word, the whole mob stopped as though wounded by a sudden impression.

"Don't you see his beard in the shape of a U? He's not wearing a badge on his coat nor a mourning band on his hat."

"Unitarian dog!" "Buenos Aires dude!" "He rides like a gringo." "Arrest him." "Shear him!" "Beat him up!" "He carries a holster to put on airs." "All those scummy Unitarians put on airs." "I'll bet you can't shake him up a bit, Matasiete!" "What do you mean, he can't?" "Of course he can!"

Matasiete (Killer-of-Seven), the chief butcher, was a man of few words and much action. When it came to violence, agility, skill with the cleaver, the knife, or a horse, he acted without saying anything. They had doubted him. He put spurs to his horse and galloped with free reins after the Unitarian.

The rider was a young man about twenty-five, attractive and elegant in appearance. While that stream of comments was

pouring out of those lawless mouths, he had been trotting toward Barracas, never fearing any danger. However, noticing the
hostile looks of that group of slaughterhouse dogs, he was reaching automatically with his right hand toward the holster on his
English saddle when a glancing blow by Matasiete's horse
against his mount sent him flying. He landed face down and
motionless.

"Hurray for Matasiete!" the mob yelled, falling on his victim, like vultures on the bones of a cow slaughtered by a tiger.

Still dizzy, the young man cast a fiery look at the ferocious
men, then at his horse that remained motionless nearby. In his
pistols lay his hope for satisfaction and vengeance. Matasiete
jumped down beside him and with one of his big hands grabbing his necktie, he held him. At the same time he pulled his
dagger from his belt and held it at the young man's throat.

A loud guffaw and a hoarse cheer again encouraged him.
What nobility of soul! What bravery in the Federalists! Always
falling in flocks like vultures on their helpless victim!

"Cut his throat, Matasiete! He was eyeing his pistols. Cut
his throat the way you did the bulls!" "That Unitarian scoundrel, give him a shave!" "He's got a neck like a violin for slit-
ting." "Stretch it! Play the *Resbalosa* on him!"

"Yes, let's see," Matasiete told them, and with a laugh he
slid the edge of his dagger across the neck of the fallen victim,
holding him down by his right knee on the man's chest, and
seizing the prisoner's hair in his left hand.

"No, don't cut his throat!" It was the distant voice of the
Slaughterhouse Judge, riding up on horseback.

"Take him to the shack, to the shack! Get ready the court
and the shears. Death to the Unitarian savages! Long live Rosas,
the Restorer of Law!"

"Hurray for Matasiete!"

"Kill him!" "Hurray!" the crowd kept shouting as they
dragged the unfortunate young man, securely tied, to the torture
table, amid insults and blows, as the rabble had once escorted
Christ.

The room inside the shack had in its center a big, heavy

table always covered with glasses and cards except when it was used for torture and execution by the Federalist mob of the slaughterhouse. In a corner could also be seen a smaller table with writing material and an account book. Around it were grouped several chairs including one for the Judge. A man, apparently a soldier, was sitting in one chair, playing a guitar and singing *Resbalosa*, a very popular Federalist song, when the mob trooped in and pushed the young Unitarian toward the middle of the room.

"Teach him the *Resbalosa*," one of them shouted.

"Commend your soul to the devil." "He's as wild as a mountain bull, but we'll tame him." "Get the scissors and the whip!" "Off to court with him!"

"Silence and be seated!" the Judge shouted, dropping into his chair. They all obeyed while the young man, still standing in front of the Judge, exclaimed in a voice full of indignation:

"You infamous rabble, what do you intend to do with me?"

"Calm yourself!" the Judge told him with a smile. "No need to get upset. You'll soon see."

The prisoner, in fact, was shaking in his rage. His body seemed to be in convulsion. His pale, livid face, his voice, his trembling lips, all showed the spasmodic beating of his heart, the agitation of his nerves. His eyes of fire seemed about to fly out of their orbit. His straight, black hair was standing up. His bare neck and ripped shirt front gave a glimpse of his pulsing arteries and the panting of his lungs.

"Are you trembling?" asked the Judge.

"With anger because I can't get my hands on you!"

"Think you'd be strong enough to take me on?"

"I'm very willing to try it, you scoundrel!"

"Let's have the horse clippers. Give the Unitarian a clipping!"

Two men seized him, one by his bound arms, the other by his head, and in a minute they had cut off the beard beneath his chin, as the spectators laughed and cheered.

"How about a drink of water to refresh him?" the Judge suggested.

"I'd like to make you drink vinegar, you scoundrel!"

Immediately a small Negro stepped up with a glass of water in his hand. The young man kicked his arm and the water splashed over the spectators.

"He's incorrigible!" someone remarked. "But we'll tame him."

"Silence!" said the Judge. "Now you're shaved Federal style. All you lack is the mustache. See that you grow one. Now let's see. Why aren't you wearing the Federal badge?"

"Because I don't want to."

"Don't you know that the Restorer ordered it?"

"Such livery is for slaves like you, not for free men!"

"Free men can be forced to wear it."

"Forced by bestial violence. That's your weapon, you scoundrels. The wolf, the tiger, and the panther use the same kind of force. You ought to walk on all fours, like them."

"Aren't you afraid the tiger will tear you?"

"I prefer that to having crows like you pick me apart bit by bit, now that you have me bound."

"Why don't you wear a mourning band in your hat for the heroine?"

"Because I wear mine in my heart for the country that you scoundrels have assassinated."

"Don't you know that the Restorer ordered it?"

"You slaves ordered it to flatter the pride of your master and pay him infamous tribute."

"Don't be insolent or I'll cut out your tongue!"

"Down with the trousers of that stupid dandy. Tie him to the table and use the rod on his bare behind!"

Hardly had the Judge given the order when four bloodstained bullies hoisted the young Unitarian to the table, holding his arms and legs.

"You'll cut my throat before I let you do that, you scoundrels!"

They gagged him with a cloth and then began taking off his clothes. The victim twisted, kicked, and bit. At times he relaxed like a reed, then became stiff as iron. His spine writhed like a serpent. Drops of sweat, big as pearls, flowed down his face. Fire seemed to come from his eyes, froth from his mouth. His veins blackened against the white of his skin as if bursting with blood.

"Tie him down first!" the Judge ordered.

"He's like a mad dog," one of the mob commented.

Turning his body face down, they tied his ankles to the legs of the table and were going to do the same with his hands. But to do so, they had to untie them from behind his back. Feeling them released, the young man, in a brisk movement that seemed to exhaust all his strength, raised himself by his arms, got to his knees and then fell back, muttering: "Cut my throat rather than strip me, you dogs!"

Now that he was exhausted, they tied his wrists, then went on taking off his clothes. A torrent of blood gushed from the mouth and nostrils of the victim, and flowed across the table. Then he was still. The bullies stood motionless and the spectators were stupefied.

"That Unitarian savage burst with rage," one of them commented.

"He had a river of blood in his veins," remarked another.

"Poor devil! All we wanted was to have a little fun with him and he took the thing seriously," the Judge commented, wrinkling his tiger-like brows. "We'll have to report it. Untie him and let's go."

They carried out the order. They locked the door and in a moment the mob was following the horse of the Judge who rode silent and with bowed head. The Federalists had concluded one more of their many noble deeds.

In those days, the throat-cutting butchers of the slaughterhouse were the apostles who proclaimed by whip and dagger the Federation of Rosas, and it is not difficult to imagine what sort of Federation could come from their heads and knives. They used the term "Unitarian Savages," an expression coined by the Restorer, the patron of the "Guild," to describe all decent men of good heart, all patriots, friends of enlightenment and liberty. And from the preceding episode it is easy to see that the focal

point and center of the Federation was to be found in the
slaughterhouse.

W.K.J.

DOMINGO FAUSTINO SARMIENTO
1811-1888   Argentina

The published works of Sarmiento, a soldier, a newspaper man, and a president, number fifty-three volumes.
Best known is *Civilización i barbarie—Vida de Juan
Facundo Quiroga: aspectos físicos, costumbres, i ábitos
de la república argentina* (Life in the Argentine Republic in the Days of Tyrants, or Civilization and Barbarism, 1845), written to show the Chileans the state of
barbarism into which his Argentina had lapsed under
Dictator Juan Manuel Rosas. The book is composed of
three parts. The first and most interesting is a sociologi-
cal discussion of the interaction of people and land. The
second part is devoted to Commander Facundo (1790-
1835), a partisan of Rosas'. It asks, if the underling is so
terrible, what must the overlord be like? Least interesting is the third part, analyzing Rosas' rule and suggesting a plan for Argentina's future greatness; yet its pro-
gram may have helped Sarmiento's election to the
presidency of Argentina in 1868, while he was in the
United States studying the American educational sys-
tems.

FACUNDO

Part I. Chapter 2
The gaucho tracker

The most conspicuous of all the gauchos, the most extraordinary, is the tracker. All the inland gauchos are trackers. In
prairies so extensive where paths and roads cross in all direc-

tions, and the fields where the beasts feed or wander are open, it is necessary to know how to follow the tracks of an animal, and distinguish it from thousands of others, to know whether it is travelling slowly or fast, loose or on a rope, with a pack or without. This is a home-taught and popular science. Once I came upon a road that crossed one from Buenos Aires and the peon who was guiding me cast a glance, as usual, at the ground.

"A fine Moorish mule came along here. Here is the string of animals of Mr. Zapata. The mule was saddled and passed here yesterday."

The man was from San Luis; the horses were coming back from Buenos Aires, and it had been a year since he had seen the Moorish mule whose tracks mingled with those of a whole string of horses on a path two feet wide. This gift, that seems incredible, is common knowledge; the man was just a cattle driver, not a professional tracker.

The tracker is a serious, circumspect person, whose declarations are accepted by the lower courts. The consciousness of the ability he possesses gives him a certain reserved and mysterious dignity. Everybody treats him with consideration, the poor because he can harm them by slandering or denouncing them, the land owner because his testimony may be necessary.

A robbery has taken place during the night; hardly has it been discovered when everybody hurries to find a clue to the thief, and once found, it is covered with something so the wind won't blow it away. Then the tracker is summoned. He sees the track; he follows it, glancing at the ground only from time to time as if his eyes saw clearly a track that to the rest is imperceptible. He follows along the streets, across a yard, into a house, and pointing at a man that he finds, he says coldly: "That's the man!" The theft is proved, and rare is the criminal who denies the accusation. For him, even more than for the judge, the statement of the tracker is sufficient evidence. It would be foolish to deny it. He surrenders to this witness whom he considers God's accusing finger.

I myself once knew a gaucho named Calibar who was a

tracker for forty years in one province. Now he is eighty years old, bent by age, yet full of dignity and preserving his venerable appearance. When people talk of his fabulous reputation, his remark is: "I'm nothing. You should see what my boys can do." The boys are his sons, who learned under a famous teacher.

About Calibar they recount that while he was away in Buenos Aires, somebody stole his valuable saddle. His wife covered a footprint with a bowl. Two months later Calibar came back, saw the track, now almost erased and invisible to other eyes. He said nothing more about the affair.

A year and a half later, Calibar was walking along a street in the suburbs. He entered a house and there was his saddle, grimy and practically worn out. He had recognized the tracks of the thief two years after the crime.

In 1830 a convict condemned to death had escaped from jail. Calibar was hired to track him down. The poor man, foreseeing that he would be followed, had taken all the precaution that the threat of the gallows suggested. Useless precautions! All they did was make his discovery certain, because with his reputation at stake, Calibar's self respect made him work so hard that he ruined a man but proved his marvelous sight.

The fugitive took advantage of all the roughness of the soil so as not to leave tracks. He walked on tiptoe for blocks, then climbed low walls and crossed and recrossed areas. Calibar followed without losing the tracks. If for a moment he missed them, on finding them he would exclaim: "Where would you go disappearing on me!"

Finally he reached a ditch in the suburbs whose course the fugitive had followed to fool the tracker . . . useless! Calibar followed the bank easily, without hesitation. Finally he stopped, looked at the weeds, and said: "Here's where he stepped out. There's no footprint, but these drops of water on the grass indicate it." He entered a vineyard; Calibar studied the mud wall surrounding it and said: "He's inside."

The group of soldiers had wearied of looking for him and had returned to report the uselessness of further search. "He hasn't left," was the brief reply that the tracker gave without moving, without making any new examination. He hadn't left, that was true, and the next day he was executed.

In 1831 some political prisoners planned a jail break. Everything was prepared, the outside help was ready. Just as they were about to leave, however, one said: "What about Calibar?" "That's right," said the others terrified, "Calibar!" Their families arranged for Calibar to be ill for a couple of days following the escape, and so they were able to make their get-away.

What mysterious power does the tracker have? What microscopic ability is developed in those men's organs of sight? What a sublime creature has God made in His image and likeness!

Part II. Chapter 1
The youth of Facundo Quiroga

There lies between the cities of San Luis and San Juan an extensive desert that, because of its complete lack of water, receives the name of "The Wasteland." The appearance of those solitudes is, in general, sad and forlorn, and the traveller coming from the east never passes the last reservoir or cistern without filling his drinking horn with sufficient water. In this wasteland once took place the strange scene that follows.

The knife fights so common among our gauchos had forced one of them to flee the city of San Luis on foot to the Wastelands, carrying his saddle on his shoulder, in order to escape the police. A couple of friends were to join him later as soon as they could steal horses for the three.

Hunger and thirst were not the chief perils awaiting him in that desert, but rather a man-eating puma that for a year had been following the tracks of travellers and more than eight of them had fallen victims to his taste for human flesh. It sometimes happens in those countries where beast and man fight for control of the region, that man falls beneath the bloody claws of the wild beast; then the puma begins to prefer human victims and is known as a man-eater. The magistrate of the district near the scene of its devastation calls together the best hunters, and under his directions, they set out after the killer who rarely escapes the sentence of death imposed by law.

When our fugitive had walked about six leagues, he thought he heard a puma bellowing in the distance and his nerves tingled. The puma roar somewhat resembles the sound made by a pig, but more shrill, prolonged and strident, and even when there is no reason to be afraid, it causes an involuntary tightening of the nerves, as if the flesh was stirred by the announcement of death.

Moments later the bellowing sounded louder and nearer: the puma had come upon the track. At some distance the fugitive saw a carob tree. He increased his speed, and broke into a run, because the roars sounded more frequently, more distinctly than before.

Finally, discarding his saddle beside the road, the gaucho approached the tree. In spite of the weakness of its trunk, he was able to climb into its branches, fortunately some distance from the ground, and though it still swayed, he could find a place among the foliage that partly concealed him. From there he witnessed events on the ground.

The puma increased its speed, sniffing the earth, roaring more frequently as it sensed the nearness of its prey. Passing beyond the spot where the fugitive left the road, the beast lost the scent. Angrily it circled till it came upon the saddle that it slashed with one stroke of its claw. Then finding the scent and raising its glance, it spied the man whose weight was making the slender tree sway like a reed when birds alight.

No longer did the puma roar. Its leaps carried it to the tree, and almost instantly two claws seized the slender trunk six feet from the ground, causing it to tremble in a way to upset the nervous gaucho. The wild animal tried to leap up at him; it circled the tree, measuring its height with red and blood-thirsty eyes, and finally bellowing in rage, it crouched on the ground, waving its tail, its eyes fixed on its prey, its mouth open and dry.

The situation lasted two mortal hours. The uncomfortable position of the gaucho and the terrifying fascination that the motionless, blood-thirsty glare of the puma exercised on him had started weakening him, and the moment was approaching when his nerveless body would have fallen into those open jaws, when the far-off sound of galloping hoofs brought hopes of salvation.

His friends had seen the spoor of the puma and were coming, though without hopes of saving him. The saddle located him and to loosen their lasso and toss it over the maddened beast at bay was the work of a second. The beast caught in the rope could not escape the many knife thrusts of the vengeful man who was to have been its victim. "That's when I learned what it meant to be afraid," General Juan Facundo Quiroga used to say to his officers when he recounted this episode later.

W.K.J.

BARTOLOMÉ MITRE
1821-1906   Argentina

Mitre, who began his literary career as a poet, wrote his last verses before 1854. He also made translations from Italian (*The Divine Comedy*), and from Latin and English. He turned to prose, first in his *Historia de Belgrano y de la independencia argentina* (The History of Belgrano and the Argentine Independence, 1858-59), and then in his other major work, *Historia de San Martín y de la emancipación sudamericana* (The History of San Martin and the South American Emancipation, 1888); these made him Argentina's greatest historian. His latinized vocabulary reveals his classical background. Mitre also founded *La Nación*, one of the world's great newspapers. In these, and in many other ways, he contributed to the greatness of his nation, which he served as president from 1862 to 1868.

THE HISTORY OF BELGRANO

Introduction

What at the end of the eighteenth century was called the Vice-regency of the River Plate, within which Argentina became an independent nation, was made up of a vast territory that covered a quarter of South America. Situated at one extremity of the new continent, it extended from 55 degrees of south latitude to nearly ten degrees within the Tropic of Capricorn.

The terrain ascended gradually from the horizontal pampas of the River Plate basin to the summits of the lofty mountains of Peru that form the watershed of South America. Its great rivers in the austral section, running from north to south through the sloping plains, articulate the territory extremely well, forming a magnificent fluvial system that brought the people of the mediterranean region into contact with the coast, all of them emptying into the great estuary of the Plata, to which they could contribute, along with the volume of water, all the products of the various zones that they traverse . . .

When the Argentine revolution began, in the first decade of the eighteenth century, the population of the whole viceregency hardly reached 800,000 inhabitants, of which almost half were natives, either living in a savage state or incorporated into the civic life that formed its sum total.

With this minute and heterogeneous population, the revolution for Argentine independence began, out of which developed on the South American continent six republics, of which were constituted from the incoherent elements of the old viceregency, four independent nations that today (1857) number nearly six million inhabitants.

Two human currents contributed to the founding of this colonization, depositing through nearly three centuries in the lap of its bastard population the germs of European civilization that fatal laws were to modify. One came directly from the Mother Country, Spain, crossing the seas and occupying and populating the shores of the River Plate basin by rights of discovery and conquest, fertilizing them by work. The other came from the ancient empire of the Incas, subjugated by Spanish arms as they explored the interior of the continent that extended from the Pacific to the Atlantic, occupying territory under the same rights and exploiting it under a system of feudal servitude . . .

The Conquistadores, or more properly the colonizers from the River Plate, were occupying a land inhabited by nomad tribes with no social cohesion, having no precious metals and without resources to meet the needs of civilized living. The indigenous occupants of the soil, following their native customs, bowed tamely under the yoke of the conqueror. The most bellicose did try to dispute possession of the coast, but at the first clash surrendered their territory and took refuge in the deserts of the interior where only time and a compressed population could conquer them in an indefinitely prolonged war of conquest.

Colonization in the River Plate region, then, was unique in that the establishment, formation, and gradual development was not due to the attraction of precious metal, even though that was the first lure. Baptized by a deceitful name, "Silver River" and "Argent Land," that only the future was to make come true, defrauded in its hopes, its capital took form on prairies covered by weeds where only savages could exist, amid sterile mountains that limited its expansion, and virgin forests populous with wild animals, surrounded by chaotic or swampy terrain that comprised its vast expense of territory, and with no resources beyond its sylvan products and primitive agriculture that scarcely sufficed for the basic requirements of the Indians. So was born and so developed Argentine colonization in the midst of hunger and misery, seeking its sustenance in Mother Earth and growing strong amid dolorous suffering, offering to South America the unique example of a society that was the daughter of reproductive toil.

W.K.J.

CIRILO VILLAVERDE
1812-1894   Cuba

Born and educated in Santiago, Villaverde completed
his studies in Havana where he became interested in
writing. His *Cecilia Valdés o La Loma del Angel*, 1839-
1879, has some of the Romantic flavor of Cooper and
Scott, though combined with Realism. It covers the Cuban scene from captain general to slave, with characters
based on actual people in accurate geographical settings.
In this description of mid-nineteen century colonial customs, Villaverde produced the first anti-slavery novel;
its first part preceded *Uncle Tom's Cabin* by thirteen
years. Its freshness, beauty, and emotional intensity
make it readable even today. Its heroine, Cecilia, is a
beautiful mulattress who is loved by the mulatto Pimienta. Her father is an ignorant Spaniard who became
rich through slave-trading.

CECILIA VALDÉS

Part I. Chapter 17

José Dolores Pimienta declared that the dance for the colored
people would be held in Soto's house. It occupies the west corner of Jesús María Street, where it meets the Monte Road op-
posite the parade ground. One enters the house across a wide
porch with wooden railings. From it through tall windows wide
open, anybody could enter and share in the party. In the square
patio, covered by an awning, they set up refreshment tables.
The orchestra played in the dining room, people danced in the
very large parlor, and in the other rooms the dancers relaxed and
friends and sweethearts talked.

The only decorations of the parlor was a hanging damask of
red, the national color, caught up above the doors and windows
by blue ribbons. Wax candles in huge chandeliers provided the

illumination that gleamed through the prisms that multiplied and broke the light into all the colors of the rainbow.

By using the phrase "Fashionable Dance," they meant it was to be very formal, very different from dances of the white people, not only because of the type of music, but because of the attire of both men and women. The women were to wear skirts of white satin, a blue band across their breasts and a marabou feather in their hair. The men wore black frock coats, pique vests, and white silk ties, besides short trousers of naneen, flesh-colored stockings and low shoes with silver buckles in the style of Charles III whose statue, made by Canovas, stood at the end of the Prado, the present location of the Fountain of the Indies.

In order to enter and share in the festivities, more than the special costume of the men was needed. They had to present a ticket in the vestibule to the committee stationed there to greet and look after the women. At first this arrangement was strictly observed, but when the time for dancing approached, Brindis and Pimienta, the chief receptionists, delegated their authority to assistants less scrupulous. Because of this lack of supervision, several individuals entered later that night who although formally dressed, had no tickets and were not even laborers.

Among this number was a Negro of average height, rather stout, with a full, round face, and with balding spots on both sides of his forehead that by the time he was forty would make him completely bald. Although dressed in the prescribed style, his coat was too tight, his vest was rather short. His stockings were discolored with age, his shoes lacked buckles, and the collar of his shirt was riding so high it almost covered his ears, perhaps because his neck was so short and thick.

Because of his appearance, the balding Negro was the target of all eyes from the moment he entered the ballroom. He realized this, since he was no fool and therefore was hesitant at first, shunning the brightest lights of the parlor. But toward eleven o'clock he got up nerve to join the circle of men around the prettiest girls and he even picked up courage to invite one of them to dance a courtly minuet, which was so graceful that the couple attracted general attention. Several times he approached the group courting Cecilia Valdés, the most beautiful of the women in that heterogeneous gathering. He looked at her for a long time out of the corner of his eye, then moved away with visible evidence of scorn.

On one such occasion, an official of Uribe's Tailor Shop, observing him from nearby, followed him out of the room, put his hand on the man's shoulder familiarly, and said:

"Listen! Are you here?"

"Well, what about it?" the Negro replied turning and shaking from head to foot.

"What are you doing around here, Smarty?" the official went on with still greater familiarity.

"Please tell me," replied the other angrily, "when and where I ever harmed you?"

"Don't come here, pretending to be a big shot, because I know who you are, and you know who I am. So quit play-acting. You might fall off the stage and end up in the kitchen."

"Well, what do you want of me?"

"Nothing. I don't want anything of anybody. I was just noticing you giving the eye to the prettiest girl at the dance, and it roused my curiosity."

"Does what I do matter to you?"

"More than you can imagine."

"Are you trying to defend that young lady?"

"She doesn't need it. Women aren't like kings that everybody is supposed to honor. Whether you like her or don't, doesn't matter."

"Then leave me alone."

"You're ungrateful," said the official seriously. "It's not your fault, it's mine for paying attention to somebody so inferior to me, you cook and . . . slave!"

The enraged Negro raised his hand to strike his insulter, but for his own reasons, he did not hit him. He had entered the house without invitation, he was an intruder, and any scandal would damage him. So he contented himself with muttering a threat that he would get his revenge after the dance. He turned his back and started away, a departure that amused the official.

He laughed when he described the incident to his friend José Pimienta, but neither thought much about it.

From early in the evening, the floor was crowded with people of all colors, sexes, and conditions, that jammed both windows of the porch and made a lively picture. There was hardly room for the men to stand between dances, elbowing each other and almost concealing the women seated around the floor. Cecilia, with Nemesia and Missie Clara, Uribe's wife, had chairs facing the street, half way between the dining room door and the sitting room, and whenever the groups of men who came to talk to her permitted it, the exclamations of admiration of her unusual beauty could be heard from the group at the door.

Sometimes amid the comments about her attractiveness could be heard expressions of pity because, taking her for a white girl, it was natural that people would be surprised to see her there and would suspect of low taste anyone who mingled so intimately with colored people. Cecilia, meanwhile was thoroughly enjoying a triumph that comes to few women of her youth and beauty . . .

Even a casual observer could notice that there was a difference in her treatment of Negroes and mestizos. The latter often led her out for a contradance. With the blacks, however, she danced only minuets. When the balding Negro approached, she did not give him a definite refusal. She only said she had the next dance taken, that she was rather tired, etc.

Finally when she visited the refreshment table, he left the doorway and approached close enough to touch her shoulder with his chin.

"So the Young Lady doesn't think me worthy of being her partner tonight?"

"What are you saying?" Cecilia demanded.

"I'm saying that the Young Lady has snubbed me."

"If you think so, I apologize. I had no such intention."

"The Young Lady told me she was tired, but went right out to dance with somebody else. The Young Lady need not look for explanations. I realize why she snubbed me. She sees that

I'm black, poorly dressed, without friends in the group, and she probably figures that I'm nobody, just some crude ragamuffin."

"You're mistaken."

"No, I'm not. I know what I'm saying just as I know who the Young Lady is."

"Sir, you're mistaking me for somebody else."

"I know the Young Lady better than she realizes. I've known her since she started nursing and crawling. I know her father, as well as I know these hands, and I have good reason to know the mother that looked after her for a year."

"But I don't know you . . ."

"Does that matter? I understand. I must tell the Young Lady however that she scorns me because she thinks that on account of her white skin, she is white. But she's not. Maybe the Young Lady can fool others, but not me!"

"Did you come here to insult me?"

"No, señorita, I'm not in the habit of insulting people who wear tunics. If the Young Lady wore slave's clothing, believe me, I wouldn't insult her like this. But I don't like the haughty attitude the Young Lady displays toward me."

"We've talked long enough," Cecilia interrupted him, turning her back on him.

"Just as the Young Lady wishes," said he, greatly enraged. "However let me suggest she lower her proud neck a bit because if her father is white, her mother is no more white than I am. In fact, the Young Lady is the reason that I've been separated from my wife for more than twelve years."

"How am I to blame for that?"

"Because my wife is the real mother of the Young Lady, since she looked after her from birth, since her own mother couldn't nurse her child because she was crazy."

"You're the crazy one," cried Cecilia.

Nemesia and Missie Clara approached their friend and tried to take her to the other room. But some of the men, hearing the loud voices, hurried up to see what was happening. Pimienta was the first to question her.

"It's nothing. This black man," she declared disdainfully, "persisted in trying to quarrel with me since he sees I'm a woman."

"You coward!" cried Pimienta, a meek lamb suddenly changed into a lion. And he swung at the man, but missed him. When the others restrained him, he demanded:

"Who are you?"

"I'm who I am," came the fearless reply.

"What are you looking for here?"

"Whatever I like!"

"Well, get out of here or I'll kick you out."

"I'd like to see you try."

"You dog. You must be a slave! Get out!"

                                                        W.K.J.

MANUEL DE JESÚS GALVÁN
1834-1910   Santo Domingo

Enriquillo (1879), based on the chronicles of Padre Las Casas, is not only the best historical novel of the period, but it ranks high among the works of Romanticism. In addition, it is the forerunner of the Indianist Movement of the next century. Set in Santo Domingo in the early sixteenth century, it comprises three parts and 125 chapters. Though the sentences are long and, to present-day tastes, involved, its style was universally admired.

ENRIQUILLO

Guarocuya, son of an Indian chief, has been baptized in the Christian faith, under the name of Enrique. Padre Las Casas brings him word that his aunt, Higuemota, widow of a Spanish nobleman and mother of Mencia, is dying, and takes the young Indian to her. She lives only long enough to get his promise to marry Mencia. Enrique is so moved by the experience that he contracts an illness, described by Dr. Gil Pérez, the Viceroy's erudite physician, in Part I, Chapter 31:

"I arrived at the convent and with the permission of the reverend prior, whom I besought in the name of Your Excellency, I was taken to the cell occupied by the young invalid, who is a fine physical specimen, with admirable qualities. The fever, *febris acuta*, had found abundant material to feed on, *abundatia sanguinis*; and his delirium proved to me that he had a dangerous rush of blood to the head, *congestio inminens*, but following the precepts of Avicena in such cases, I extracted blood from both arms, prescribed a *pedilivium*, footbath, boiling, *fervidus*, and afterward I remained to observe him for more than an hour until I saw repose conquer the patient, *restauratio causa requietionis*. I have now left him fast asleep, with his feet wrapped in cloths soaked in warm oil, *oleum calefactum*; and I assure Your Excellency that if the friars taking care of him make him follow the practices that I prescribed, that is, diet and rhubarb tea, within a month he will have recovered his health, *pesanabit*; but I must tell Your Excellency that I am dubious, because a layman is living among the friars and he was inconsiderate enough to dare to contradict me and to call me to my face 'ignoramus,' *stultus*."

The doctor pronounced the last words with a gesture comically tragic.

"Who could have been so bold?" exclaimed the Viceroy, Admiral Diego Columbus, unable to control a chuckle.

"A *quidam*," replied the doctor, "whom I have seen several times among your visitors and whom I have heard the friars call Doctor Las Casas. In all events, if he is really a doctor, he should respect knowledge a little more."

The Viceroy invites the Indian to come to court, and he appears there in Part II, Chapter 3, entitled:

PRESENTATION

Enrique's recovery was rapid, much more so than could have been foreseen from the words of Doctor Gil Pérez. Perhaps Bartolomé de Las Casas, who carefully supervised the care of the sick man, had continued his rebellion against the authority of the learned doctor; the result, in any case, was that within three weeks Enriquillo, completely free from fever, howbeit still pale and weak, left his cell and strolled wherever he wished in the patios of the convent though the predictions of the doctor had been a month as the shortest time in which the invalid, if he followed instructions absolutely, would regain his health, and so the defiance of science was successful.

Still filled with grief, the young man, hardly able to believe that for so short a time he had seen alive his Aunt Higuemota, whom he considered the being to whom he owed the greatest tribute of love and gratitude, could console himself only when Las Casas, always compassionate and practical, reminded him of the obligation embodied in the last words of the young and unhappy widow, at her death. According to Las Casas, that wish ought to be more binding than any written will upon the three witnesses of that sad scene: Enrique, the girl Mencia, and Las Casas himself; and so upon Enriquillo, concluded the foresighted doctor, lay the double obligation of resignation and restoration of strength so that he might look out for the future of his young cousin and fulfill the sacred request of her dying mother.

The effect of these timely words upon Enrique is indescribable: from that instant, convinced that his sorrow was shameful and unworthy, he changed his expression, showed himself determined to face the tests and struggles of life, and only a slight hint of his customary mournful expression gave evidence of the melancholy deep within him, despite his struggle to conceal it.

Realizing this progress, Las Casas arranged with Diego Velásquez (commander of the army) to present his protegé to the Viceroy and his wife, and for the interview the Spaniards provided Enrique with mourning clothes which, with his face, naturally pale and made more so by his recent illness and by the emotions of the moment, gave a mark of distinction to the young Indian. With an air of triumph, Diego Velásquez remarked about it to Las Casas, because his vanity made him anxious to have the young man create a favorable impression at court.

When Enrique was ushered into the presence of the Viceroy and his wife, Doña María de Toledo, both of them greeted him with unusual friendliness. Encouraged by the kindness of the royal couple and by the prompting of Las Casas, Enrique lost no time in expressing his desire to see his cousin, thereupon Doña María took him at once to her chambers and then to a beautiful garden within the Fortress where Mencia, sad and silent, was listening without interest to the conversation of the ladies of the court.

When she saw Enrique, she jumped up and, running to him, threw her arms around him and kissed him on the cheek. The young man, restrained by his sensitive instinct, was less responsive, contenting himself with seizing a hand of the lovely girl and with looking at her with a gentle smile and with tears that, in spite of himself, ran down his cheeks. Doña María, though much moved, tried to conceal her feelings by saying:

"Go ahead, Enrique! Kiss your cousin."

The young man cast an indefinable glance at the kind noblewoman and muttered to himself:

" 'Kiss your cousin!' That is what *she* told me just before she died, and didn't give me time to follow her wishes."

"Of whom are you talking, Enrique?" asked Doña María.

"Of somebody no longer alive, of my beloved Aunt Higuemota, who just before her death said what you just said: 'Kiss your cousin,' in the presence of Doctor Bartolomé de Las Casas, and she added as her final farewell: "Kiss her who, if God hears my prayers, will some day be your wife.' " And Enrique took the lovely head of Mencia between his hands, kissed her brow tenderly, and broke into tears.

The compassionate grand lady could not see through her

tear-filled eyes, but making an effort to control her emotions, she
tried to distract the young man, saying to him:

"Well, then, won't Mencia be your wife as soon as you are
both old enough to marry?"

"If I didn't think so," Enrique replied, "what interest would
I have in living? I must look after my poor cousin, and only for
that reason do I want to preserve my life."

*After Doña María rejoined her husband and Las Casas, she
repeated the conversation to the Viceroy and suggested that Enrique come to live at the court, that "the sacred betrothal sealed
by death" be made official, and that plans be made to see that
Higuemota's dying wishes be carried out. The chapter ends:*

All of them agreed with the generous resolution and it
seemed as though from that day on, the happy future of the two
orphans was certain, but those fleeting and affectionate illusions
did not long endure in the fated course of events, because the
determinations of the human will always find the road of evil
wide and easy, therefore when they seek good and are inspired by
virtue, they are certain to be obstructed by many obstacles, and
not even faith in the sanctity of the purpose nor the most energetic persistence in the struggle is enough to conquer them.

*Most of the Spaniards felt less friendly toward the Indians,
and the novel contains many examples of their cruelty. Sure that
only flight can save the several thousand Indians of whom Enrique is now chief, he rides out with his best friend, Tamayo,
looking for a refuge for his followers. His search is recounted in
Part III, Chapter 35, entitled:*

THE BAHORUCO MOUNTAINS

The time was autumn, but autumn in the fortunate valleys of
the Maguana River neither dulls the brilliant green of the grassy

plains nor strips the trees of their showy foliage; instead it seems as if the vegetation, when it senses a lessening in the heat of the summer sun, clothes itself in the finery reserved in other climates for the spring, in order to express its homage of gratitude to the fertile Prince of Creation.

Since Enriquillo was endowed with keen feeling and capable, not only because of a delicate instinct but also because of his superior intelligence, of that simple yet sublime enthusiasm that a love for beauty engenders, he was forgetting his troubles as he rode along, followed by faithful Tamayo and by the no less faithful mastiff that always went along with them. The morning was cloudless; the fields stretched wide and lonely; the air was balmy; the breezes, touching with their invisible wings the light, waving grasses, murmured mysterious and unforgettable melodies.

Amid these splendors of nature, the young chief felt the need for communicating his impressions to another intelligent and sensible being, and thinking Tamayo capable of appreciating them and of feeling the inspiration of breathing freely in that vast expanse, he tried to express his own feelings to his sullent companion, every time he noticed some strange and seductive object in that panorama, only to have each attempt frustrated as Tamayo, unwittingly parodying a famous Athenian cynic, hacked away at Enriquillo's enthusiasm. When the chief called the attention of his companion to the fantastic changes in the distant horizon, he would receive a chilling response:

"If we get there, we won't find anything like that. It *seems*, but it really *isn't*. It's just like the hopes of us poor Indians."

Fifteen minutes later, Enriquillo tried again.

"Look at this lovely savannah! It's this sort of scenery that makes Padre Las Casas believe that our beautiful land was Adam's Garden of Eden."

"Then we Indians are like Adam after he sinned," the inexorable Tamayo replied.

"Look! In the distance," Enriquillo insisted, "those peaks! In the sunlight they look exactly like a city with its big buildings, like those of Santo Domingo."

"What hard work and how many lives they have cost the poor Indians!" the uninspired Tamayo retorted.

Tired of trying to play on the untaught strings of Tamayo's inert feelings, Enrique kept to himself any further original and poetic observations, and they rode on in silence.

In the remainder of the novel, Enriquillo and his followers for fifteen years escape the efforts of the Spaniards to capture them. Finally, in 1533, Charles V of Spain commanded that Enriquillo and his vassals be permitted to live in peace in Santo Domingo.

W.K.J.

JOSÉ MÁRMOL
1817-1871   Argentina

Hatred of Argentina's gaucho dictator, Juan Manuel de Rosas, drove Mármol to Uruguay where he wrote Argentina's first novel, *Amalia*, in two parts (1851, 1855), which depicts the dictator's tyranny and cruelty. Like its chief character, Mármol himself had been arrested in 1839. Escaping to Montevideo with other progressive young Argentines, he wrote poetry, drama, and part of *Amalia*. After Rosas' overthrow in 1852, Mármol returned to Buenos Aires to perform political and diplomatic duties. Part of Rosas' bad reputation is due to the fact that only his enemies wrote about him.

AMALIA

Chapter 1

On May 4th, 1840, at 10:30 P.M., six men were crossing the patio of a small house on Belgrano St., in the city of Buenos Aires. Reaching the vestibule, dark like the rest of the house, one of them stops and says to the others:

"One further precaution."

"At this rate, we'll go on all night taking precautions," answers another of them, apparently the youngest of them all. From his belt was hanging a long sword, half concealed by the folds of a long blue cloak that was hanging from his shoulders.

"No matter how many precautions we take, it'll be too few," replies the one who had first spoken. "We mustn't all go together. There are six of us. Let three leave first. We'll take the sidewalk across the street. A minute later the rest will leave, but stay on this side. We'll meet where Balcarce crosses this street."

"Good idea!"

"All right. I'll go first with Merlo and this gentleman," said the young man wearing the sword, and pointing to the one who had just spoken. He pushed the door latch, opened the door, threw a corner of his cloak across his face and crossing the street with the people he had indicated, he followed Belgrano St., toward the river. The other three men left two minutes later and after closing the door, headed in the same direction.

After continuing several blocks in silence, the sword wearer's companion said to him, while the one called Merlo still walked silently, wrapped in his cloak:

"It's a sad thing, my friend. This is the last time, perhaps, that we'll walk the streets of our own country. We are leaving to join an army that is going to have to do some fierce fighting, and God knows what will happen to us in the war."

"How very true," his friend answered him. "But this step is necessary. However—" he added after several seconds of silence— "there is one man in this world who has a different opinion. He thinks it is the duty of Argentines to remain in Buenos Aires."

"In spite of Rosas?"

"In spite of Rosas."

"Bah, he's either a coward or a member of Rosas' secret Mashorca."

"No, neither one. He's brave almost to the point of rashness, and his heart is the purest and noblest of our generation."

"What does he want us to do, then?"

"He wants all of us," said the man with the sword, "to remain in Buenos Aires because the enemy we must fight is here,
and not in the army, and he has arguments to prove that fewer
will die in a street revolution than in four or five months of
battle with little chance of victory."

*At the river, Merlo betrays them, and four of them are killed
by Rosas' Mashorca. Eduardo Belgrano, the wearer of the
sword, though wounded in the thigh, escapes with the help of
Daniel Bello, the "rash idealist" alluded to. Daniel takes him to
hide at the house of his cousin, Amalia, and they fall in love.
When a servant, a member of Rosas' spy network, reports a
strange man living there, María Josefa, the elderly sister-in-law
of Rosas who is at that time believed to be the brains of the
dictatorship, pays a call on Amalia.*

Part III. Chapter 9
The first act of a drama

Of all those present, Amalia was the only one who did not know
María Josefa Ezcurra, but when she entered the parlor and got
a close view of that thin, sharp, and repulsive face, she couldn't
help having a vague impression of disgust, a certain distrust, and
a fear that made her put only her fingers into the extended hand
of the old woman. When handsome Agustina Mansilla, the dictator's sister, said to her: "I'm delighted to introduce you to
Madame Ezcurra," a nervous shiver passed like an electric shock
through Amalia's body and, without knowing why, her eyes
sought out Eduardo.

"Didn't you expect me this afternoon in this bad weather?"
Agustina went on, speaking to Amalia, as all found chairs in
front of the fireplace. Whether by chance or design, María Josefa sat beside Eduardo.

"It is a pleasant surprise," Amalia assured Agustina.

"María Josefa insisted we must come, and since she knows
how happy I am to visit this house, she herself ordered the
coachman to drive us here."

Daniel began scratching one ear, staring at the fire as if it absorbed his whole attention.

"Apparently we're not the only ones who think of you," Agustina went on. "Here is Madame Dupasquier who hasn't come to call on me for a year, and here is Florencia who has been avoiding me, and consequently here is her sweetheart señor Bello. And I also have the pleasure of seeing señor Belgrano who hasn't been seen by anybody for years," went on Agustina, who knew all the young people of Buenos Aires.

The eyes of María Josefa passed over Eduardo from head to toe as if he absorbed her entire attention.

"It was just chance," Amalia remarked. "My friends seldom drop in on me."

"But you're so well-off here that your solitude is almost enviable," was María Josefa's comment.

"I live comfortably, señora."

"Barracas is a healthy part of the city," the old woman went on. "I hope the young gentleman is recovering." She looked at Eduardo.

Amalia grew red. Eduardo spoke up.

"Señora, there's nothing the matter with me."

"Oh, excuse me. You looked pale."

"That's my natural color."

"And since I don't see your patriotic red badge, and you are wearing such light clothes, I thought you were living here."

"Clothes are a matter of taste," Daniel broke in to avoid either a lie or a revealing remark. "The Scotch live in a chilly climate but go bare-legged."

"That's all right for gringos. We're living in Buenos Aires."

"Florencia, why don't you play something on the piano?"

"Very well, Mama. What would you like to hear, doña Josefa?"

"Anything."

"Very well. Sit here beside me. I sing badly but for you I'll play and sing my favorite composition, Rosas' *Birthday Song*. Will you turn the pages?" Florencia stood before María Josefa to make her invitation more urgent.

"My dear girl! It's hard to get up where I'm sitting."

"Oh, come on!"

"What a girl!" said the elderly woman with a Satanic smile. "All right. All right. Excuse me, señor Belgrano." As she spoke, on the pretense of needing support she put her bony hand on the left leg of Eduardo and rested on it the whole weight of her body. The pain shot through him because her hand exactly covered the most sensitive spot of his deep bullet wound. He snapped his head back, unable to choke off an exclamation: "Ouch, señora!" He slumped in his chair, almost fainting and pale as a corpse.

As soon as she leaves, his friends rush Eduardo to a safe place. A little while later, six of Rosas' soldiers gallop up to arrest Eduardo. The only man there is Daniel Bello, protected by a document affirming his loyalty as a member of Rosas' Federalist party.

W.K.J.

VICENTE PÉREZ ROSALES
1807-1886   Chile

Pérez Rosales was the son of a wealthy and patriotic Santiago family. His career ranged from smuggler to senator, including gold hunting in California. Educated partly in France and partly in Spain, he had the opportunity to meet many of the prominent figures of Europe. Through his service in Germany as official agent for Chilean colonization, and through his first piece of writing, *Ensayo sobre Chile* (Essay on Chile, 1855), he attracted many new citizens to his country.

It was, however, as the author of the delightful *Recuerdos del Pasado: 1814-1860* (Memories of the Past) that Rosales left his mark on Chilean literature. Though lacking in character analysis, it is full of anecdotes. First published serially in *La Época*, 1882, it went into several editions, the third one "corrected and augmented"

the year of the author's death. While Pérez Rosales
claimed no literary aspirations, his *Memories* is one of
Chile's most original works, providing fascinating reading throughout its twenty-five long chapters.

MEMORIES OF THE PAST

Chapter I. How Santiago in 1814-22 was not even a shadow of the Santiago of 1860

What was Santiago like in 1814? How did it compare with the
city that today, in spite of its short existence, is such a progressive place, combining the more or less well-founded pretensions
of a big city with the smallness appropriate to a village?

Santiago in 1814 was a delight for its fortunate inhabitants,
but for those recently arriving it was, except for its enchanting
Chilean sky and the imposing aspect of the Andes, a forbidding
and sad settlement whose low and crude buildings, though bor-
dering straight streets, were lacking in any architectural taste.
Diminishing the worth of this jewel of the so-called Kingdom of
Chile was its unattractive setting, because, although it was built
on the fertile plain of the Mapocho River, its expansion was
limited to the north by the wasteland of the Mapocho, to the
south by the Cañada dumps, to the east by the wastelands of
the Santa Lucia slopes, and to the west by those of San Miguel
and San Pablo.

If the surroundings of Santiago were wastelands, what term
would fit the fields extending beyond it, granted the apathetic
and satisfied nature of its ceremonious sons?

Only the eastern valley of the town, thanks to the waters of
Chile's Manzanares River and to the numerous small streams
that surge from the foothills of the Andes, was truly a garden
spot compared to the uncultivated fields extending toward the
north, east, and south of our capital.

The plains of the Maipo, a veritable oven where the summer
sun heartlessly baked the thirsty stony ground, produced, in-

stead of trees, discolored rosemary, and instead of pasture, fugitive rat grass. There in the poetic words of our *huaso* cattle rustlers, not even the chirp of a sparrow was heard.

Who, contemplating the satisfied sluggishness of our material way of weaving our life, could have guessed back then that with the progress of time those wastelands first visited by the turbid Maipo in 1920, the year that this river united part of its flood of water with the scarce and always disputed water of the Mapocho, would become the same land where today the locomotive puffs and whistles through the cool woods that surround a thousand rustic possessions where industry, art, and the conveniences of life seem to have found their natural lodgings? Who would have imagined that those filthy lands that developed into a city beyond the dump heap of the ancient Cañada would be transformed into parks, sumptuous residences, and what is more, that that very wasteland would turn into the Alameda de Delicias, a promenade that, I can say without blushing, the most attractive city of cultured Europe may well desire for itself? All are miracles, the legitimate descendants of our immortal 12th of February, 1810, when, having definitely broken the barrier between us and the rest of the civilized world, we resolved to develop according to our own voluntary pattern.

But let's not get ahead of our story.

Santiago, that twenty-four years after the epoch to which I refer had only 46,000 inhabitants, appeared when seen from the top of Santa Lucía Hill, a wooded village composed of country houses lined on either side of streets whose narrow walks were frequently invaded by spurs coming from temples and convents, or from pilasters of houses more or less pretentious belonging to rich citizens, —something that should not cause surprise, since the Church and Wealth never forget their invading tactics.

Our capital had only one market place and one main plaza, the site of not only the chief commercial houses, but the cathedral, a convent of nuns, the residence of the authorities, the town hall, and the inexorable public jail that, as in all towns of Spanish origin, displayed its ancient iron grating and the dirty hands of the criminals who, holding onto the bars, chatted with their daily visitors. It was not unusual to see, mornings outside the arcade of the unhappy building, a couple of bloody corpses, laid out there by the police, waiting to be claimed by their families . . .

In the middle of that plaza that served as well for ceremonial parades and bullfights as for the drilling of the soldiers, was an enormous bronze basin always surrounded by water sellers who, after ladling the water into the casks on their donkeys, by gourds, set out to sell drinking water to the citizens. And here and there usually stood gallows for murderers, though their gloomy presence did not free that aristocratic square from the lethal and ever-present clubs that they called a "rolling pin." . . .

Foreign luxury had not yet invaded us, and so the parlors of our rich citizens revealed only Chilean luxury. Instead of wall paper, white wash; instead of extensive carpets of pile, Indian matting or woven rugs occupying the center of the room with the rest of the floor, bare under the chairs whose position was determined by the rigid moral requirements of the time, because those destined for the ladies were always across the room from those occupied by the masculine sex. Figure out for yourselves from this strategy, unfavorable for battles of love, the mutual anguish of sweethearts, although it is rumored that they made up for it later, either through the bars of the windows facing the street or over the walls of the yard.

In addition, inlaid wooden tables, with heavy silver candlesticks and religious images. On the walls, a couple of mirrors with filagree frames, a picture or two of the family saint, and a frightful portrait of some important ancestor, done in the style of Josephus Gil. Illumination was provided by wax candles, and in winter the chill was taken out of the air by thorn charcoal, in braziers of heavy silver in the middle of the parlor.

Families less well off decorated their parlors with similar luxury on a lesser scale; however, except for the presence of a piano, not very plentiful at that time, or a clavichord, instruments which the poor replaced by a guitar hanging from the wall; and the wall-to-wall carpeting, for which in the poorer houses a rag rug had to do, to see one parlor was to see them all . . .

One who saw Santiago in 1814 and came back to it in 1825 could say truthfully: Either the recent great political and social changes have taken too much time to let them prepare for the city a costume less threadbare, or Santiago was born to remain forever unchanged.

However, let us not make fun of our modest cradle. The ragged villages of Santiago and Concepción belonged to our parents, and from their tatters came the giants to whom we owe our country and our liberty. Having described the scene of my earliest period, I shall continue to put down chronologically according to the passing years, the little that age has not erased from my memory.

W.K.J.

ALBERTO BLEST GANA
1830-1920   Chile

Chile's great historical novelist and interpreter of the customs of his country was Blest Gana, a forerunner of Modernism. His father was a physician of Irish origin and his mother came from Chilean aristocracy. His reading of Balzac decided him to write about Chilean society as he did in an early short story, "Una escena social" (An Episode in Chilean Society, 1853). In 1860 he won a literary prize with his first novel, Aritmética en el amor (Arithmetic in Love), which was highly praised for its realistic descriptions of Chilean social life. Later came Martín Rivas (1862), subtitled novela de costumbres político-sociales (a novel about political and social customs), the most popular, and one of the best of his fifteen novels. It describes the first clash between the middle class and the aristocracy during Chile's political uprising of 1850-1851, and covers every phase of Santiago life from the division of social classes and the ways of life of the rich and the poor to religious events and trips to the market.

Later, while living in Paris, Blest Gana wrote his greatest historical novel, Durante la reconquista (During the Reconquest, 1897), a lengthy study of Chile before 1818. Some of his last books deal with Chileans who, like himself, lived abroad.

The hero of *Martín Rivas* is a country boy who comes to Santiago to study law. He lives with the family of his father's friend, the aristocratic Dámaso Encina, and falls in love with Encina's daughter, the haughty Leonor. Here is a conversation between Leonor and her brother Agustín, just returned from a journey in Europe.

MARTÍN RIVAS

Chapter III

At four o'clock, the oldest child of don Dámaso was tapping at the door of Leonor's room. He wore a blue frock coat and light trousers that fell over patent leather boots whose heels revealed small gilded spurs. In his left hand, he carried a whip with an ivory handle, and in his right hand, an enormous half-smoked cigar. He knocked, as we have said, and he heard his sister's voice: "Who's there?"

"May I come in?" Agustin asked, partly opening the door. Then without waiting for an answer, he entered with an air of extreme elegance.

Leonor was combing her hair before a mirror. She turned her head to welcome her brother.

"Oh!" she exclaimed. "Here you are with your cigar."

"Don't make me throw it away, sister," said the elegant young man. "It's an 'Imperial' that costs two hundred pesos a thousand."

"You might have finished it before coming to see me."

"I tried to. I went to talk to mama, but she drove me out and said the smoke choked her."

"Have you been riding?"

"Yes, and since you're so nice about my cigar, I'll tell you something you'll be glad to hear."

"What is it?"

"I met Clemente Valencia."

"What about it?"

"He was most enthusiastic about you."

Leonor compressed her lips in a gesture of scorn.

"Come on!" Agustin told her. "Don't be a hypocrite. You know you like him."

"Not any more than a lot of others."

"Maybe, but most of the others don't have 300,000 pesos."

"Yes, but he's not very good looking."

"Nobody is ugly with all that money, sister!"

Leonor smiled. It would have been hard to say whether it was on account of her brother's maxim or because she was pleased with the appearance of her hair.

"In these days, sister," the well-dressed young man went on, lounging in an arm-chair, "money is the first consideration."

"Or maybe good looks," Leonor replied.

"Are you trying to tell me you prefer Emilio Mendoza because he's handsome? Break down and confess. You know I adore you."

"There's nothing to confess. I don't love anybody."

"I guess it's no use. We might as well talk of something else. Did you know we've got a lodger?"

"So I heard, some young man from Copiapó. What's he like?"

"Poorer than poor," said Agustin with a gesture of scorn.

"I mean, what does he look like?"

"I haven't seen him. He's probably some pink-cheeked, sunburned farmer." Then he looked at his sister who had finished with her hair. "Why you are *charmante!*" Even though he had learned little French while abroad, he used all the phrases and words possible to make people believe he knew it perfectly.

[In the law classes at university, Martín Rivas' old-fashioned clothes contrast with the fashionable attire of most of the students, and his attention to study, among students interested *chiefly in social life, makes him conspicuous. One day he meets one of the older students.*]

Chapter VIII

He was a young man of twenty-three or twenty-four, with a face pale and almost effeminate that made more noticeable his black and shining mustache. A mass of hair with a part in the middle of the forehead, fell in long locks behind his small ears. His eyes, without being large, seemed to gleam with the spark of a keen intellect and the fire of a lofty masculine heart. His energetic expression went well with the elegant proportions of his body, of average height but well formed. The students called him Rafael San Luis.

At the beginning of the class Rivas watched the newcomer with interest until the young man observed him and said something to his companion. At that moment, the professor questioned Martin about a legal point which was being discussed. His reply brought an angry retort from the student who had just given a different answer. Martin was quick and vigorous in his reply. His substantiation of his correction made the other student turn red with anger.

After class he approached Martin arrogantly.

"Correct me, if you like," he said, haughtily, "but don't ever again use that tone of voice."

"I won't put up with anybody's arrogance, and I'll use whatever tone of voice people use to me," Martin told him. "And now that you've brought it up, let me tell you, I'll take lessons only from the professors and only in what pertains to their subject."

"The young man is right," exclaimed Rafael San Luis, joining them. "Miguel, you had no right to get angry when he was only answering the professor's question. Besides he's a newcomer, and he deserves at least some consideration and hospitality."

Martin turned to him timidly.

"I feel I owe you my thanks for what you've just said in my behalf," he said. "And I beg you to accept it with the sincerity that I offer it."

"So I do," Rafael replied, extending his hand with frank cordiality.

"And since you were willing to take my side," Rivas went on, "I beg you that whenever you can, you will give me your advice. I'm new in Santiago and I don't understand its customs."

"It looks to me as if you don't need advice," Rafael replied. "What predominates in Santiago is pride, and you seem to have a large supply. And now that we're mentioning it, I might tell you that I spoke up because they told me you were poor and that you knew few students. Here people pay most attention to outward appearance, an attitude with which I don't agree. Your poverty and isolation attracted my sympathy for reasons that have nothing to do with this matter."

"Well, I certainly appreciate it and hope we can get better acquainted."

"I'm afraid I will be a sad acquaintance," San Luis told him with a melancholy smile, "but I have had certain experience that may perhaps help you. Anyway, time will tell. I'll see you tomorrow."

With these words, he walked away, leaving a strange impression in the mind of Martin Rivas, who remained pensive, following him with his eyes.

[*Meanwhile Agustin becomes infatuated with the ambitious Adelaide Molina, one of the three children of a lower class family, who had a son by San Luis. Her brother Amador under threats of death forces Agustin into a fake marriage, though don Dámaso had planned an excellent match between his son and Matilde, daughter of a wealthy friend. She, however, loves San Luis. When Agustin confesses to Martin, he buys Amador's confession of the trick and meets the other sister Edelmira. Matilde discusses with Leonor her marriage to San Luis.*]

Chapter XLII

"Since you're not in love," she said, seizing Leonor's hands with sweet abandon, "you can't understand my happiness."

Leonor fixed on her a profound look, of the kind pertaining merely to the body when the soul is wandering far afield.

"Listen," her cousin went on, "when I'm absent from Rafael, I think of nothing to say. Perhaps a love like mine has no words to describe its full extent. But what interest could you have in all this?" she added, noticing that Leonor was only pretending to listen.

"But I do!" Leonor replied with a gentle smile.

"You don't understand me."

"I understand you very well."

"What? Are you in love?" In the vivacity of Matilde's question could be seen that for a moment her woman's curiosity was stronger than her desire to discuss her own love.

Leonor answered quickly, blushing.

"Me? Of course not, Matilde!"

"You're fibbing."

"What makes you think so?"

"Because you're not the same Leonor you used to be. When were you ever before pensive as I often see you now? Come on! Give! Which of the two is it, Clemente or Emilio?"

Leonor thrust out one lip in a gesture of magnificent disdain. Matilde named a number of other men among Santiago's high society, only to receive the same reply. Finally she exclaimed:

"I wonder if it's Martin."

"Oh, don't be silly!" But Leonor's cheeks flamed.

"Well, why not?" Matilde went on. "Martin is interesting."

"Do you think so?" asked Leonor, pretending the utmost indifference.

"I find him so. What difference if he is poor?"

"Oh, it's not that," Leonor exclaimed, raising her brow with regal majesty.

*As Leonor confesses her growing love for the poor lodger, she
sees a note from Edelmira Molina to Martin in which the two
appear to be in love. Don Dámaso hears that Martin has ad-
vised Edelmira not to marry Ricardo Castaños, who comes from
the lower class, and that he has helped her to escape from her
parents' house—whereupon he turns him out of the Encina
house. The other Molinas break up the marriage of San Luis
and Matilde by showing her San Luis' son. Rafael begs for Martin's help, but he returns to Copiapó for the summer vacations.*

*Back in Santiago for the 1851 school year, Martin is per-
suaded by San Luis to join the Liberals' revolution to end the
twenty years of Conservative power. On the eve of battle, he
sends a farewell letter to Leonor, who has learned from Edelmira
that Martin has been faithful to her. Street fighting starts.*

*In the group gathered at a corner on San Isidio, Martin and
Rafael aim their guns at the soldiers who have just left their
barracks, and order the unarmed rebels to take guns from those
who have fallen.*

Chapter LVIII

That was the most brutal moment of the bloody conflict. The
fighters, so close to each other, shouting insults at their enemies,
could aim well and even see the results of their shots. The noise
was deafening; men fell by the score on both sides. The spectators, who since dawn had been looking on, had now fled from
danger, to let the rival armies fight it out, forgetting that every
shot reddened the soil of Chile with the blood of one of its sons.
Bold fearlessness in the face of danger, obstinate tenacity in defense and attack, undoubted passion as well as heroic cold-
blooded attitude were national attributes evident on both sides
in that supreme moment.

The two cannons against which Rivas, San Luis, and their
companions directed their deadly volleys from the street corner, fired less frequently because the rain of bullets had killed
the two officers in command as well as most of the soldiers. Attacking in the confusion and smoke, the revolutionists were able

to seize the pieces that death had left without defenders. Martin and Rafael arrived together at the guns that had caused so much carnage among their followers.

"Victory! Victory!" shouted San Luis.

Hardly had the echo died when the main gate of the barracks opened and a fearful volley of bullets caused frightful slaughter among the revolutionists.

San Luis seized Martin's arm and shouted:

"Fire! The enemy is in trouble." Then throwing his arms around Martin's neck he groaned:

"They've wounded me. I can't stand!"

[He is taken to a nearby house for surgery, where it is discovered that Martin also has a slight wound in the arm. San Luis dies, asking Adelaide to forgive him. Some government troops under Amador Molina almost capture Martin, but he escapes to the Encina house where Leonor hides him. Finally, Ricardo Castaños tracks him down. Edelmira promises to marry Castaños if he will help Martin Rivas escape. Later when peace has come, Martin returns to Santiago to marry Leonor, while Agustin marries Matilde.]

W.K.J.

JUAN MONTALVO
1832-1889   Ecuador

The greatest pamphleteer of his time and one of the continent's masters of prose, Montalvo used his pen to glorify his country. He described the great moments of its history, as in the poetic prose of *Pichincha*, included in *Siete Tratados* (Seven Treatises, 1882). He boasted that his political attacks overthrew García Moreno, the political "boss" of Ecuador who had exiled him. After Moreno's assassination, Montalvo directed his attacks against Ecuador's next dictator, Veintimilla. Juan Montalvo was a phrase-maker who combined the literary style of the past with the style of his own time, giving his work a sense of balance and purity, if not serenity. It was not surprising that, as a classicist, Montalvo was the author of *Capítulos que se le olvidaron a Cervantes* (Chapters That Cervantes Forgot), a continuation of *Don Quijote*, not published until after his death.

ON PICHINCHA

One day a boy climbed to the heights of Pichincha; he was only a child, yet he knew where he was, and had his head and his heart full of the battle. The mountain in the clouds, with its scarf of mist falling down to its waist, seemed a masked giant, terrifying. The city of Quito, at its feet, lifted its thousand towers to heaven: the green hills of this lovely city, fresh and graceful, surround her like gigantic uncut emeralds, set with apparent carelessness in her broad girdle. Rome, the city of hills, has neither so many nor more beautiful ones. A sound barely reached the heights; it was confused, vague, fantastic, that sound composed of a thousand sounds, that voice composed of a thousand voices, always emanating and ascending from great towns! The ringing of bells, the beat of hammers, the neighing of horses, the barking of dogs, the creaking of carts, and the thousand laments coming from no one knows where, sighs of shadows, uttered perhaps by hunger from its fireless dwelling and rising on high to mingle with the laughter of pleasure and infect it with melancholy. The boy heard, heard with his eyes and with his soul, heard the silence, as it says in the Scriptures; he heard the past, he heard the battle. Where had Sucre been? Perhaps here, on this very spot, on this green stair; there is where he passed by, farther over is where he broke into a run, and finally, on that side he shot at the fleeing Spaniards.

The boy caught sight of a white bone, a bone half hidden amid the grass and the wildflowers; he went over and picked it up. Had it belonged to one of the royalists? Had it belonged to one of the patriots? Was it a holy or an accursed bone? Child, do not say that! There may have been accursed men; there are no accursed bones. You should know that death, although cold as ice, is a fire which purifies the body; first it corrupts it, decomposes it, dissolves it; then it deodorizes and cleanses it. The bones of the dead, washed by the rain, shaped by the air, polished by the hand of time, are the remains of the human race, not of this nor of that man. No, the bones of our enemies are not enemy bones; they are the remains of our fellow men. Child, do not throw this away in disdain. . . . The bones of our fathers who died on Pichincha are now the prize of nothingness; their very dust has taken a more subtle form, turned into spirit, and disappeared into the invisible amphora in which eternity gathers the members of the human race.

Anon. Pan American Bulletin, 68 (1934)

UNLIMITED POWER

. . . Our previous worries now take the form of actualities. We previously hinted that Veintimilla would not want to be bound by the Constitution and laws, even though he had them drawn up according to his desires. This man was not born to be a constitutional president, but rather to be master of a people that by God's high judgments had fallen into his possession. This miserable nation must be largely responsible if, from tyranny after tyranny and dictator after dictator, when it expected to free itself through the efforts of a majority of its citizens, it wakes up to find itself once more under a dictator. A nation is blameworthy, just as people are; often it thinks it has done the necessary penance; but in reality the blackest guilt is still deeply stamped on its heart. When it struggles against threats and scorns bribery at the election booth; when it steadfastly confronts the poison glance of the oppressor; when it faces fearlessly and gets rid of known evils; when it prefers the fruits of labor to the wages of infamy; when it respects schools and sites of higher learning; when it does not flee like a coward from its pledges;

when it keeps the sacred fires of the Fatherland burning, then a nation is free of guilt. It has a right to liberty and is master of its fate.

Suffering is a virtue; moderation and temperance are virtues, but they can reach a stage where they become shameful faults, having lost all resemblance to propitious character and peaceful divinities. Suffering through cowardice is not suffering, but rather endurance, like the despicable non-resistance of stupid animals. Patience that springs from fear, far from being meritorious, is infamous. Noble and valiant souls suffer in silence as long as their honor is not involved, but woe to anybody who tempts them too far! Vacillators, miserable people without bravery or honor, on the other hand, put up with anything. Anyone stronger than they may strike them and beat them, as if such equalizers as bullets and swords did not exist.

We are speaking of individuals. Nations are always stronger than their oppressors whom they outnumber. If nations would learn the secret of unity, there would be no tyrant. His advantage lies in the fact that jealousy and disinterest divide the slaves. If the Holy Spirit descends on them in the form of a public conscience, then love of country and liberty, the force created by these divine tongues is immense. Nothing can resist it. Thrones crumble, crowned heads fall into the abyss, haughtiness disappears with a howl, the executioner flees in panic, the infamous prisons tumble, and oppressors great and small die or sink trembling to their knees. Such is a nation when exercising its holy anger . . .

Other nations had their dictators, Caesar, Caligula, Rosas of Argentina, Melgarejo of Bolivia, and Gutiérrez of Peru. They were foreigners. What have we to do with them? But we do have the responsibility for Flores, García Moreno and Borrero . . .

García Moreno, what a man! Yes, indeed, what a man! Born to be great, if only he had not possessed the flaw of a nature impelling him toward evil. A person of great intelligence, a wise tyrant, an incredibly brave and bold giant, full of inventiveness and craft, rich in ways and expediencies, a keen imagination, a strong will. What a pity! García Moreno could have been the greatest man in South America if his powerful faculties had not been dedicated to the nefarious task of oppression and tyranny. García Moreno, adored by his many followers; supported by the clergy; feared and loved by the military class; an unusual man, mysterious to women; full of force, power, ability, with a physical and moral life to last for years, killed unexpectedly one day by an assassin. The poor man is kicked across the plaza. A dog dies no more ignominiously. The fact is that in addition to his abilities, really great abilities, he was unjust, ambitious, arbitrary, oppressive, a tyrant. It was a deserved death, a good death . . .

                                                                W.K.J.

JORGE ISAACS
1837-1895   Colombia

Specific in its details but universal in its appeal, the Colombian novel *María* (1867) is perhaps the most typical example of the Latin American sentimental novel, although it appeared in the year that marked the beginning of Realism. Its author, Jorge Isaacs, was born in Cali, son of an English Jewish father and a Spanish mother. Though some critics compare his novel to *Paul and Virginia* (1788) by Bernardin de Saint-Pierre and to *Atala* (1801) by Chateaubriand, these French novels were closer to Romanticism and were entirely created in the imagination of their authors. *María*, while of the Romantic tradition in which even strong men were not ashamed of displaying their emotions, is so realistic in its descriptions of nature that it could be a guide to the Cauca valley. That it truthfully portrays the author's own home life is attested by its dedication "To the Brothers and Sisters of Efraín." At the age of eleven, Isaacs went to a boarding school in Bogotá and later to London. During his absence, his father's ward, whom Jorge loved, married someone else. In the novel, *María*, the daughter of a widower cousin is also lost to the hero

during his absence. The novel has had many editions
and several translations including one into Hebrew in
1962; it has been called the representative Spanish
American novel. It was the first South American work
to be selected as a textbook for Spanish students in the
United States.

MARIA

Chapter 1

I was still a young boy when they sent me from home to start
my education in the —— School, founded only a few years earlier in Bogotá, yet by then famous throughout Colombia. The
night before my departure, after the family gathering, one of my
sisters came into my room and without saying a word, because
sobs choked her voice, she clipped off a lock of my hair. When
she left, her tears were wet on my neck.

I fell asleep sorrowfully, filled with a vague foreboding of
many sorrows ahead of me. That lock of hair taken from a boy's
head, that precaution against death amid such abundant life,
made my mind wander during my sleep among the many spots
where unheedingly I had spent the happiest hours of my life.

In the morning, my father had to loosen the arms of my
mother from around my neck, wet with her tears. My sisters
with their farewell kisses wiped them away. Maria humbly
waited her turn, then stammering her goodbye, touched her
blushing cheek to mine, chilled by the first sensation of sorrow.

A few moments later, I was following my father, who hid his
face from my eyes. The hoofbeats of our horses on the pebbly
path drowned out my last sobs. The murmur of the current of
the Zabaletas, whose banks lay to our right, grew fainter and
fainter. We were already rounding one of the hills along the
path where we used to get our first glimpse from the house of
expected guests. I looked back for a last glimpse of those I loved.
Maria still stood under the vines that climbed around the windows of my mother's room.

(After six years of studying, Efraín returns home for a four months' vacation before leaving to study medicine in England. He describes the first meal.)

Chapter 3

At eight o'clock we went to the dining room, with its picturesque view toward the east. From it could be seen the bare summits of the mountains, against the starry background of the sky. The desert breeze gathered perfume in the garden, from the roses that surrounded us. When it died down, for a moment, the murmur of the river could be heard. Nature seemed to be displaying all her evening beauty as if to welcome a friendly guest.

My father sat at the head of the table, and had my chair placed at his right. My mother sat as usual on his left. My sisters and the children took any seats, but Maria sat across from me.

My father, grown gray during my absence, kept looking at me with satisfaction, with a mocking yet affectionate smile that I have never seen on any other lips. My mother, who was the happiest of all, never said a word. My sisters tried to make me taste what they had cooked, and blushed whenever I complimented or commented. Maria kept her eyes resolutely hidden from me, but in the moments when I caught a glimpse of them, I couldn't help noticing that they had the brilliance and beauty of women of her race. Only once between her prettily commanding red lips did I see the regular curve of her teeth. Like my sisters, she wore her long dark-brown hair in two braids, into one of which she had thrust a pink.

She was wearing a dress of light muslin, almost blue, but only the lower part was visible since a purple scarf of fine cotton extended from her white throat over her bosom. When she pushed back her braids as she leaned over to eat, I admired her beautifully molded arms and her hands as delicate as a queen's.

(The narrator takes part in the life of the community, riding with his father, and hunting. He falls in love with the shy Maria. And so the days pass.)

Chapter 13

One afternoon as I came down from the mountain, I thought I
saw worry in the faces of the servants in the corridor. My sister
told me that Maria had suffered a nervous attack, and though
adding that she was still unconscious, tried to calm my anxiety.
Forgetting everything, I entered the room where Maria lay, and
fighting back a frenzy to press her against my heart and restore
her to life, I approached the bed. My father was seated at the
foot of the bed. He looked at me intensely then turning toward
Maria, seemed to be accusing me. My mother was there, too,
but she did not raise her eyes because, knowing I loved Maria,
like a good mother, she pitied me.

I stood motionless, looking at her without daring to ask what
was the matter. She seemed to be sleeping. Her face, deadly
pale, was half concealed by her disheveled hair. In it I saw the
flowers I had given her that morning, now crushed. Her contracted forehead revealed unbearable pain, and there were drops
of perspiration on her temples. Tears that had tried to escape
from her closed eyes glistened under her lashes.

My father understood my anguish. He got up, but before he
left, he took her pulse.

"She's getting better," he told me. "Poor girl! It's the same
disease her mother had."

Her breast rose as if in convulsion, but she only sighed.
When my father left, I stood at the head of the bed and oblivious to my mother and Emma, I raised Maria's hand from the
pillow and bathed it in the tears I could no longer hold back. I
realized my misfortune. It was the same disease her mother had,
an incurable epilepsy of which she had died while still very
young. The thought was mastering my whole being and almost
destroying me.

I felt a slight movement in the heavy hand to which my
breath could not bring back any warmth. She was starting to
breathe more easily, and her lips seemed trying to say something. First was a mumble, then came my name, clearly distin-

guishable. I leaned over her. Perhaps I called her. Slowly her eyes opened, as though hurt by an intense light. She looked at me as if trying to recognize me. Half conscious, she demanded: "What is it? What happened to me?"

My mother and I tried to quiet her, but in a reproachful tone that I did not understand at the time, she went on: "Don't you see? I was afraid of this."

After the effort, she seemed profoundly sad. I came back that night to see her, according to the restrictions set up by my father. When I was telling her good night, she seized my hand.

"Goodbye till tomorrow" she whispered and emphasized the final word as she always did when our conversation at night was broken off.

(*When his father asks if he still wants to marry Maria, Efraín says "yes." Before he leaves for Europe, however, the doctor tells him that Maria does not suffer from the disease that killed her mother. A neighbor, Carlos, courts her, but she refuses him. She will wait for Efraín, who in spite of a business reverse met by his father, is still planning to go abroad. He says goodbye to his family.*)

Chapter 47

All had taken a tearful farewell. My sister Emma, who was the last, realizing that I was looking around as I released myself from her embrace, pointed to the door of the family chapel. I went inside. The yellow light of two candles illuminated the altar. Maria, seated on the rug almost concealed by her white dress, uttered a little cry when she saw me, then let her head fall onto the chair against which she had been leaning, when I came in. Hiding her face, she held out her right hand toward me. Half kneeling, I covered it with tears and kisses. As I got to my feet, she jumped up suddenly as if afraid that I would leave, and sobbed on my shoulder. Only then did I know the depth of my sorrow.

My lips rested on her forehead. Startled, Maria drew back

her head with a whirl of her curls. Hiding her face against my breast, she extended her arm toward the altar. Emma, who had just come in, caught her as she fainted and made a beseeching gesture for me to go. I obeyed.

(*He and Maria exchange several letters during the year spent in London. Then a friend arrives from Colombia with word from the doctor that if Efraín wants to see Maria alive, and perhaps save her life, he must come at once. He takes the next boat to Buenaventura, and arrives at Cali, by canoe and mule-back but it is too late. Maria has died of epilepsy. Broken-hearted but determined to complete his medical training, he decides to go back to England. On his way, and in the final chapter he visits her grave.*)

Chapter 49

That afternoon I set out on my return determining to visit the cemetery and Maria's grave. I bid farewell to the others, after we all went to the chapel where kneeling and weeping, we all prayed for the soul of her we had loved so much. I had no voice to say a last friendly word to them, and they would have had none to reply to me.

A short distance from the house, I paused at the top of the descent, for a final look at my beloved home and its surroundings. Of the hours of happiness that I had spent in it, I carried with me only memories; of Maria, only the gifts she had left for me when at the edge of the grave.

After a ride of an hour, I dismounted at the entrance to the village cemetery, a garden spot surrounded by a fence. I passed inside, through the bushes and between the crosses on the graves. As I rounded a clump of tall tamarinda, I came upon a white pedestal, spotted by rain, on which was an iron cross. On a black tablet, half hidden by poppies, I made out: "Maria."

To that terrible monologue of the soul in the presence of death—of the soul that questions, curses, begs, cries out—that cold and deaf grave that my arms were embracing and my tears were bathing gave a reply all too eloquent.

I left my wreath of roses and lilies on the cross. Then I gave to Maria and her grave my last farewell. I had already mounted my horse when a bird flew over my head with a sinister croak that I know well. I saw it fly to the iron cross, alight on one of its arms, flap its wings, and utter again its terrifying cry.

Torn with emotion, I set out at a gallop over the lonely plain whose vast horizon the night was darkening.

                                                          W.K.J.

JUAN LEÓN MERA
1832-1894   Ecuador

The first novelist of Ecuador and author of the outstanding Indianist novel of the Romantic period, Juan León Mera was a self-taught teacher, poet, historian, critic, and conservative politician. Conservative, too, was his *Cumandá o un drama entre salvajes* (Cumandá or a Drama Among Indians); written in 1871, it was sent in manuscript to the Royal Spanish Academy that made its author a corresponding member in 1874. When it was finally published in 1879, it was praised by Juan Valera as South America's most impressive novel.

Cumandá was originally based on a legend that Mera had heard from the English explorer Richard Spruce, but he made a number of changes after reading *Atala*. Many novels idealizing the Indians and glorifying nature appeared in Latin America, but none equalled the poetry and the realistic descriptions of primeval forests and Indian customs found in *Cumandá*.

CUMANDÁ

During an uprising against the Spaniards in 1790, the Indians have killed all but José Domingo Orozco and his son Carlos.

The broken-hearted father becomes a missionary in the jungles where Carlos meets an Indian girl, Cumandá (White Duck), child of Tongana and unbelievably beautiful, despite her savage environment.

Chapter II

Between the Palora and the Upiayacu Rivers rises a long sloping hill. Down its south side flows a clear stream that bathes several palm trees and twisting vines, one with pink flowers, another with white blossoms. One day almost at dawn, the daughter of Tongana made her way to this favorite spot of hers. She paused to look at the palm trees and spoke to them as if they could understand her, and started to sing as she swung on the vines, dipping her bare feet in the water and occasionally peering among the branches and the rushes along the bank toward the river mouth, covered by mist.

She was awaiting the foreign poet who delayed so long that in her heart she began to fear, to become uneasy, to be filled with anguish, because the morning was passing and it was urgent that she talk with him and let him know that the next day she and her whole family would be leaving for Palora, to be absent for several weeks.

Finally in the distance a black spot moved between the mist and the water. It was the young stranger who tied up his canoe and leaped ashore.

"White friend," the Indian girl told him, "you are cruel. The voice of the cricket had not ceased nor the glow of the firefly faded when I left my bed to meet you, and you have taken so long to come! Are you beginning to forget the path to the palm brook?"

"Cumandá, you accuse me of being cruel, and really you are the cruel one, since you reproach me without realizing that it wasn't easy for me to get here. Don't you see how the river has risen and the current increased? I have been paddling since before dawn. I am completely exhausted."

"You are right," the Indian girl interrupted him. "I hadn't noticed how high the river is."

"So you see, Indian sister, that I am right, and you are the unjust one."

"True, true, White brother. You have disarmed me. I did wrong in uttering bitter words. Forgive me and sit here beside me because my tongue has important things to say to you . . . White man, my heart does not know fear, but now it trembles like the leaf on the branch when the wind blows, because I think I hear behind me the steps of the *mungía*, who resembles the devil that harms Christians. But since I am a Christian . . ."

"So you have told me several times, but are you really a Christian, Cumandá?"

"Of course! My mother told me that when I was very young, they wet my head with miraculous water. My father does not want us to be Christians, but good Pona has secretly taught me some things and I have recently learned more because you, as a Christian, like them."

"You don't know how happy it makes me to discover that you are a Christian. But what were you saying about a *mungía?*"

"I make the sign of the Cross. I pray to the Holy Virgin, and it leaves me alone. It can come now, if it wants to. I'm not frightened here beside you."

"My beloved!" Carlos exclaimed. "Your presence transforms me. You bring life to my heart and strength to my soul. Among all the girls of my race no matter how beautiful, I have never found any like you to charm and conquer me. Even without study, you have learned the art of capturing the most stubborn heart without pretense or flattery."

"Foreign brother, you speak a language like that which the good spirits use, capable of making the shy bird and the fiercest animal alike love you. How did the women of your land ever let you come to this wilderness? Oh, friend, I like you more than the honey of the *guinde* blossoms or fish in the river. I feel toward you something that I can't explain and I hope from you something I cannot put into words, though just the idea of it thrills me with delight."

"That thing you can't describe is love, true love that you feel toward me and that you have no need to hope for, from me, since you already possess it."

"Yes, that must be it. I love you. Oh, White man, you will be my husband or I shall cease to live. Why should I live without you? Strip the bark from a tree and you will see how quickly it dries and dies. You are for me the protecting bark."

She tells him that there will be an Indian canoe festival in which she will play the most important rôle. He wants to attend it and she obtains his admittance among spectators.

Chapter VII

Long before dawn the camp was astir, with the Indians paddling their light canoes over the mystic waves of the Pastaza. It was a whole village gently transported to the lake in the palms of the aquatic deities as a reward for their piety in making the pilgrimage . . .

A large number of canoes tied to the lake shore and decorated with fragrant branches, flowers, and feathers of all colors and varieties were ready to obey the oars and break the crystal surface of Chimano Lake that reflected them. One raft, larger than the others, moored to a post, rocked among the other crafts. In its center stood a chair draped in tiger skins and with a back of interlaced bows and lances. The border of the rustic barge was decorated with green festoons, plumes of feathers, and covering of pretty tortoise shell and snake skins. Twenty lances of chonta wood with points painted red hung from the festoons, each one decorated with the shrunken head of an enemy warrior that seemed to scowl at being forced to witness the festivities of the terrible fighter who had killed him. Between the lances were vines of *chambira* palm interwoven with white lilies, fruit, birds, and fish. That was the floating throne of the king of the fiesta. It had something of terrifying grandeur about it, worthy of the ancient *curaca* who would soon be elected to occupy it . . .

At a signal from a tambourine, the voting begins. One by one the spectators advance toward Yahuarmaqui, who sits among them. They address him with a word or phrase indicating their choice of him, like: "You are brave." "You are like lightning." "You have conquered many enemies." Each voter thrusts a pike into the ground before him and returns to his place. At the conclusion, a jungle of these weapons, decorated with cords and human hair, surround the old man with the bloody hands. The most honored among the ancient warriors counts the votes and announces the choice, and the new king, amid cries of enthusiasm and the sounds of primitive musical instruments that echo through the jungle, jumps onto the raft and seats himself upon the throne . . .

Canoes containing the young men and the virgins to take part in the festivities are ready on the shore . . . Cumandá finally appears and gracefully enters her canoe that trembles like a leaf. All gazes are fixed on the daughter of Tongana. What beauty and grace!

First the young men, representing hunters, fishermen, artisans, etc., present their gifts to the king of the festival. Then the various girls offer him fruits and grains.

Finally, like a *guinde* suddenly appearing among the foliage, Cumandá approaches alone in her light canoe shaped like a shuttle and covered with beautiful flowers. Nothing more beautiful, fantastic or enchanting has ever been seen in the jungles of Oriente. She is more than the Virgin of the Flowers, more than the Queen of the Fiesta, more than the Spirit of the Lake. She is a bit of the sun, fallen onto the waves and transformed into a magic and divine being who attracts all eyes, inflames all hearts, and awakens all spirits to an indescribable admiration. The crowd utters a gasp of surprise and admiration that becomes muted to enjoy the marvel that moves on the water.

Yahuarmaqui stands like a statue, but on his granite brow

is depicted his shock at seeing the magnetic movements of the girl. From her canoe she throws onto the raft of the old warrior a rain of wild *norbos*, myrrh, roses, and the other myriad exquisite and nameless flowers of the transAndean jungles.

A burst of applause begins. The tambourines and fifes voice the popular approval and all the Indians press closer to see her and to snatch the blossoms floating in the water.

Chief Yahuarmaqui marries Cumandá and orders Carlos to be killed, but a friendly chief saves him. Cumandá fleeing from her husband, learns at Orozco's mission that her husband has died. As his wife, she must return to be buried with him, or else Carlos will be tortured. She returns.

Orozco comes to save them both but she is already dead. The wife of Tongana shows him a squirrel skin pouch that identifies Cumandá as Orozco's missing daughter Julia, supposedly killed along with her mother in the massacre. Carlos dies. Orozco is recalled by his bishop to Quito, and the Indians, keeping fresh flowers on the double grave, tell the tragic story of the white missionary and his two children.

W.K.J.

CLORINDA MATTO DE TURNER
1854-1909   Peru

Mrs. Turner, the Peruvian wife of a British doctor, followed González Prada's advice to use national themes, and wrote about the plight of the Quechua Indians in several novels. *Aves sin nido* (Birds Without Nests, 1889) is the best known. It narrates the love of the two illegitimate children of a priest, Pedro de Miranda. One is supposedly the daughter of the poor Indians, Juan Yupanqui and his wife Marcela, who are oppressed by their landowner, the church and the government. The other is believed to be the son of the governor. At the end, they discover they cannot marry and are therefore "birds without nests." The power of this socially significant book lies in its description of the hopes and fears of the Indians, and its pictures of the depravity of their oppressors.

BIRDS WITHOUT NESTS

Chapter VI

When, after her talk with doña Lucía, Marcela returned to her small hut, carrying a world of hopes in her heart, her daughters were already awake. The youngest was crying, grief-stricken, after awakening and finding her mother gone. There were sufficient signs of her, along with a handful of boiled corn, to calm the innocent future heroine of this novel who, in spite of being born among the rags of the hut, nevertheless cried the same salty, crystal tears as the children of kings.

Marcela carefully took the sticks of the portable loom which she placed in the center of the hovel, with the help of her older daughter, Margarita, having already prepared the threads of the warp, in order to continue weaving a well-made little poncho, streaked with all the colors that the Indians prepared from brazilwood, cochineal, the *amatto* tree, and the flowers of the *quico*.

Never did Marcela take to her daily labor with a happier spirit. And never did the woman build more castles in the air about the best way to tell Juan her good news.

For this very reason, the hours seemed eternal, but finally the evening twilight arrived, covering the valley and its inhabitants with its subdued shadows. Day bade farewell to the singing doves that soared away in all directions in search of a kindly tree. This was when Juan returned, and no sooner had she heard his approaching footsteps than Marcela hurried out to greet him. She helped him pen the oxen within their fence. She scattered grain in the stable, and when her husband finally took a seat beside the hut, she began to speak to him nervously, uncertain whether her news would be well received.

"Juanucho, you know Señoracha Lucía, don't you?" asked Marcela.

"Sure, since I go to Mass, Marluca; everybody gets acquainted there," Juan replied indifferently.

"Well, I spoke to her today."

"You? What for?" asked the surprised Indian, looking intently at his wife.

"I'm upset by everything that's happening to us. You've made me see plain enough that our life is full of despair."

"Did the tax collector come?" Juan interrupted her. She replied calmly and confidently:

"No, thank heavens, he hasn't come. But listen to me, Juan. I believe this lady can help us. She told me she would talk to the authorities, and that you should go . . ."

"Poor Marcela, you're like a desert flower," said the Indian, shaking his head and reaching for little Rosalia who was affectionately clutching his knees. "Your heart is like the fruit of the cactus; pick off one and another sprouts without need of care. I'm much older than you, and I know what it means to cry out in hopeless despair."

"Not me, even though you tell me I'm like a prickly pear. It's better to be like me than like you, a lowly peppergrass flower that withers and never grows again after being touched by the human hand. The hand of some sorcerer has touched you, Juanuco, but I've seen the face of the Virgin in that of Señoracha Lucía," Marcela said, looking up at her husband and laughing like a little girl.

"Maybe so," Juan replied, sadly, "but I come home from work worn out and without any bread for you, you who are my Virgin, and for these little ones of mine." He gestured toward the two little girls.

"You complain more than necessary, Juan. Perhaps you don't remember that when the father priest comes to his house with his pockets full of silver from the collection plate on All Saints Day, there's no one to welcome him as I wait for you with my arms stretched out, and no affectionate kisses with which these two wait for you. Ingrate! You think of bread. Don't we have cold corn and cooked potatoes whose odor calls its invitation to us from the stove: You will eat! . . . Ingrate!"

Marcela's face was flushed. The hope with which Lucía had filled her had caused a change in her, and her logic, mingled with what her heart told her, that voice inherent in a woman's heart, was irresistible, convincing Juan who was taking two pots of black clay off the stove. The whole family settled down to a delicious, though frugal, dinner.

After dinner, when the hut was enveloped in the black shadows of night, there was no light except what was given off by the feeble flames from the *molle* wood that occasionally flickered bright from the stove. They all went to rest in a common bed that stood on a wide adobe support; a hard bed that because of the love and resignation of the Yupanqui couple, had the comfort and softness provided by the feathers that Love let drop from its white wings.

A bed of roses where love, as the primitive sense of tenderness, exists without the dangers and mysteries of the dark nights that the city comments on, in a lowered voice, unable to keep its secret.

When this story eventually moves its scene to the richest city of Peru, toward where the characters are heading, perhaps we can draw a parallel between the awakening of the countryside and the sleeplessness of the capital . . .

Hardly had it become light again when Juan's family awakened, held morning prayers, crossed themselves, and began the chores of the new day. Marcela, whose mind was aflutter with thoughts, was first to speak:

"Juanuco, I'm going right away to Señora Lucía. You seem uncertain and silent, but since yesterday my heart has never stopped giving me assurance."

"Go ahead, then, Marcela. Go ahead, because I'm sure the tax collector will come today. I had a dream about him, and there's nothing else we can do," the Indian answered. His attitude seemed to have changed noticeably under the influence of his wife's words and the superstition revived by his dreams.

George Karnezis

RICARDO PALMA
1833-1919   Peru

Peru's greatest man of letters, Ricardo Palma, began his
literary career at the age of thirty-nine with the writing
of his first *Tradiciones* (Traditions); he continued to
produce series of these works until near the end of his
long life. According to Palma, a *tradición* was an anecdote with a slight flavor of truth, written in a witty,
lively style, and full of local color and local, idiomatic
speech. The principal series of these contributions to
history and legend were written between 1872 and 1883,
and the last was published in 1911. Numbering several
hundred, *Tradiciones* cover Peru's history from earliest
times down to the war with Chile in 1879. "La camisa
de Margarita" (Margarita's Bridal Nightgown) is typical of the form; more than a short story explaining a
folk legend, it provides the antiquarian author with a
setting for extraneous historical material.

MARGARITA'S BRIDAL
NIGHTGOWN

It is quite probable that some of my readers have heard old
women of Lima say, when they wanted to stress the rising prices
of some article: "Why, it's more expensive than the nightgown
of Margarita Pareja!"

I would have remained with my curiosity unsatisfied about
the identity of that Margarita whose nightgown became a subject of comment, if I had not happened to run across an article
in *La América* of Madrid, signed by Ildefonso Antonio Bermejo
(author of a notable book about Paraguay), who briefly touches
upon the girl and her bridal nightgown. It got me started on
unraveling the mystery so that I was able to get the details of the
history you are about to read.

I

Margarita Pareja was (along about the year of 1765) the pampered daughter of don Raimundo Pareja, Knight of Santiago and Collector General of Callao. She was one of those Peruvian beauties who, through their loveliness, cause even the devil to cross himself and throw rocks. She had a pair of black eyes like a couple of torpedoes loaded with dynamite that caused explosions deep inside the heart of the young men of Lima.

About that time there arrived from Spain a haughty young man, a Madrileño from the City of the Bear and the Strawberry Tree, by the name of Luis Alcázar. He had a wealthy bachelor uncle in Lima, of ancient Aragonese lineage, who was prouder than a king's son. Until he should inherit his uncle's wealth, our don Luis was living as penniless as a church mouse and suffering the blackest unhappiness. When I say that even his rags were bought on credit, to be paid for when he came into his fortune, I think I give you the idea.

During a procession in honor of Santa Rosa, Alcázar first looked upon the charming Margarita. The girl caught his eye and shot an arrow into his heart. He uttered some compliments to her and although she did not give him yes or no, she made him understand by smiles and the other weapons of a feminine arsenal that the young man was a dish very much to her taste. To tell the truth, as if I were in a confessional, each of them fell deeply in love with the other.

Since Love never thinks of Arithmetic, Luis never considered that his present poverty might be an obstacle to their love, and so he went to Margarita's father and without beating about the bush, asked for her hand.

Don Raimundo was not at all interested in the young man's request, and courteously dismissed him, saying that Margarita was still too young to think of marriage because, in spite of her eighteen Mays, she was still playing with dolls.

But that wasn't the real mother of the calf. The truth was that don Raimundo had no wish to be father-in-law of a pauper, and he said as much in confidence to some of his friends, one of whom passed the remark on to don Honorato, as his Aragonese uncle was named. He, who was prouder than the Cid, shook with rage.

"The nerve of him! Insulting my nephew! Many families would sing with joy to get such a son-in-law, since there is none better in all Lima! Did you ever see such insolence? Who does that cheap collector think he is?"

Margarita, who was ahead of her century, since she was as nervous as a girl of today, whined, tore her hair, stamped her feet, and if she didn't threaten to take poison, it was only because phosphorous matches had not yet been invented. She lost color and flesh; she wasted away visibly; she talked of entering a convent; and she was thoroughly disagreeable.

"I'll be the bride of Luis or of God!" she would scream every time she had an attack of nerves, which was at least once an hour.

The Knight of Santiago got very much upset. He summoned physicians and herb doctors, and they, one and all, predicted that the girl would die of consumption, and that the only cure was something that could not be bought in a drug store. Either marry her off to the man of her choice or carry her off in a coffin under palms and flowers. That was the medical ultimatum.

Don Raimundo (first of all a father), dashed away like crazy to the house of don Honorato, without stopping for his cloak or his cane.

"I've come to get you to consent to a marriage tomorrow between your nephew and my daughter, because otherwise she'll be dead by the next day."

"Impossible!" said the uncle flatly. "My nephew is a 'pauper,' and what you need to look for, for your daughter, is someone rolling in wealth."

Their talk was stormy. The more Raimundo begged, the more angry grew the Aragonese, and the father was about to give up in despair, when don Luis, entering into the argument, said:

"Uncle, it is unchristianlike to punish somebody who isn't to blame."

"Do you want to marry her?"

"With all my heart, esteemed uncle."

"Very well, my boy. I consent because you want it, but on one condition. Don Raimundo must swear to me before the altar that he will not give his daughter a single penny now or leave her a peso of inheritance."

That started new and more agitated discussion.

"But, my dear señor!" Raimundo argued. "My daughter has more than twenty thousand dollars of dowry."

"We refuse the dowry. Your daughter will enter her husband's house with nothing but the clothes on her back."

"At least let me provide the furniture and her trousseau."

"Not a pin! If you don't agree, goodbye, and let the girl die."

"Be reasonable, don Honorato! At least my daughter needs a gown to replace the one she'll be wearing."

"Very well. I'll agree to one slip, so you won't accuse me of being obstinate. I consent that you supply her bridal nightgown, but that is absolutely all."

The next day don Raimundo and don Honorato went early in the morning to San Francisco Church and knelt before the altar to hear mass, and according to the agreement, the moment the priest was elevating the Host, Margarita's father spoke.

"I swear to give my daughter nothing beside her bridal nightgown. May God punish me if I lie!"

I I

Don Raimundo Pareja fulfilled his oath literally because never again in life or death did he give his daughter anything of value.

The Flemish lace that adorned her nightgown cost $2,700, according to Bermejo's account, apparently copied from *The Secret Accounts* by Ulloa and Jorge Juan. In addition, the drawstring at the neck was a chain of precious stones worth $30,000.

But the newlyweds made the Aragonese uncle believe that the gown was hardly worth a doubloon, because he was so stubborn that if he had known the truth, he would have forced his nephew to divorce her.

So let's agree that the wedding nightgown of Margarita Pareja was very deserving of the fame it attained.

W.K.J.

IGNACIO MANUEL ALTAMIRANO
1834-1893   Mexico

Altamirano, a full-blooded Aztec Indian, was taught to read only because his father was mayor of his native village, Tixtla. Ambitious and hard-working, he earned a law degree and was appointed to the Mexican Supreme Court in 1867. He began writing stories to interpret his Indian ancestors to other Mexicans. One of the stories is "La Navidad en las montañas" (Christmas in the Mountains); it reveals Altamirano as a Romanticist in subject, but a Classicist in expression.

His most famous novel, El Zarco (The Blue-Eyed Bandit), was written between 1861 and 1863. Parts of it were read by the author in the Hidalgo Lyceum, of which he was the sponsor, but it was not published until eight years after his death. Simply written, it contrasts the noble-hearted Indian blacksmith Nicolás with Zarco, the revolutionist-turned-bandit, both rivals for the love of beautiful Manuela. Charmed by the robber's presents, she runs away with him to his mountain home where she is quickly disillusioned.

THE BLUE-EYED BANDIT

Chapter 21. The orgy

One afternoon Zarco galloped in very happy. During the day, he and his bandits had ridden on a foray. He jumped off his horse at the door of the chapel that they had taken as their home, and hurried in to find Manuela, who, as usual, was shut away in a curtained bedroom that she had improvised.

"Here's something," the bandit told her. "So you won't be so unhappy," and he put into her hand a pouch full of gold pieces.

"What's this?" Manuela asked in disgust.

"Look and see what it is," Zarco said, emptying the coins onto the bed. "My boys brought me back a Frenchman they picked up near Chalco, practically at the capital. He's plenty rich. His family already sent a hundred gold pieces and tomorrow they'll send five hundred more."

"Heavens!" gasped the frightened Manuela.

"What? Don't be squeamish! That's a fine way to be! You ought to be glad, not scared, because this money is going to make us rich. I'll give the boys part of the ransom, but we'll grab the big share and then pretty soon we'll sneak away to Morelia or Zacatecas or to Hell and gone, where they won't know who I am, and we'll buy a farm or build a house because, the way you are, I can see you'll never get to like this life. But you promised me . . ."

Without showing that she knew she was being reproached, Manuela looked at the gold, then answered indifferently:

"Listen, Zarco. Even if you don't bring me any more money, I beg you to let that man go."

"What are you talking about?" Zarco demanded in a hoarse voice that betrayed his savage anger. "Are you crazy, Manuela, to say things like that? Not bring you any more, you ungrateful girl, when I risked the lives of my boys to kidnap that man to get money for us so I could buy you jewels and silk dresses and everything you want? And now you come out with this pity and this request. If that's the way your mind works, why didn't you marry that Indian? He isn't a bandit. But as long as you're with me, either shape up to the life I live or you'll die." Zarco came closer, opening his eyes, lowering his voice, and dropping his hand onto his pistol.

Manuela trembled at the explosion of anger. But before any-

thing else could be said, a loud commotion broke out, shouts
and the strumming of guitars, and into the chapel burst some of
the robbers, Salomé Plasencia, "Dry Stick," Tiger, Linares, and
a score of bandits more, all hilarious and all apparently drunk.

"Zarco!" one of them yelled. "You're rich now, buddy, and
we're going to throw a dance to cheer up the dame you brought
from Yautepec, who is dying of unhappiness."

"Come on, trot her out and let her dance the waltz, the
polka, and the schottische with us!"

"Come on, Manuela. We mustn't disappoint my pals," said
Zarco, taking her by the hand. She let herself be dragged from
behind the curtain like a victim, and even managed a smile.
"Here I am, boys. And here's my girl, ready for the dance."

"Come on, Blondie!" cried Salomé, waving a bottle in one
hand. "You're coming to the dance we're throwing to celebrate
the adventures of Zarco. Come on, and quit looking as sad as
the Virgin of Solitude on Good Friday!"

"O.K., O.K.!" Zarco told them. "Go and look after the music
and the liquor and I'll bring along Manuela. You go and get
dressed for the dance, honey, and I'll come for you."

"You're jealous, Zarco," Salomé commented mockingly, giving him a slap on the back. "You're jealous, and you know that
doesn't go down with us. We'll let you get away with it for
awhile, but don't keep it up, because it's not right."

Manuela trembled. Everything promised new dangers for
her. As soon as she reached her quarters, she called one of the
women to help her dress. When Zarco arrived, he found Manuela ready for the dance and very lovely in spite of her pallor
and loss of weight. Since the dance was taking place in rooms
inside the old manor house, the couple climbed the rickety stairs
and quickly reached the salon that gleamed with wax candles and
was full of smoke. The bandits were all there enjoying themselves.

When Manuela came in with Zarco, a spontaneous shout
greeted them,—hurrahs, compliments, oaths, all coming from a
hundred mouths twisted by drink and debauchery. All the famous bandits were there, covered with silver and with weapons

handy. Manuela shuddered. The moment that Zarco released her arm, up stepped a colossal and horrible mulatto who inspired her with repugnance. He wore a bandage that covered part of his face, but his enormous mouth was still visible, full of shining white teeth, with the two eyeteeth projecting against his lower lip. He seemed completely sheathed in silver as if to outshine the rest of his companions.

"Come on and dance with me, Blondie," he addressed Manuela, seizing one of her delicate white arms in his paw.

In spite of herself, Manuela stepped back in fright, and tried to rejoin Zarco for protection. The mulatto held onto her, laughing.

"Hey, Zarco," he called, "the Kid's trying to run away and not dance with me. Give her the word."

"What's the matter, Manuela? Why won't you dance with my friend, Tiger? I told you that you were supposed to dance with all of them. That's why you're here."

Resigned, and even wearing a pitiful smile, she let herself be led to the dance floor by that ugly and repulsive man. After a couple of turns around the crowded floor, trampled and pushing fifty pairs of bandits and their partners, all of them drunk, Tiger pulled her out of the crush. Pushing back his big hat and staring at her with his only free eye, he told her:

"Listen, Kid. Ever since I first saw you with Zarco, I've liked you. And I told the Fox, Yellow's girl, to tell you so, not so you'd like me after a while, but so you'd know right away. I don't know whether she told you."

Manuela did not answer.

"Well, if she didn't, I'll tell you now, frankly, that you'll end up crazy about me."

"Me?" echoed the surprised girl.

"Yes, you!" Tiger assured her. "You'll see. Just slip me the word that you could go for me and I'll knock off Zarco right away. Otherwise, I'll wait and we'll see what happens."

"Zarco shall know about this!" she cried, twisting away.

"Tell him, dearie, tell him," replied Tiger with a scornful and sinister smile. "That Zarco, that you love because you think he is a man, is nothing but a coward. So go and tell him, and I'll sit right here and wait."

When she went looking for her lover, she saw him coming toward her, scowling, white with anger. She thought at first that he was jealous of Tiger and she was afraid of a fight. But Zarco, with a satanic smile and a voice hoarse with anger, shouted:

"Now I know why you've been moping these past days. The Fox told me. She said you regretted running away with me . . . that you realized you don't love me . . . really . . . that the only one you love is that Indian, Nicolás . . . That you're sorry you turned him down and you don't like the life here with the Silver boys, and the first chance you get, you're going to skip out."

"I never said anything like that!" Manuela broke in.

Suddenly, a messenger rides in with news of the death of Manuela's mother from the shock and sorrow the latter caused her by her flight, and announcing that some of their fellow bandits have been wiped out by government troops. The bandits call off their dance and prepare to ride to avenge the death of their comrades.

W.K.J.

II

POETRY

INCA POETS

Peruvian Indians were still reciting their poetry when the white men who could write it down arrived. (The Indians had no written language.) Years after he had left Cuzco, Garcilaso Inca de la Vega, whose mother was an Inca princess, remembered four lines of a *Jailli*, or sacred hymn, that he set down. In his *Relación de antigüedades deste Reyno del Perú* (Account of the Ancient Things of This Kingdom of Peru, 1613), Juan de Santacruz Pachakuti Yanki Salkamaywa preserved another *Jailli*, "Himno de Manco Quápaj," about the legendary founder of the Inca dynasty. The supreme lyrical form, however, was the *Wayñu*, a melancholy love song written in five-syllable lines. It had a musical accompaniment and was danced by a couple facing each other and clasping hands. As can be seen by the following sample, the Indians knew rhythm, but not rhyme.

GARCILASO'S JAILLI

Cayllallapi   In the nearest spot
puñunqui   you will sleep,
chaupi-tuta   and at twelve o'clock
samúsaj.   I shall come.

(*An authority on Inca poetry, Jesús Lara, explains that this is a symbolic hymn in which the powerful but invisible god Viracocha is telling his sister, the Princess of Heaven, who carries water in a jar, that he will find that jar, break it, and cause a rain storm.*)

WAYÑU

Flower of Kantuta
Blood turned to brightness,
Born lovely maiden
For my caresses,

Princess delightful,
Eyes full of starlight,
Fresh as a garland
And my good fortune,

When I behold you,
You act so shyly
Like timid blossom
Hid in the meadow.

'Mid all the tempest
Of my ill fortune,
You are the rainbow;
Peace do you promise.

Triumphant bright star
From the clouds peeping,
Condor who, wheeling,
Flies through my day dreams,

Rainbow triumphant
O'er the abysses,
What my eye glimpses
First in the morning,

Sun at its zenith
Caught for a moment,
Like passion flower
Does your hair charm me.

Like precious jewel
In my heart prisoned,
You are the touchstone
Of my deep passion.

You are a soft dove
With voice sweet as honey,
Lovely companion;
Of my heart, partner.

You wear a garment
Woven of flowers,
Golden threads shining,
Web of my being,

Its fringes fastened
Tenderly to me,
Guarded securely
By my two pupils.

How your enchantment
In my brain dancing
Fills every moment
With exquisite pleasure.

W.K.J.

HYMN OF MANCO CAPAC

Viracocha,
Powerful foundation of the world,
Thou commandest:
"Let this be man!
Let this be woman!"
Lord of the sacred fountain,
Thou governest even the hailstorm.
Where art thou?

—As if I were not thy son—
Above,
Below,
In the middle,
Or in thy seat of supreme justice?
Hear me,
Oh, thou that stayest in the ocean of heaven,
And who also livest in the seas of the earth,
Oh, Ruler of the world,
Creator of man!
Lord and princes, with their unclean eyes,
Long to see thee.
But when I am able to see
And know and travel
And understand,
Thou wilt see me and know of me.

The Sun and the Moon,
The Day and the Night,
The time of abundance
And of cold are controlled,
And at the suitable place
And the appointed time,
They will arrive.

Thou who hast given me
The royal sceptre,
Hear me before I fall,
Conquered and dead.

Susan Louise Shelby

NAHUATL POETRY

Mexico

Early chroniclers in Mexico preserved a number of
poems in the Nahuatl language, including one called

"Canto de los pájaros de Totoquihuatzin, Rey de Tlacopan" (Song of the Birds of Totoquihuatzin, by the King
of Tlacopan) which was probably composed in honor of
the king, rather than written by him. The syllables *to*
and *ti*, added to complete the lines, represent a sort of
play on words without any textual meaning. As a sample of the language of the Mexican Indians, two lines
of another poem, "The Creation of the Sun and the
Moon," are also given.

THE CREATION OF THE SUN
AND THE MOON

In oc yohuayán, in ayámo tona, in ayámo tláthui
Auh níman no icuac motláli in tlétl in óncan tlecuílco.

Still lasts the darkness, still sun unborn is, still comes no dawning,
But moments later bright fire is kindled in ardent furnace.

SONG OF THE BIRDS

I am beating the drum. Enjoy it, my friends.
Say: totototo tiquiti tiquiti.

Let the benignant flowers in the house of Totoquihuatzin say:
Toti quiti toti tototo tiquiti tiquiti.

May the earth enjoy happiness; totiquiti toti,
Toti quiti toti tototo tiquiti tiquiti.

My heart is a fine jewel: tototo.
The flowers with which I adorn myself are of gold.
Variegated are the flowers that some day I shall bring in homage.
Totiquiti. Oh, how I sing: Tiquiti tiquiti.

Come, intone the song in your heart: Tototo.
Here do I offer gardens of roses and painted books.
Totiquiti toti—that someday I shall bring in homage.
Totiquiti toquiti tiquiti tiquiti.

W.K.J.

FRANCISCO DE TERRAZAS
1525?-1600?   Mexico

The son of a general with Hernán Cortés, Terrazas was the first native-born New World Spanish poet, whom some suspect of having learned his craft from the Spaniard Gutierre de Cetina during his visit to Mexico. Here is an example of the excellent sonnets that Terrazas wrote in the Italian manner.

TO A BEAUTIFUL
BUT HEARTLESS COQUETTE

Renounce those threads of twisted gold that close
In glinting ringlets round my captive will,
And on the virgin snowdrift in repose
The tinted whiteness of these roses spill.
Of pearls and precious corals that adorn
This mouth enticingly, be thou but shorn;
And to the heavens, by which thou'rt envied still,
Return the stolen suns that thou hast worn.

The grace and wisdom, which as symbols stand
Of knowledge springing from the Source Divine,
Surrender to the far angelic sphere;
And thus renounced the gifts of Nature's hand,
Behold that which remains to thee is thine;
To be ungrateful, cruel, vain, austere!

Peter H. Goldsmith

ALONSO DE ERCILLA Y ZÚÑIGA
1533-1594   Chile

Thanks to Ercilla, one of the courtiers of Philip II, Chile
is the only New World nation to be honored by an epic
poem. He reached South America at the age of 21,
anxious to avenge the death of Valdivia and fight in the
army of García Hurtado de Mendoza. However, rivalry
with his commander and a growing admiration for the
enemy slowly reversed the tone of the *Octavas reales*
(Royal Octaves) that he wrote each night at the campfire on any material that was at hand. While considering
the Spaniards as an historian, he took a poet's view of
the Indians, and ended by praising the Araucanians.

Finally returning to Spain, he gathered his verses together, all 21,072 lines, and published them gradually
in 1569, 1578, and 1589 under the title *La Araucana.*
Once completed, the work contained 37 cantos. It inspired other epics in the New World, but only Oña's
El arauco domado (Arauco Tamed, 1596) even re-
motely approached the literary value of Ercilla's poem.
La Araucana proved to Spaniards like Cervantes that
South America, too, possessed culture.

LA ARAUCANA

Canto I

Sing Muse—, but not of Venus and her chuck,
And amorous jousts in dainty lists of love,
Favors and forfeits won in Beauty's siege
By soft assaults of chamber gallantry;
But of the valiant deeds and worthy fame
Of those who far on surge-ensundered shores,
Bent the proud neck of Araucania's race
To Spain's stern yoke, by war's arbitrament.

Yet not their feats alone inspire my pen
To stamp their glory on the epic page,
But of their foeman too—, attend, and hear
Of stubborn tribes no common king obey,
But each its rival chief; of customs strange,
Rare arts and curious crafts; and if I praise
The conquered brave, so shall my words exalt
The worth of those who were their conquerors.

Chile my scene; a fertile land remote,
Hard by the border of Antarctic seas,
Home of a stiff-necked people, bred to arms,
Renowned in war, by neighbor nations feared;
Whose hot distempered blood alike rebels
At rule domestic and at stranger yoke.
No king among themselves they own, nor e'er
Have bowed the knee to foreign conqueror.

Due North and South the Chilean coastline runs,
Fronting along the West the Southern Main;
Upon the East a range of cloud-capped peaks
Shuts in the plainlands for a thousand leagues;
Midway between the North and South is where
Our scene of war is set; here that fierce tribe
I speak of dwells; mild Venus here no part
Has in men's lives; but Mars alone is lord.

Robust and strong, hairless of lip and chin,
Well-grown and tall above the run of men,
Of ample shoulders and capacious breasts,
And brawny limbs thick-set with stubborn thews,
Ready and nimble and high-spirited,
Haughty and daring, reckless in assault,
Hardy and tireless, bearing undismayed
Cold, hunger, heat, and all extremities.

Nor ever has a king by force subdued
This haughty people to his vassalage,

Nor has the foot of an invading foe
Left shameful print upon Arauco's soil,
Nor neighbouring tribe so temerarious
To try the battle with their furious hosts.
Untamed and feared by all, they live or die
With haughty neck unbowed to God or man.

No lengthy chronicle shall here detain
The labors of my war-recording pen;
Let history's larger hand abridge the page
And purge her tale of dull prolixity;
What service here each battle to recount,
The numbers and the names of those that died,
Before the remnants of Arauco's host
Laid down its arms before victorious Spain.

Walter Owen

Canto II

Especially admired by Voltaire, who compares him to the Homeric Nestor, Colocolo advises the Indians on choosing their leader. (This translation follows the original rhyme scheme.)

Ye Chiefs, defenders of your native land,
Your lust for power is not what saddens me,
When I behold you striving for command
Of what is mine by right. This should not be,
But I resent it not, for Death's cold hand
Will force me soon to face Eternity;
Not thought of self, but warm, deep love for you
Inspires my final counsel; hear me through.

As slaves, can we seek honor, noble station,
And hold ourselves, Ye Chiefs, in high regard,
When all the world perceives our degradation,
A conquered race? The Spanish yoke is hard!
How can we rest supine, in subjugation,

From all our ancient heritage debarred?
Better to rise in battle, fight for life,
Than waste our strength in tragic, tribal strife.

What madness clouds your minds, O Pine-tree dwellers?
Drives ye to slay your own proud-hearted race?
Raises your swords in hate, Ye Tyrant-quellers,
Against your kin? What folly, what disgrace,
To kill your own! Ye Christian-dog expellers,
Drive aliens out who have usurped your place!
If ye would die, smite those whom ye abhor.
Die not, O Chiefs, in fratricidal war!

I am not sad to see this warlike flame
That fires your hearts; instead it gives me joy.
But still I fear this valor may defame
Your honored past. Our land ye may destroy
In civil strife, and gain eternal shame
If stubborn, bloody violence ye employ.
Cut, if ye must, your country's throat, but first
Cut this old throat of mine,—and be accursed!

Kill, if ye must, my aged body, broken
By dire misfortune's blows. The sharp-edged sword
May still my voice before my words are spoken.
Easier it were to die, by all ignored,
Sweet were an early death, if by this token
Tyrants were slain and Freedom's sway restored—
But that is vain. Seeking the public good
I'll raise my voice, be heard, be understood.

Ye Chiefs! Equal alike in strength and daring
Dowered by Heaven's gift with equal state
At birth, of wealth and noble name, all sharing
Alike in power and courage, Chieftains great
And strong, be not cast down, be not despairing.
Rise and control the world! It's not too late!

By scorning precious gifts, by sloth imbued,
Have ye now sunk to this vile servitude.

But it shall pass. I know your warlike soul
Will flame for Freedom, strike the Tyrant down!
Choose, then, your leader. One shall have control,
Obeyed by all, that all may win renown.
Who longest bears this great tree's heavy bole
Upon his back,—him shall we captain crown.
Since we are peers, by strength we choose today
Our battle chief, to lead us to the fray.

Read Bain and W.K.J.

Caupolican is chosen. After several victories, he is captured by the Spaniards and sentenced to death. Ercilla relates his execution in the thirty-fourth canto.

Shoeless, unkempt, with warbonnet forgot,
Bent by the weight of long and heavy chain,
With rope around his neck, its end a knot
By which the jailer dragged him out in pain,
Hemmed round by sea of weapons and a lot
Of curious eyes that stared and stared again
To see if what they saw were really true
(Though seen by eyes, the fact more dubious grew):

Like that, the Indian reached the gallows side
Which was about a bowshot from the fort,
A pike's height from the ground upraised, and wide,
In plain sight of the mob that thronged the court.
There with his usual energetic stride,
Unhesitating and without retort,
He climbed the narrow steps as carelessly
As though from prison he had been set free.

Then came the eager executioner,
An ill-clad negro slave, from overseas.

Caupolicán considered him a cur
Who'd come to carry out the court's decrees.
Although with calm and patient character
He had endured the earlier insults, these
He'd not endure. He raised his noble head
And in a voice shot through with rage, he said:

"Is there no sword of all these brandished here,—
Those swords that, in the past, with savage might
Slashed Araucanian throats from ear to ear,—
Will grant me such oblivion here tonight?
Whatever means ill fortune takes to jeer
And mock a prisoner in hopeless plight,
It shall not be that hand of baseborn man
Shall touch the noble chief, Caupolicán."

He paused and with his foot half-raised in air
(Although impeded by the weighty chain)
He kicked so hard the ill-kempt negro there
That he rolled, wounded, to the ground again.
Then, shocked by insult to his name so fair
And urged by rage, the chief with great disdain
Struck off the hands outstretched, himself to take,
And hurled his body on the sharpened stake.

It seems to me that I am saddened still
As when I heard details, that by-gone day,
Of this cruel deed. O why should people kill?
I was not there, My King, I was away
On conquest bent, according to your will,
Upon the distant Isle of Chiloé.
If I had been there at the time, I vow
Caupolicán would still be living now.

W.K.J.

PEDRO DE OÑA
1570-1643   Chile

The first native-born Chilean writer, Pedro de Oña, was the second of Chile's epic poets. His *Arauco domado* (Arauco Tamed, 1596) was intended to restore to García Hurtado de Mendoza the glory taken from him by the poet Ercilla, who bestowed it on the Indians instead in his *La Araucana*. Oña must have planned a sequel to these nineteen cantos, numbering 16,000 lines, for at the end, Caupolicán is still alive and the Indians are still "untamed."

After Oña's father was killed by Chilean Indians, the boy was sent to Peru to be educated. Later he fought against Ecuadorean rebels whom he described so mercilessly that the first edition was suppressed after 120 of the 800 printed copies had been sold, and the Peruvian printer had to flee to escape imprisonment.

Oña's epic of the Araucanian struggle is more personal than Ercilla's. Ercilla was the epic poet; Oña was a lyric poet who turned to the epic because of his predecessor. They used the same meter, but Oña's poetry is more sensitive, imaginative, and more artistic in its handling of the eight-line stanza. His metaphors are more striking, and his language is less restrained than Ercilla's. Oña mixes European and New World cultures; his Indians know Greek mythology. While chronology is forgotten and veracity is sacrificed to poetry, the style is impressive and the war scenes spirited.

As a sample of Oña's various styles, a selection from the fifth canto has been translated here, from the bucolic beginning in which Caupolicán and his wife, Fresia, are resting in the forest, to the ferocious attack by 20,000 Indians on the Spanish fort of Penco.

ARAUCO TAMED

The sinuous brooklet plashed in rippled pleats,
And formed into a chain of purest glass
Throughout the placid, pleasant wood of shrub,
Descending from the rocky mountain top,
And with sonorous, easeful murmuring
Dispatched the rich vein into deep of sea,
Crisscrossing it to make in varied wise
Sharp elbowed bends, and havens of pause and rest.

. . . .

'Twas here Caupolicán siesta took,
Impassioned, with his Fresia, hand in hand,
Recalling to remembrance, dreams of yore
In tender style and amorous images,
Nor was he here solicitous of war,
Nor with responsibilities concerned
Of office, for where love holds fast the fort,
Scarce enters any other paltry care.

Provoked and stimulated by the site,
He was invited by soft indolence
To souls communion with his cherished wife.
To harmony of word, breast, face, and mouth,
And hand. To tunes Love exquisitely played
For him, he sang: "Sweet glory, sweetest life,
Who tastes like me a boon so rare and high
Without fear's inner stress, without alarm? . . .

"Ah!" Fresia answered him, "beloved lord,
It is no trait of perfect love, and pure,
To live in deep contentment's nest secure
Without misgivings and anxiety
In that the bitter chalice never fails
To follow banquet-feasts of tenderness,

No happiness can come, if e'er it came,
And evil not impede it on its road . . .

Together they descended to the stream
Which beckoned them with freshness, quickening, cool,
And also since Apollo harassed them
With ardor which he then supremely showed.
Gallant of gesture, the son of Leocán
Disclosed his corporal texture, hero's mould,
Broad chest and shoulders, massive-muscled thigh,
Flesh well proportioned, and puissant bone . . .

His winsome Fresia, who attended him,
Unable to bear standing there aloof,
With sprightly movement threw her cloak aside
And disattached her slender tunic's stays.
The selfsame frigid waters she inflamed,
Filling with marveled fright the fuscous glade,
And Phoebus halted with express intent
The better to enjoy this vision rare . . .

Whilst in this sport the lovers both engaged
And soaked of skin, were making at cost of love
A spark-filled forge of waters in the lake
By magic of dear passion's wonted power,
There suddenly appeared before their gaze,
Diluting present pleasures with surprise,
The fury of Megaera in disguise,
Who in this manner spake unto the Chief:

"Lend not thyself to pastimes of delight!
Return unto thyself, Caupolicán!
The lordship of the world lies in thy palm,
If thou but knowest to arrive with ready steps.
Know that a hundred Christian swaggerers,
Spared by the fury of the insane sea,

Have raised on Penco's hill a feeble wall,
Commanded by a fledgling insecure . . .

Forthwith he took departure, fiend-possessed,
With frantic Fresia following fretfully,
Choleric, drenched, and glistening in the glen,
Sane senses alienated in her fright;
And on they marched until the golden sun,
Shunning the approach of ebon-coated night
That loomed, a hunter tracking down its prey,
Withdrew to sanctuary of the sea.

The Indian, having reached the settlement,
Applied the horn to swollen cheek and mouth.
Reverberated the horrid-sounding peal
There in the most occult recess of Hell,
Blaring from hand to hand through his domain.
Eftsoons were almost all the braves convoked
Because they came, snatched up to whirling flight,
Borne on by that demonic virulence . . .

In three swart squadrons, close-packed and aligned,
The enemy presented battle's gift,
With crude skin covered, and with fine-meshed mail,
And waving gaudy standards, fluttering flags;
Already those whose fiery hearts most flared
Were on the march progressing toward the wall,
Indued with a thousand heads and tails and hides
Of foxes old, of tigers and of lions . . .

The rampart braced, the terreplein's lofty mound
That served the barren bluff as coronet
Was crowned already with thick martial rows
That mounted, iron in hand and grit in breast.
No nook, no crevice there was not brimful
Of those who risked their persons in defense.

Already all assumed the die was cast,
Though life at hazard was a precious stake . . .

Of these, lithe Gracolano was the first,
A lad courageous, strong, robust, and bold,
And he was foremost there for having pledged
The generalissimo Caupolicán
That he, anticipating all the rest,
By virtue of his lustrous-proved repute
Would enter those vallations crisp with arms
Oping through weapons' midst a vasty path . . .

He finally broke through the weapons' mass,
Uprearing, although choked with blood and blows,
His nimble feet to the widened counterscarp,
His valor and his name into the stars,
Where making many glimpse the starry lights,
At our expense he verified his boast,
As faithless as o'erbearing and arrogant
Oh woe, his deeds o'ertopped his brazen word! . . .

We beat them back, repulsed them from the wall
With tough-hewn pike-staffs and voracious swords,
With lance-thrusts jabbing and with poniard stabs
Whose din made mountain throb like bleeding hearts;
But the adversary, like unmoving rocks,
Pounded by waves the North Wind reinforces
Held in this war the stronghold of their souls,
And rocketing through air, kept gaining ground.

Thus fought the Christian and barbaric hosts;
Considering their inequality,
On equal terms so great did they contend
That neither party garnered loss or gain;
And this was so, despite the fact that all
With hands inhuman multiplied the shock

Of strokes so fell that rear ranks trampled down
For very haste the vanguard's fugitives.

Amidst stentorian, booming batteries
Before his soldiers hoisted on the wall
Appeared that bravest lion magnanimous,
The dauntless Don García preeminent,
As in the middle day appears the sun
So scintillating in the water's waste,
Or as a rainbow greets the dazzling eye,
Strung through the storm-clouds rifts in prismed grace.

. . . .

In sovereign style, with noble bearing grave
He goaded on his squadron in such straits;
O'er lofty words he set high deeds to save,
How rare a hap! His own life and the state's.
Less can it hap to me, whose voice abates,
Whose singing dies, to breast exhaustion's wave,
Unless for such an effort Heaven send me
The canto's song a new-voiced breast will lend me.

Charles M. Lancaster and Paul T. Manchester

BERNARDO DE BALBUENA
1562-1627
Mexico-Puerto Rico

Father Balbuena, a contemporary of Góngora was educated in Spain and developed his own brand of baroque
poetry. He first lived in Jamaica, then in Puerto Rico.
His earliest piece of writing was a poetic description of
New Spain, "Carta del bachiller Bernardo de Balbuena
a la señora doña Isabel de Tovar y Guzmán descri-
biendo la famosa ciudad de México y su grandeza" (Letter from the student Bernardo de Balbuena to doña Isabel de Tovar y Guzmán describing the famous city of
Mexico and its grandeur, 1604). Each line of the original provided the substance of one whole chapter in the

expanded version, written in Italianate tercets. In Puerto
Rico, Balbuena showed his talent for epic poetry in *Bernardo* (1624); this imitation of Ariosto's *Orlando furioso*
earned him his reputation as Puerto Rico's first literary
figure. When Dutch pirates sacked San Juan in 1625,
his residence and most of his books and writings were
burned.

LETTER . . . DESCRIBING THE GRANDEUR OF MEXICO

Argument

About the famous site of Mexico
The origin and grandeur of its walls,
Its houses, streets and forms of courtesy,
Its letters, virtues, quantity of crafts,
Its bounties, sources of mankind's content,
Its never-ending Spring and all its signs,
Illustrious government, religion, state,
All in my discourse finds embodiment.

Chapter I

About the famous site of Mexico

Oh, thou, heroic beauty, sage profound,
Miraculously to mankind was given;
Thine is the land where myriad gifts abound.

Cradled on plains from sandy deserts riven
On which the peaceful South Sea, foaming, breaks
Producing Orient pearls, as gifts from Heaven!

Detracting from your valor, history makes
Thee less, and Time, destroying with its flame,
From thy rich textured web more glory takes,

Yet never can destroy thy glorious name!
Listen awhile, My Lady. Lend your ear
To one whose lofty purposes and aim

Are to present to thee a spot held dear
That thou mayest love the city that the world
Esteems, where'er the sun's revolving sphere

The glory of its living rays has hurled;
And if my pen gives up its pleasant task
Of praising thee, 'tis only that I've whirled

From what exceeds my feeble power, yet mask
My weakness. Of thy beauty I'm in awe.
Instead I'll grant the boon thou deigned to ask.

Thine was the stated wish that I should draw
A portrait of the grandeur and the might
Of Mexico, whose face thou never saw.

Whether the task imposed be hard or light,
My feeble powers grow strong at thy command,
And I, to serve thee, take my pen and write.

This is my picture of that mighty land,
Bathed by a temperate and cooling wind
Where no one ever thought a town could stand.

Upon the loveliest spot that man could find,
Almost beneath the fertile tropic arch
Grow perfumed flowers and shrubs of every kind

As April, clothed in roses, follows March
And in the tropic sea engendered grow
Bright pearls in mighty depths, where sun rays parch
The earth. Upon two crystal lakes below

There floats a soft and delicate crust,
And on it stands a city raised by man
With buildings, towers, and spires upthrust,
Goodly proportioned in majestic plan.

                                                                    W.K.J.

"AMARILIS"
Seventeenth Century   Peru

There are many speculations on the identity of the
writer of a *silva* (a lyrical verse form with both long
and short lines) addressed to Lope de Vega and signed
"Amarilis." Some claim it was written by Lope's Spanish mistress, Marta de Nevares Santoya, whom he often
called "Amarilis." However, most authorities believe the
poem was actually sent from Peru, either by Maria de
Alvarado, granddaughter of a conquistador, or by Maria
Tello de Lara. "Amarilis" was often used as a pen name
by women named Maria. Lope is suspected of having re-
touched the *silva* himself. In any case, it was included
in *La Filomena* (The Nightingale, 1621) under the
title "Amarilis a Belardo," a pen name used by Lope de
Vega. Besides professing admiration for the great Spanish dramatist, the writer expressed curiosity about details of his life. That provided the excuse for his reply,
"Belardo a Amarilis," addressed to his "Amarilis indiana." Whoever the author was, the poetry was good
enough to create suspicions that Lope had had a hand
in it.

AMARILIS TO BELARDO

When great Pizarro came in his tiny ships,
He founded cities and gained such wondrous fame
That history cannot find words to tell it . . .

By his command, here in a lofty valley
That is so favored by its site and clime
That Spring forever dwells here,
Under the smile of an ever-kindly sun,
The city of León was planned and built
And, blessed by happy fortune
Became the home of many glorious heroes . . .
I could, Belardo, if it were my wish—
And Heaven would not, I think, reprove my pride—
Tell of the deeds of those, my ancestors,
Who helped to conquer all this vast, new world;
And helped, besides, to found this pleasant town
Where they ruled vassals as men should who have
Pledged blood and life in duty to their king.
But that would weary you . . .

I have a sister and we two were born
Of noble parents whom death snatched away
Ere we were scarcely free of swaddling bands;
But heaven was kind, and sent a sainted aunt
To guard and guide us in our infancy.
Men say that of the beauty that kind fate
Bestows on girls of this far, happy land,
My sister and myself have modest parts;
Nor do we lack our share
Of worldly goods and store of jeweled toys . . .

I and my dear Belisa (Thus I call
My sister who has dubbed me Amarilis)
Are devotees of more than one sweet Muse:
I, for my part, incline toward poesie;
But my dear sister, of more fiery blood—
Perhaps the heritage of our warrior sires—
Finds herself drawn to the more vigorous arts.
And not long since, her virtues were the prize
Of a happy bridegroom who laid fame and fortune
Upon the hymeneal altar, as a pledge

Of the honest love he bears her.
But I, alas, must tread a lonelier path,
Resigned to live a quiet spinster's life,
Yielding my virgin heart
Into God's tender hands,
Praying that of His kindness and His mercy
He will forever guard my purity
Safe from all harm . . .

After telling him that she has read and enjoyed many of his works (incidentally using some of the Gongoristic language in her sentences), she confesses that she is drawn to him in spirit, and sends her soul in search of a mystic solution, *to lay at his feet.*

Thus in the end, Belardo, do I bring
My soul—still virginal—as pledge to you.
Accept my gift, you who so well will know
Its humble worth. And if perchance you send
Some words to tell me that you've made a place
For me in your great heart, I'll be content.

Surely it must seem strange to you that one
In this New World should praise you as I do—
You, who have heard ten thousand shout your fame!
But let my rustic Muse attempt to do
The tasks that I insist that it essay,—
A task a hundred Tassos would not risk . . .
Rude verse, what mighty wind will smooth your way
And bear you forth from this bright Indian land,
And bring you swiftly to Belardo's heart?

Set out, frail bark. Let go your winged sail
And bear my wingless soul to port at last!

James C. Bardin

JOSÉ EUSEBIO CARO
1817-1853   Colombia

With another poet of New Granada, José Joaquín Ortiz
(1814–1892), Caro founded Colombia's first literary
journal, *La Estrella Nacional,* in 1836. As a humanist,
thoroughly acquainted with Horace and Vergil, whose
Aeneid he translated, Caro wrote lofty and technically
perfect, though cold, poetry. His advanced thinking and
noble political ideas gave him leadership, though his humility prevented his making use of it.

ON THE LIPS OF THE LAST OF
THE INCAS

Today arriving on Pichincha's slope,
The deadly cannon of the whites I flee,
Like the sun a wanderer, like the sun aflame,
Like the sun free.

O Sun, my Father, hearken! Manco's throne
Lies in the dust; Thy altar's sanctity
Profaned; exalting thee, alone I pray,
Alone but free.

O Sun, my Father, hearken! A slave before
The nations of the world I'll not agree
To bear the mark. To slay myself I come,
To die while free.

Today Thou wilt perceive me, when afar
Thou dost begin to sink into the sea,
Singing Thy hymns on the volcano's top,
Singing and free.

Tomorrow, though, alas! when once again
Thy crown throughout the east will shining be,
Its golden splendor on my tomb will fall,
My tomb, though free.

Upon my tomb the condor will descend
From heaven, the condor, bird of liberty,
And building there its nest will hatch its young,
Unknown but free.

Alfred Coester

SOR JUANA INÉS DE LA CRUZ
1648-1695
Mexico

Called by her contemporaries "The Tenth Muse" because of her literary achievements, Sister Juana, born Juana de Asbaje, was a child prodigy who took holy orders. Her cell in Mexico City became the center of the capital's intellectual life, visited by the Viceroy and by church and political leaders.

Sister Juana was a versatile writer who led a fascinating life. One of her major prose works was "Respuesta a Sor Filotea de la Cruz" (Reply to Sister Filotea de la Cruz, 1691), an autobiographical letter defending her interest in knowledge. Its sincerity in her baroque age is unusual. Her poetry, perhaps her chief claim to immortality, runs from the deeply spiritual to the amusingly human. She also wrote several plays and many *loas* (or introductions to plays), following the formula of Golden Age Spain. Her private library was the largest in New Spain until, criticized for being more interested in temporal than spiritual affairs, she sold the books, concentrated on religious activity, and finally died nursing the sick during a plague epidemic.

SONNET

(The poet would gainsay the praise given to a portrait of her . . .)

This trickery of paint which you perceive
With all the finest hues of art enwrought,
Which is false argument of colors taught
By subtle means the senses to deceive—
This by which foolish woman would believe
She could undo the evil years have brought
And conquering in the war against time fought
Could triumph over age, and youth retrieve—

Is all a futile ruse that she has tried,
A fragile flower tossed against the wind,
A useless bribe the power of fate to appease,
A silly effort of mistaken pride,
A base desire, and viewed in rightful mind,
Is dust, a corpse, a shade—is less than these.

Beatrice Gilman Proske

REDONDILLAS

Stupid men, quick to condemn
Women wrongly for their flaws,
Never seeing you're the cause
Of all that you blame in them!

If you flatter them along,
Earn their scorn, their love incite,
Why expect them to do right
When you urge them to do wrong?

You combat their opposition,
And then gravely when you're done,
Say the whole thing was in fun
And you did not seek submission.

You expect from action shady
That some magic will be done
To turn courted courtesan
Quickly into virtuous lady.

Can you think of wit more drear
Than for one with lack of brain
To smear a mirror, then complain
Since it is not crystal clear?

Yet with favor and disdain
You the same results have had,
Angered if we treat you bad,
Mocking if we've loved in vain.

She who's modest cannot hold
Man's esteem. We're all thought naughty.
If we don't accept, we're haughty;
If we welcome you, we're bold.

Since there's only scorn or pain
Lurking in the love that burns you,
Luckiest is the one who spurns you.
Just go on, then, and complain!

Which will have the greater blame
In a passion, erring, faded:
She who falls, by man persuaded
Or he whose begging brings the shame?

Do not look surprised or rave
When guilt's placed at your own gate!

Love the girls your whims create
Or create the sort you crave

Tempt us not to acquiesce,
Then with justice can you censure
Any girl who dares to venture
Near you, seeking your caress.

Women need be strong, I find,
To stay safe and keep unharmed
Since the arrogant male comes armed
With Devil, flesh, and world combined.

                                                                    W.K.J.

ANDRÉS BELLO
1781-1865   Venezuela

Though Venezuelan by birth, Bello was really the classic
figure of the entire continent as humanist, historian,
grammarian, philologist, and educator. He founded
Chile's National University. Longing for home during
his nineteen years in England, he wrote "A la agricultura de la zona tórrida" (To the Agriculture of the Torrid Zone), in 373 lines, which appeared in 1826 in the
London magazine that he published. It became one of
the best-known nineteenth-century Spanish American
poems. Based on Virgil and Horace, it first describes the
typical products of Tropical America, then contrasts city
life with country life, and finally calls for a return to the
soil and reconstruction after the victorious battles of the
revolution, ended in 1824. The first and last sections,
showing Bello's classical training as well as his Romantic
inclinations, are translated here. Six-syllable and ten-
syllable lines are mingled with irregular rhymes.

TO THE AGRICULTURE OF
THE TORRID ZONE

Hail to thee, fertile zone,—
Where the enamored sun in daily rounds
Enfolds thee, where beneath thy kisses shows
All that each various climate grows,
Brought forth from out thy grounds!—
In spring thou bindst her garlands of the ears
Of richest corn; thou giv'st the grape
Unto the sopping cask; no form nor shape
Of purple, red or yellow flower appears
Unknown to the soft bowers;
The odors of the thousand flowers
The wind's delight afford;
Across thy pasture sward
The countless flocks go grazing from the plain,
Whose only boundary the horizon sets,
Unto the surging mountains, where
Lifting the snows into the inaccessible air
They hold their parapets.
Thou givest, too, the beauty of the cane
Where honey sweet is stored
That leaves the beehive in disdain;
Thou in thy coral urns bring'st forth the bean
Which soon as chocolate in the cup is poured . . .
Thine is the wine the pierced *agave* stores
To glad Anáhuac's joyous sons; and thine
The fragrant leaf whose gently steaming pours
With solace when their hearts aweary pine.
Thy jasmines clothe the Arab brush,
Whose perfumes rare the savage rage refine
And cool the Bacchic flush;
And for the children of thy land
The stately palm-tree's fronds are far displayed
And the ambrosial pineapple's shade.

The yucca-tree holds forth its snowy breads;
And ruddy glow the broad potato beds;
The cotton bush to greet the lightest airs
Its rose of gold and snowy fleece prepares.

            . . .

For thee the rich banana's heavy tree
Displays its sweetest store—
The proud banana, richest treasury
That Providence in bounteousness could pour
With gracious hand on Ecuador!
It asks no human culture for its aid,
Ere its first fruits are displayed,
Nor with the pruning-knife nor plough it shares
The honorable harvest that it bears.
Not even the slightest care it needs
Of pious hands about it shed,
And to its ripeness so it speeds
That hardly is it harvested,
Ere a new crop is ripened in its stead.

            . . .

Oh, youngest of the nations, lift your brow
Crowned with new laurels in the marveling West!
Give honor to the fields, the simple life endow,
And hold the plains and modest farmer blest!
So that among you evermore shall reign
Fair Liberty enshrined,
Ambition modified, and Law composed,
Thy people's paths immortal there to find
Not fickle nor in vain!—
So emulous Time shall see disclosed
New generations and new names of might,
Blazing in highest light
Beside your heroes old!
"There are my sons Behold!"—
(You shall declare amain)—
"Sons of the fathers who did climb
The Andes' peaks in years agone,—

Of those who great Boyaca's sands upon,—
In Maipú and in Junín sublime,—
On Apurima's glorious plain,
Did triumph over the lion of old Spain!"

Thomas Walsh

JOSÉ JOAQUÍN DE OLMEDO
1780-1847
Ecuador

Testifying to his civic leadership, Olmedo's tombstone
bears the inscription "Father of His Country." As a
poet, his neo-Classic "La victoria de Junín: canto a Bolívar" (The Victory of Junín: Canto to Bolivar, 1825),
celebrating the battles of Junín and Ayacucho during
Ecuador's struggle for independence, reached a high
point in poetry; however, in this poem, the author sometimes abandoned Classicism for unrestrained enthusiasm, fiery metaphors and wild imagination that provoked protests, even from Bolivar, regarding the historic
inaccuracies of his battle descriptions. The influence of
Horace can be seen in some passages. This thousand-line
poem is too long to be quoted here, but in a similar vein
and shorter, Olmedo wrote the following poetic tribute
to General Juan Flores, Ecuador's first president, in
1835. Spontaneous and full of warmth, it expresses the
poet's horror at the civil war that followed the revolution. Flores reciprocated with verses addressed to
"Omero mio," a pun on Olmedo's name and Homer.

TO GENERAL FLORES, CONQUEROR
OF MIÑARICA

How the infant eagle spurns
  All the perils of the air,
While his heart within him burns
  After loftier spheres to dare;

Reaching in his upward flight
Regions entranced in pure unclouded light,
Till with transport he has won
To gaze undazzled on the mid-day sun;
And, with his strength untried
Hopes mid the joys of Heaven forever to abide.

Suddenly struck faint and blind,
   Naked in the face of day,
At the mercy of the wind,
   See him falter on his way.
Watch him shuddering descend
On the long path that seems without an end,
Till, all risks and perils past,
He sinks into the forest shades at last;
Finding himself, how blest!
Safe in the welcome shelter of his native nest!

So in ambitious youth, my muse
   Lured me in daring ways to run;
And urged my untrained song to choose
   Temples and altars of the Sun.
Ever would my verse repeat
The joys that crowned the Incas' lofty seat.
In glowing strains would I retrace
The peaceful triumphs of their blameless race.
Of laws and faiths I told;
That the new world might learn—how gladly—from the old.

As I reached the lofty sphere
   Striving higher yet to grasp,
Sounds of doom rang in my ear,
   Laurels withered in my clasp.
Down I sank, lost and alone,
Fading before my eyes the distant throne.
In vain the call to arms

Rang through the nether world with wild alarms;
It struck a deafened ear.
I felt no love or hate, no hope or fear.

Where contending oceans rave,
  Freedom's youngest, fairest child
Rose like Venus from the wave;
  Heaven and Earth before her smiled.
Crowned with roses, breathing spring,
She hovered o'er me on her pausing wing.
The joys of all the western world
Found me with harp unstrung and banner furled.
Not Junín's deathless name
Could wake a thrill of triumph in my listless frame.

But Genius never dies—his breath
Rouses the dull, deafened ear;
Wakes a throb of life in death;
  Warms the ice-cold pulse with cheer.
So it was now with me—the earth
That had so lately hailed the new Republic's birth,
Now with angry passions stirred,
Changed in a moment, as at one brief word;
And I awoke to see
What had been, what was now, and what was yet to be.

What has roused the savage horde
  Sweeping o'er the new won land?
Fierce Rebellion waves the sword,
    Lifts his poison cup in hand;
Law and Freedom he proclaims;
Gold and Power and Vengeance are his aims.
Toward the rising sun he calls
For safely on the unconquered Andes' walls;
And toward the setting day
On the Pacific's Queen urges his desperate way.

Who is the chieftain heaven-sent,
  For whom an outraged people sigh?
On whom all eyes, all hearts are bent.
  And all united voices cry?
Strong as true and brave as wise
Sent for our aid and comfort from the skies;
Faction before his glance gives way,
Like bats and owls of night at break of day;
And at his magic name
Awakes from far and near the trumpet-call of Fame.

Flores! The name breathes of delight.
  From every mountain top it sounds!
Flores! it echoes from the height
  And every hill and dale rebounds!
Till waves upon the rocky shore
Mingle their watery voices with the roar;
As when the thunder shock
Scatters the shepherds and their trembling flock;
So, at that one name's sway
Rebellion's gathering forces waver in dismay.

Mark that dusky stifling cloud
  And the struggling forms within;
Now more faint and now more loud
  Comes the muffled roar and din.
There is Miñarica! There
Passion and anger fight with black despair!
Too well the advancing hero knows
That friend and brother swell the list of foes.
He bids the tumult cease,
And offers them the outstretched hand and pledge of peace.

He makes no presumptuous taunt,
  Harbors no vindictive thoughts;
For the brave can freely grant
  Pardon when it is not sought.

For these, alas! it is too late.
False pride, blind hatred, urge them to their fate.
The generous proffer they disdain,
And the door closes, ne'er to ope again.
The hero draws his sword,
The mute sign of appeal unto a righteous Lord.

As the sunbeam from the cloud
    Bursts, withdraws, and bursts again;
Then of fuller radiance proud
    Bathes with lustre hill and plain;
So the hero's lightning blade
Now here, now there, now hidden, now displayed,
Sweeps o'er the trembling field
Till all his foes are forced to fly or yield.
Some for grace freely given, pray;
And over those who fly, his generous pity throws its sway.

Hail to thee, hero, blest of heaven!
    Thou arm, thou bulwark of our land!
Before thy sword our foes were driven!
    Behind thy shield, uncrushed we stand!
A heavy price for peace we paid;
And now we look to thee, still undismayed,
To guard our new-won state,
Science and law and art to consecrate!
To raise our flag again
That it may float in pride before the eyes of men.

Royal Andes, bow your head,
    To salute the Conqueror!
Hail, ye waves, his welcome tread,
    Nearing the Pacific shore!
Where our queenly city waits
To open wide her shining silver gates;
Where our temple fanes are dressed
With flowers for his name, our brightest and our best.

And songs of praise ascend
For him, our people's chief, defender, leader, friend!

Agnes Blake Poor

JUAN CRUZ VARELA
1794-1839   Argentina

The Varela family had good reason to hate Dictator
Juan Manuel de Rosas. Florencio, the younger son, was
assassinated by his dreaded *mazorca,* and Juan died in
exile in Uruguay. His talent for lyrical poetry was evident in "Al triunfo de Ituzaingó" (To the Triumph of
Ituzaingó), in which he minutely described that battle.
As a patriot, he attacked the merciless Spaniards in "Al
incendio de Cangallo" (To the Burning of Cangallo),
deploring their burning of the town of Cangallo in Peru,
in 1822. In the poem "25 de mayo de 1838 en Buenos
Aires" (May 25, 1838, in Buenos Aires), describing the
celebration of Argentina's Independence Day, he shows
how President Rosas, legally elected for a second term in
1835, was already assuming the dictatorial powers he exercised for the next seventeen years.

MAY 25, 1838 IN BUENOS AIRES

(extracts)

"Welcome to this hallowed day,
Welcome to thee, morn of May,
    In fresh beauty beaming.
Dawn is blushing in the skies
Waiting for the sun to rise;
    Every flag is streaming.

"Purest white and azure blue
Send back each celestial hue

To the King of Heaven.
Every wish unspoken waits
Till he bursts the golden gates,
    And the sign is given.

"Then will echoing cannon roar
All along the silver shore
    Where blue waves are playing;
Every hand and every voice
Join together to rejoice;
    Every heart is praying.

"Happy tears the mother sheds,
Over her children's infant heads
    Silent thanks bestowing;
And the warrior, worn with strife,
Feels the current of new life
    In his pulses flowing."

With his hand upon my head,
Thus an aged warrior said,
    Morning proudly greeting.
I who heard was but a boy
But I shared the old man's joy;
    And my heart was beating . . .

What Mays were those of old! What songs, what flowers!
How quickly ran the twilight's happy hours!
How sweet with evening came the welcome rest!
How safe the babe slept on his mother's breast!
How bright the visions treasured memories gave
To gild the dreams of the exhausted brave!
But they are past, forever, ever past;
And I, who speak today have seen their last.

And now the dawn of May awakes once more
Over a silent town and lonely shore.

No welcome greets the coming of the light.
Each square and street is hushed like dead of night.
In every house the closed and guarded rooms
Hold the oppressive atmosphere of tombs;
And its pale inmates, trembling with each breath,
Hear in each random sound the threat of death.
Some unknown spy may rouse the tyrant's power;
His vengeance may descend at any hour.

Perhaps a little later in the day
Some prowling negro band may wend its way,
And barbarous songs and savage dances raise
Where once was heard the hymn of joy and praise.
Why wonder? 'T is a tale but too well known,
    How with success came fratricidal strife,
And they who once had monarchs overthrown
Now cower before a despot of their own,
    And quail with dread of the assassin's knife.

Sons of my fatherland! Shatter the chain
    That palsying tyranny around you flings,
And show the world that it was not in vain
    You broke the fetters forged by foreign kings.
Recall your past of high immortal deeds,
    And pledge yourselves to do and dare again.
It is the desperate venture that succeeds;
    Awake! Arise! And quit yourselves like men!

Fair city, throned beside the silver gates!
    Queen of the balmy breezes of the West!
Arouse thyself and know that fortune waits,
    Even on the throb of one heroic breast;
For what though death his purpose consecrates?
    'Tis by a hero's death his life is blest.

Agnes Blake Poor

OLEGARIO VICTOR ANDRADE
1841-1882   Argentina

Born into poverty in the provinces, Andrade had little
leisure or preparation for his proposed career as author.
He earned his living in newspaper work, but he did not
publish the first of the poems that were to make him the
greatest Argentine poet of his time until he was thirty-
six. "El nido de cóndores" (Condors' Nest, 1877), about
San Martin's crossing of the Andes, was followed by his
four other great poems in the tradition of Walt Whit-
man—even to awkward images and occasional vulgar
diction, but full of inspiration and patriotism. His final
poem, "Atlántida, canto al porvenir de la raza latina en
America" (Atlantis, Song to the Future of the Latin
Race in America) was written in 1880 and published
the year before his death.

POEM TO ATLANTIS

. . . The passing centuries the secret kept,
But Plato saw it dimly when, beyond
The Aegean Sea, he gazed upon the shadows
Falling softly on Hymettus' peak,
And spake mysterious words with restless waves
That ground beneath his feet. He knew the name
Of this last child of Time, destined to be
The Future's bride, where dwells eternal Spring;
And called it Fair Atlantis.
But God thought best to give the mighty task
To Latin men, the race that tamed the world,
And fought its greatest battles.
    And when the hour was struck, Columbus came
Upon a ship that bore the fate of Man,
And westward made his way.
The wild tumultuous Ocean hurled against

The tiny Latin ship the black north wind,
While whirlwinds roaring fiercely rode astride
The lightning's blood red steed.
Forward the vessel moved and broke the seal
Of Mystery; and fair Atlantis woke
At last, to find her in a dreamer's arms!

Often the victor over thrones and crowns,
The restless spirit of the ancient race
Had found fulfilment of its noblest dreams,—
Abundant space and light in distant zones!
With armor newly forged, nor dragging now
The blood-stained winding sheet of a dead past,
Nor weighted down by blackest memories,
Once more it ventured forth in eager quest
Of liberty and glory.

Before it lay a vast, unconquered world.
Here, resting on the sea, 'neath tropic skies,
And bathed in the white light of rising dawn,
The Antilles lift their heads, like scattered birds
That utter plaintive cries
And dry their snowy wings that they may fly
To other, distant shores.
Here rises Mexico above two seas,
A granite tower that even yet would seem
To spy the Spanish fleet as it draws near
Across the Aztec gulf;
And over there Colombia, lulled to sleep
By the deep roar of Tequendama's fall,
Within its bosom hides unfailing wealth.

Hail, happy zone! Oh, fair, enchanted land,
Beloved child of the creative sun
And teeming home of animated life,
The birth-place of the great Bolívar—hail!

In thee, Venezuela, all is great:
The flashing stars that light thee from above;
Thy genius and thy noble heroism,
Which with volcanic force and deafening crash
Burst forth on San Mateo's lofty peak!
Outstretched below the Andes' mighty chain,
Like one who weeps above an open grave,
The Inca's Rome doth lie.
Its sword was broken in the bloody strife,
And in obscurity its face was sunk.
But still Peru doth live! For in a virile race
Defeat doth spell a new, a nobler life.
And when propitious toil, that heals all wounds,
Shall come to thee at last,
And when the sun of justice shines again
After long days of weeping and of shame,
The ripening grain shall paint with flowers of gold
The crimson cloak that o'er thy shoulders floats.

Bolivia, namesake of the giant born
At Mount Avila's foot,
Hath kept his lively wit and valiant heart,
With which to face the storm and stress of life.
It dreams of war today; but also dreams
Of greater things, when 'stead of useless guns,
The engines made of steel
Shall boldly bridge the vales and scale the hills.

And Chile, strong in war and strong in toil,
Hangs its avenging arms upon the wall,
Convinced that victory by brutal strength
Is vain and empty if it be not right.
And Uruguay, although too fond of strife,
The sweet caress of progress ever seeks;
Brazil, that feels the Atlantic's noisy kiss,
With greater freedom were a greater state;

And now the blessèd land,
The bridge of glory, which the Plata bathes
And which the Andean range alone doth bound!

Let all arise, for 'tis our native land,
Our own, our native land, which ever sought
Sublime ideals. Our youthful race was lulled
E'en in the cradle by immortal hymns,
And now it calls, to share its opulence,
All those who worship sacred liberty,
The fair handmaid of science, progress, art . . .
    Our country turns its back on savage war
And casts aside the fratricidal sword,
That it may bind upon its haughty brow
A wreath of yellow wheat,
Lighter to wear than any golden crown . . .
The sun of ultimate redemption shines
On our belovèd land, which strides ahead
To meet the future, and with noble mien
Offers the Plata's overflowing cup
To all the hungry nations . . .

                                        Elijah C. Hills

ESTEBAN ECHEVERRÍA
1805-1851   Argentina

Living in Paris at the time when Hugo, Dumas, and
other Romanticists were prominent figures on the French
literary scene, and familiar with the Romanticism of
Byron and Scott, Echeverría was a liberal both in literature and in politics when he returned to Argentina. His
poem "Elvira o la novia del Plata" (Elvira or the Bride
of La Plata, 1832) was a product of French Romanticism, for the movement did not begin in Spain until
1833. His *La cautiva* (The Captive Woman), about

"two souls united by the double bonds of love and misfortune," was not only his greatest poem, but Latin America's first poetic legend based on native themes and local scenery. The poet declared, "Poetry among us must reflect the colors of the physical nature that surrounds us and be, at the same time, a vivid picture of our customs and dominant ideas. The desert is our richest patrimony."

Later Echeverría showed himself an even greater master of prose in the short story "El matadero" (The Slaughterhouse). His contemporaries declared that Echeverría had founded Argentina's national literature.

THE CAPTIVE WOMAN

I. The Desert

(i.e., the uninhabited but fertile pampas)

"Ils vont. L'espace est grand." *Hugo*

The night was coming on. The sun
To touch with gold had just begun
The Andean peaks. Below, the plain
Mysterious stretches, without rein
In all directions, sad and grave.
So melancholy is the view,
Silent and solitary, too,
As when in twilight hours the sea,
Relaxing its activity,
Lays calming hand on every wave.

Look where one will, above, around,
Naught but immensity is found.
Like birds above the sea in flight,
There is no place where human sight
Can rest, but only dens of fierce
And wild brutes, and solitude,

And nests of birds, and unturned sod,
And grass and skies that o'er it brood;
A desert land known but to God,
Through which His eyes alone can pierce.

From time to time its dignity
By wild beast's snarl may shattered be.
Then all is silent as before
Till broken by a bellowing roar
As tigers over prey rejoice.
Sometimes a *chajá* bird will cry
Sensing afar a wandering brute;
Moodily staring at the sky
This prophet, usually mute,
In warning raises now its voice.

The sun had set. Like funeral pyre
The western skies were now afire;
Then dying out behind each hill
To make the pampas darker still,
The sky became opaque and grave.
Each trembling, twinkling distant star
Flicked on and off, and then from sight
Became obscure, then burned afar,
Like flickering candles in the night
Winking in some cathedral nave.

By now the mantle of the night
All of the earth had hid from sight.
A cloth, black as a winding sheet
Made cover for the world complete
From west to east. 'T was dark again.
Slowly descending night brought balm
For weary souls longing for peace.
They sighed while welcoming the calm
That to their labors brings surcease;
So, too, in the uninhabited plain.

Then like the sudden storms that burst
At night, with thunder warning first,
In far-off rumbles, came a sound,
Dull and confused and echoing 'round;
Splitting all space before it ceased,
It rose like screams in quiet night,
A wild, swelling, pulsing cry,
From mighty crowd in frenzied flight,
That echoed in the midnight sky,
Its clamor frightening each beast.

Far off was heard the thundering beat
Of some swift pony's flying feet.
Who was it? What unfeeling tongue
'Gainst Heaven that loud cry had flung
In silence never so defaced?
What haughty human foot would dare
To tread that land so solitary,
And with that peaceful calm to share
In action so extraordinary,
Unknown, unseen, in desert waste?

Hark! Do you hear that howling band
Of thundering savages at hand,
Waking the fields on every side?
Look! In wild onset now they ride
With horrid din and frenzied pace;
The fierce onslaught of steeds foam-flecked,
With wind-like riders, streaming hair,
Comes nearer now, its speed unchecked,
Like whirlwind never pausing there,
Its frightening swiftness covering space.

Where is it going? Whence its birth?
What joy seeks it upon the earth?
Why does it shout, fleeing what dread,
Spurring its steed to dash ahead

With never a look or slackened pace?
See! From each blood-tipped lancehead hangs,
Adorning it, a human head,
Like snarling beast with obvious fangs.
Those eyes still open and blood-red,
Betray their fury in their gaze.

Such is the proof the savage shows
Of his fierce courage toward his foes.
Treachery, too, he thus reveals,
As on his sleeping foe he steals.
On them his boastful glance he lowers.
Inhuman knives the booty made
Cutting the heads from those alive.
Now hear him shout: "Christians, you paid
Because your chiefs have dared to strive
And feud against our Indian powers.

"The straw-thatched huts where once you dwelt
The power of our might have felt.
The flames their ravaging tongues upthrust
And your proud vigor bit the dust!
Ye Christian braves, where are you all?
Why come you not in haste to free
Your wives and children from their chain?
They languish in captivity.
But should you come, then once again
Before our lances you will fall."

To taunts the Indian gave birth
The while the tortured trampled earth
Shook 'neath the hoofbeats of his steed.
Then he rode on, and stilled indeed
In the vast pampas was his cry.
Meanwhile, the night—its obscure face
Covered beneath its cloak of cloud—
Cast over that deserted space

A frightening silence, like a shroud,
In still and shadowy majesty.

W.K.J.

GAUCHO POETRY
Nineteenth Century   Argentina

Riding on horseback or sitting around the campfire,
cowboys everywhere make up poems. Here is a trio of
Argentine gaucho poems from the middle nineteenth
century.

My wife has swiped my pony;
   To Salta gone, of course.
I feel so sad and lonely.
   Oh, God, send back my horse!

. . .

If you think I'm mad about you,
   Since I'm staring at your face,
You forget how many shoppers
   Buy naught in the market place.

. . .

"Oh, Men are the very devils!"
   So all the women say.
But watch them wait for a devil
   To carry them away.

BARTOLOMÉ MITRE
1821-1906   Argentina

When Mitre was ten years old, he was sent to a cattle
ranch to learn the business. He lived among the gauchos
and learned to ride like an Indian, but he spent most of
his time reading and writing poetry, and he was finally

sent back to Buenos Aires. Soon afterwards his family moved to Montevideo out of hatred for Dictator Rosas. There he got his training as an artilleryman, and there he met the Argentine poet Echeverría, who urged him to write about the American scene. One result was "A Santos Vega" (1838), about a traditional gaucho troubadour so skilled that when he was defeated in a singing contest and died of grief, people believed his opponent must have been the devil in disguise.

Driven from Uruguay later by President Rivera's suspicions that the Argentine fugitives were conspiring against him, don Bartolomé went to Bolivia to edit a newspaper, and later to Chile, again as an editor. There, in 1849, he used a poetic form not very common in Latin America, the sonnet, for "A la América" (To America).

After he collected his poems in *Rimas* (Rhymes, 1854), Mitre abandoned verse for prose. The first version of his *Historia de Belgrano* appeared in 1858–59 and, corrected and expanded, as *Historia de Belgrano y de la independencia argentina*, in 1887. His *Historia de San Martín* was first published in 1888. A definitive edition of *Rimas* is dated 1891.

This "polygonal" man not only wrote history, but made history in many battles, including the one that overthrew his enemy, Dictator Rosas, in 1852, and in the political arena where he won a term as president of Argentina (1862–1868). He was exiled because of his refusal to accept his defeat at the polls after a second attempt. Mitre played an important role in the transformation of modern Argentina from feudalism and anarchy. And in his old age he received merited honors for his achievements in statesmanship and letters.

TO AMERICA

Pursued by the hungry, wild beasts
An untamable colt crosses the plains,
And, bound with strong fetters,

On his withers rides Mazeppa, outspread;
At length, his wild career ended,
The brute upon the hard crags drops prone
And, freed from his strong bonds,
Mazeppa arises, an anointed king.

Thus amid the shackles America groans,
Lashed to the wild colonial colt,
Followed by a band of grey hounds;
And exhausted and wounded and bloody,
She runs, falls, and then rises; then with laurels
Her forehead is crowned resplendent.

Anon. Inter-America, 5 (1922) *p.* 182

TO SANTOS VEGA (Argentine Minstrel)

Santos Vega, all thy singing
Failed to bring thee highest glory
Yet thy songs live in the memory
Of the *lower class*, like folklore:
Though they use not ink nor paper,
Yet they save them from oblivion,
Son from father learns to sing them
Oral tradition has preserved them.

Untaught bard of our vast pampas,
Like the prairies' sweetest song bird.
Thou hast given to the breezes
Songs both uncouth and sonorous:
And thy songs are oft repeated
In the forests and the pampas
By the Argentinian gaucho
And the untamed Indian wanderer.

What avails thee if thou hast lived it
Singing like a wee cicada,

To the humble guitar's strumming,
'Neath the colossal ombú?
If thine eyes are now o'erclouded
'Mid a thousand acclamations,
If thy ballads and thy glories
In the people e'er will live?

From ranch to ranch thou hast gone singing
And defeating *payadores*;
From among a world of singers
They acclaimed thee as the best;
But at length thou fellest beaten
In a duel of harmonies,
After two full days of singing,
And of sorrow thou didst die.

Like a warrior of past ages,
Fallen dead upon his buckler,
On thine instrument, now silent,
Didst thou yield thy soul to God;
At the same time, runs the story,
That thy life was ebbing quickly,
The G-string in twain was broken,
Giving out a doleful sound . . .

Thy soul inhabits the deserts;
And far in the southern lowlands,
By the side of a lone cabin,
Stands a funereal cross;
That cross 'neath a green leafed *tala*,
Solitary and abandoned,
Is ever an adored symbol
Of the lands of the Tuyu . . .

Having established the true elements of the tradition, the poet concludes his elegy by universalizing the dead hero through the collective mystery of the legend.

Sleep now, sleep now, Santos Vega,
For, as long as in the desert
Is heard afar this vague concert,
Immortal will be thy name;
It must be heard by the *gaucho*,
On his rugged couch extended,
While on the thatched roof upstanding
Crows the matutinal cock.

Sleep then until be awakened
With the pale star of the morning
The restless, vigilant drover,
Who will sing again thy song,
And which, from plateau to forest,
Off the tune or following it,
Like a mighty chorus rolls
Wildly filling all the welkin.

And while the wandering *gaucho*,
As he goes across the meadow,
Pauses anon in his gallop,
And from his courser alights,
And on the ground spreads his *poncho*
In token of meager carpet,
And prays 'neath his horse's shadow,
Santos Vega, sleep in peace.

Anon. Inter-America, 5 (1921)

JOSÉ HERNÁNDEZ
1834-1886   Argentina

Hernández was born among the gauchos and became
their spokesman in his two-part epic, *Martín Fierro*, the
finest example of the so-called *gauchesca* literature. The
first part, *La ida* (The Departure), published in Buenos
Aires in 1872, gained immediate popularity. Fifteen edi-

tions and 60,000 copies appeared in the seven years before the second part, *La vuelta* (The Return), was published in 1879. The two parts total forty-six cantos. The work was sold even in the country grocery stores, where the kind of people described in the poem bought it along with their gin and salami.

The injustice of the government to Martín and his friend Cruz served to awaken public consciousness, while the realistic description of gaucho life and customs, written in authentic dialect, has immortalized Hernández and made Martín Fierro the legendary figure of the Argentine pampas.

MARTIN FIERRO

Part I. The Departure
Canto I

I sit me here to sing my song
To the beat of my old guitar;
For the man whose life is a bitter cup,
With a song may yet his heart lift up,
As the lonely bird on the leafless tree,
That sings 'neath the gloaming star . . .

I will sing my song till my breath gives out,
I will sing when they bury me;
And singing I'll come where the angels roam
The rolling plains of their starry home,—
Into this world I came to sing,
As I sang on my mother's knee . . .

'Tis little I have of bookman's craft,
Yet once let me warm to the swing
And the lilt and beat of the plainsman's song,—
I will sing you strong, I will sing you long,

And the words will out like the tumbling rout
   Of waters from a spring . . .

I am the best of my own at home,
   And better than best afar;
      I have won in song my right of place,
      If any gainsay me, face to face,
Let him come and better me, song for song,
   Guitar against guitar . . .

I was born on the mighty Pampas' breast,
   As the fish is born in the sea;
      Here was I born and here I live,
      And what seemed good to God to give,
When I came to the world, it will please Him too,
   That I take away with me.

And this is my pride: to live as free
   As the bird that cleaves the sky;
      I build no nest on this careworn earth,
      Where sorrow is long, and short is mirth,
And when I am gone, none will grieve for me,
   And none care where I lie.

I have kept my feet from trap or trick
   In the risky trails of love;
      I have roamed as free as the winging bird,
      And many a heart my song has stirred,
But my couch is the clover of the plain,
   With the shining stars above.

And every one that hears my song.
   With this he will agree:
      I sought no quarrel, nor drew a knife,
      Save in open fight and to guard my life,
And that all the harm I have done to men
   Was the harm men wished to me.

Then gather around and hearken well
  To a gaucho's doleful story,
    In whose veins the blood of the Pampas runs,
    Who married a wife and begat him sons,
Yet who nevertheless is held by some
  As a bandit grim and gory.

Canto III

Twas long ago that with wife and sons,
  And cattle a goodly batch,
    I rode my horse among the best;
    But into the army I was pressed,
And when I came back, of all I owned,
  There was only walls and thatch.

Ah, happy was I 'neath my "rancho's" roof,
  As the bird in its feathered nest;
    My heart rose up with a father's pride,
    As I watched my boys with the rangers ride,
Alas, of all by an evil chance,
  In a day I was dispossessed . . .

Once at a merry gathering,
  I was warm and going strong,
    When all of a sudden there and then,
    The Justice came with a troop of men,
And the party came to a sudden end;
  For they took the lot along . . .

Though some that had been in the trap before,
  Made off and got clear away,
    Like a simpleton I waited there;
    I knew I had no accounts to square,
And I wouldn't run; but I soon found out
  That I was a fool to stay . . .

They formed us up at the door and said
  We must serve the Government;
    And they mixed us up with a wretched lot
    That at some other place they'd caught;
Not the devil himself, it seems to me,
  Could anything worse invent.

I knew the Judge had a down on me,
  For I'm no politician;
    On voting day I had stayed away,
    And somebody since had heard him say
That those that didn't vote for him
  Were helping the opposition . . .

But before we went off, the Judge he up
  And made us a long harangue;
    He said they'd treat us like gallant men,
    And he promised us over and over again,
That we'd only serve six months and then,
  He'd send the relieving gang.

Canto VIII

Like an ownerless horse the gaucho is,
  That everyone may ride.
    They break his back and they break his heart,
    For life he must struggle from the start,
Like the tree that without a shelter grows
  On the wind-swept mountain-side.

As soon as he's born and they've baptized him,
  They drop him and give him a whack;
    The priest says: "You'd better to work begin;
    Run off and find someone to take you in."
And into the world like a donkey he goes,
  With his suffering on his back . . .

They call him a drunken gaucho beast
   If he takes a spot of gin;
     If he goes to a dance he's an upstart boor;
     If he plays at cards he's a sharper sure;
He's a brawler if he defends himself;
   If he doesn't—they do him in.

Neither sons nor wife nor friends has he,
   To make his lot less hard.
     He's like a stray bullock that nobody owns,
     And that's only good for its hide and bones;
For what good is a bullock that doesn't plough,
   Except for the slaughter-yard?

His home is the wild; and his only friends
   Are his lasso, his horse, and knife;
     If dying with hunger and fatigue,
     He drops his loop on some sucking-pig,
They hunt him off for a "gaucho-thief,"
   And he has to fly for his life.

And if they stretch him belly-up,
   There's never a soul to care;
     By the side of the trail they let him rot,
     With never a cross to mark the spot,
Or into some hole, like a dog he's thrown,
   With a curse instead of a prayer.

Part II. The Return

Perhaps the most dramatic part of the poem is Canto IX, narrating Martin's hand-to-hand fight with an Indian whom he finds torturing a woman captive. It is condensed here.

Canto IX

The wretched victim bathed in blood
  At the Indian's feet I saw,
    The raw-hide thong from head to heel
    Had left its mark in welt and weal,
And through the rents of her tattered dress
  The flesh showed red and raw . . .

Shall I tell in a song how the angered blood
  Through my tingling pulses stirred?
    The Indian turned and our eye-beams clashed,
    From eye to eye the challenge flashed,
We knew each other man to man
  And we wasted never a word.

With the backward leap of the cornered cat
  His fighting length he chose,
    He watched me there like a beast at bay
    That knows it must either be slain or slay,
His "bolas" from his belt he loosed
  And waited for me to close . . .

That somebody there was about to die
  Was as plain as plain could be;
    There wasn't much choice what I had to do,
    There was no way out, but one of two:
To stiffen that son of Satan out,
  Before he could stiffen me . . .

He lashed the air with two "bola" shots,
  Round his head like rings they spun;
    One grazed my arm with a glancing hit,
    A hair's breadth more would have splintered it;
Those balls of stone whizz through the air
  Like bullets from a gun . . .

Aijuna! I'll say he was quick and sly—
  He missed me by simple luck;
    The blood worked up to his ugly head,
    Till like a colt he was seeing red:
He would feint at me with the right hand ball
  Before with the left he struck.

But a bitter turn Fate served me there
  As we circled round and round,
    I saw my chance and went rushing in,
    While he backed away to save his skin,
My foot tripped up in my "chiripá"
  And headlong I hit the ground . . .

Then onto my back with tooth and nail
  He leapt like a clawing brute
    He was reckless then that I'd still my knife,
    He was blind with his rage to have my life,
Not a ghost of a chance he let me have,
  To straighten and get my foot . . .

The captive that lay in her tears and blood
  Half killed by the murderous whip,
    When she saw my plight forgot her pang,
    Like an arrow there to my help she sprang,
She gave the Indian a sudden tug
  That made him lose his grip . . .

As soon as once to my feet I got
  At each other again we tore,
    Not a pause for a breather could I get
    I was soaking wet with my dripping sweat,
In all my fights, I'd never been in
  Such a touch-and-go before . . .

As madder and madder the savage grew
  I calmed down more and more,—

Until the Indian has made his kill
There's nothing his ravening rage can still,—
Till one of his whirling cords I cut
And began to press him sore . . .

I'll leave to wits more wise than mine
What I don't understand:
It seemed to me as he backward trod,
He was tripped by the wrath of Almighty God;
Where chance isn't present you'll often find
That Providence takes a hand.

As he staggered back, I leapt and closed
With lightning thrust and slash,
Though he kept his feet and escaped my grip
He lost the fight by that fateful slip;
I got home once with a scalping-chop
And once with a belly-gash . . .

The Indian felt that the horn for him
Was sounding the slaughter-blast,
His hair stood up and his eyes rolled round,
He was staggering now on the trampled ground,
He sucked his lips in out of sight
As his breath came thick and fast . . .

And there, thank God, I finished him;
Well home I rammed my knife.
I was weary and sore, but desperate,
I lifted him up as one lifts a weight;
And gutted there, from the raking steel
I threw him off when I knew by the feel,
That he hadn't a spark of life.

When I saw him dead I crossed myself,
The help of heaven to thank;
The kneeling woman beside me there,

    At the Indian's body could only stare,
And then to the skies she raised her eyes,
    And in tears on the ground she sank.

On the boundless plain by that woman's side,
    With the great blue sky above,
      I knelt and gave thanks to my patron Saint,
      While she to God's Mother made her plaint;
Through her sobs she prayed for both of us
    To the Holy Virgin's love.

Canto XXXIII

With these parting words I'll take my leave,
    Without telling you until when;
      The man who's just out for an easy lot
      Will choose his cut at a tender spot;
But I've always cut through the toughest part
    And I'll cut through the tough again.

To the eagle its nest; to the speckled cat
    In wood and brake its bed;
      The fox in some burrow makes its lair,
      But the gaucho wanders here and there
Borne on by the winds of change and chance,
    With no place to lay his head . . .

And if life fails me, this I know,
    When the news of my death is spread,
      The roaming gaucho, far away
      In the desert lands, will be sad that day,
And a sudden ache in his heart will wake,
    When he knows that I am dead.

For I've told in these songs of my brothers' wrongs,
    Their pains and their misery;
      When the tale of my life is a tale of old,

My story with pride in their hearts they'll hold,
And I'll live again for my countrymen,
When they remember me.

Walter Owen

ESTANISLAO DEL CAMPO
1834-1880   Argentina

Second in popularity only to the gaucho epic *Martín Fierro* is *Fausto* (Faust, 1870) by Estanislao del Campo. Born the same year as Hernández, and like him a soldier and politician turned journalist, del Campo started his literary career as a Romantic poet. Then he turned to gaucho themes, although he was a man of the city whose only contacts with the gauchos had been in the army, when he had commanded them. He chose for his pen name "Aniceto the Chick," after his literary idol Hilario Ascasubi (1809–1875), one of the first poets to mine the gaucho vein, who signed his works "Aniceto the Cock." Del Campo was the most cultured of the Argentine gaucho poets.

On August 24, 1866, the Colón Theater in Buenos Aires gave the first performance of the opera *Faust*. In del Campo's work, a naive gaucho who had attended that performance of the opera describes the evening to an equally unlettered chum, Laguna, whose mention of the Devil brought the Faust story to mind. Walter Owen, an Englishman living in Buenos Aires, who translated much Latin American poetry, put it into cowboy jargon.

FAUST

Canto II

Nights back I was roamin' around this town,
Sort of takin' stock here and there,
When I come on a string of coaches drawn
Outside of a slap-up theatre
That I see'd by the sign was called Colón.
The folks that had come was pilin' down
And crowdin' like crazy through the door
To a counter set 'cross the corridor.
I thought I'd step inside the hall,
I was feelin' good and rash,
So I elbowed into the free for-all,
Till I reached the place where they took your cash.

When I bought my ticket, my ribs were sore,
The crowd was wuss than it was before;
I looked behind and I'll give you my word,
They was millin' 'round like a loco'd herd;

And as if that warn't enough, by gum,
While the thick of the crowd I was takin' on,
I'm jiggered if some slick-fingered bum
Didn't "vamos" with my *facón!*

I crossed that off, though it soured my crop.
And next—as part two of my evenin's fun—
I climbed a ladder that didn't stop
Till step one hundred and one.

The loft up there is where they stow
The folks like me and you,
And down below are the town-bred crew,
All stacked up, row on row.

I had bare sat down and looked around
When the band with a bang let go,
Behind a fence, down on the ground,
Where the stage was, for the show.

At a big tarpaulin they gave a haul
With such a rush, I tell you true,
Would have bowled you over, horse and all,
If it caught you comin' through.

And behind the screen a chap appeared,
A doctor by vocation,
Called Fowst, it seems—for so I heer'd—
And well known by reputation.

He told us that all the pile of books
He had read till his eyes were dim
Weren't helpin' his case with a goldy-locks
That hadn't no use for him.

He kept snoopin' around her grazin'-patch,
Neglectin' his sleep and food,
And bleatin' all night outside her thatch,
But it didn't do no darn good.

Then he slammed his hat on the floor and fell
To cussin' worse than double,
And wound up by callin' the Fiend of Hell
To fix his particular trouble.

He should have thought twice! He'd barely spoke,
By Christ, what a scare I got!
For there in a cloud of stinkin' smoke
The Devil was, on the spot!

You ought to have seen the Devil, my word!
Skin and bone in a flappin' coat,

A hat with a feather, cats-claws, a sword,
And a beard like an old buck-goat.

Said the Devil: "I'm at your service, doc.
Just order yours most truly."
But the doctor was showin' signs of shock
Like his wits was goin' woolly.

Then the Devil again says, most polite:
"Now what can I do for you?
There ain't the least call for takin' fright.
Call your orders—I'll put them through."

"If you want *dinero*—I don't talk rash—
But I'll do you proud and proper;
And when I'm done fixin' you up for cash
Anchorena'll look a pauper."

" 'Tain't power nor money I'm pinin' for,"
Says Fowst. "Let's quit palaver.
I'm nuts on a gal, my good señor,
And my trouble's that I can't have her."

As soon as those words the Devil hears,
He busts loose with such ugly laughter
That it kept on ringin' in my ears
The rest of the evenin' after.

He stamps the floor and the solid wall
Cracks open top to bottom,
And standin' there was the doctor's gal—
I guess the doc thought he'd got 'em!

That gal was a topper for looks, my son,
Pure peach with locks like flax;
I thought I was settin' eyes on one
Of them Virgins they make of wax.

The doc gave himself his head,
Makin' tracks in her direction;
But Satan headed him off and said;
"Not so fast! She's in my protection.

"If you're ready, I'll be only too pleased
To put things in black and white.
You give me your soul; and all will be greased
For smooth-workin' . . . You got me right?"

"Okay," says the doctor on the spot.
"Just show me where I sign."
And the Devil flips out a bill he'd brought.
And gets Fowst on the dotted line.

He says to the Devil with a wink
As he hands back the contract, signed;
"Can't you fix me up with some witchin' drink?
You know what I've got in mind?"

The Devil was hot-stuff, I'll allow.
Old Fowst had no sooner said it
Than the Devil did somethin'—don't ask me how—
And Gee! . . . it's hard to credit . . .

Did you ever chance to see a grub
Turn into a butterfly?
That's somethin' how as Old Beelzebub
Made over that crocked old guy.

Old bag-coat, night-cap, and silvery hair
Went poof! and no more were seen;
And there was the doctor standin' there
As good as he'd ever been.

The Devil then waved the gal to quit;
And with some kind of magic knack,

He mended the wall where he'd busted it . . .
And they pulled the tarpaulin back.

Walter Owen

RAFAEL OBLIGADO
1851-1920   Argentina

The scholarly and talented Obligado was a member of
the America-first school of Echeverría and, like Ascasubi, the novelist Eduardo Gutiérrez, and Bartolomé
Mitre before him, he was drawn to the Santos Vega
theme. Obligado put the final touches to the legend in
a four-part poem, most of which appeared in his only
volume of poems, *Poesías*, in 1885.

SANTOS VEGA

*Santos Vega the minstrel—
A great man was he—
Died singing his love,
Like a bird in a tree.*

Part I. The Soul of the Cowboy Minstrel

When the evening is descending
Sobbing toward the west horizon,
There creeps forth a somber shadow
Over Argentina's pampas.
When the rising sun illumines
With its light serene and brilliant
All the scene of its broad acres,
Then the melancholy shadow
Flees while kissing its soft carpet
With the eagerness of anguish.

Then according to the Creoles,
On the mild moonlit evenings
By a lakeside solitary
This same shadow stays his journey.
There he seems to take on grandeur
And a sail skims o'er the water,
While he takes delight in hearing,
As though sounding for him only,
The incessant roar and hissing
As the long, gray waves roll onward.

They say, too, when nights are cloudy,
If a careless lad leaves hanging,
His guitar upon the crossbeam
Of a well-house, all unheeded,
Then the silent shadow coming
Wraps the guitar in his mantle,
And the prelude of some ballad
From its sleeping cords starts plucking,
Strings that vibrate as though wounded
By the salty tears of sorrow.

Creoles say that on these evenings
When the pampas plains are sinking
In the depth of their own vastness,
Lost without their crown of starlight,
There where hillocks are the fairest,
Where the clover grows the thickest,
Shines a torch that no one carries,
Partly veiled by misty vapor
As though waiting till the breezes
Cool the soft winds of its dreaming.

But if suddenly a tempest
Rages in the former quiet,
And the hollow thunder vibrates,
Giving words to lightning flashes,

Then a ruddy, flaming serpent
Strikes the ombú tree obliquely,
Turning all its leaves to ashes,
Curls, and strikes, and climbing upward,
From the tallest branches scatters
Raindrops, glittering and scaly.

Other times, in summer siestas,
When mirages look like rolling
Waves that sweep, immense, majestic,
From some far, fantastic river,
Stealthily, dejected, gloomy,
Down the emerald slopes descending
Comes a horseman riding slowly,
With guitar over his shoulder
To the lonely shore, and spurring,
Rides his horse into the water.

If, at that time, some lone rider,
Galloping across the pampas,
Sees that melancholy gaucho
In the distant gleam reflected,
Of that abyss of illusions,
He will cease his song a moment
And a tender prayer will utter
From the depth of his compassion.
Crossing himself, he will mutter:
" 'Tis the soul of Santos Vega!"

I, a native of this region,
Born within the land this genius
Hymned, and also sharing with him
That fierce pampas wind he loved so—
Here I kiss the land he cherished,
Share with him the land's affection,
While with pride I'm overflowing

As I think with them I'm sharing:
Echeverría's home and nation,
And the land of Santos Vega.

Part II. The Minstrel's Sweetheart

The dark night fell. For a moment
Peace and calm lay o'er the pampas,
Then melodious guitar strumming
Seemed to fill the breeze with music.
To its flourishes united
Came the sweet voice of a singer,
In a love song to his sweetheart,
Who upon the gaucho's shoulder
Bent her head with loving sadness,
So to hear each word he uttered . . .

"I'm that white cloud in the distance,"
Vega in his song was saying,
"That with the still sombre darkness,
Flees with the coming of the morning;
I'm the light that, at your window,
From the moon comes down in handfuls;
That which—when you were a youngster—
Caused your smiling eyes to open;
That which built your every daydream,
In the lagoon of the desert . . ."

Then when the first light of morning
Set the void's vast depth afire,
With its dawning glance of whiteness
That makes every dew drop sparkle;
When the sun upon the river
Cast its earliest wave of brightness,
There was seen a floating shadow

Swiftly seeking western refuge,
While the tall ombu was swaying,
O'er an ancient, lonely farmhouse.

Anon. Inter-America, *4* (1920) *and* W.K.J.

JOSÉ MARÍA HEREDIA
1803-1839   Cuba

Cuba's national poet, Heredia, is considered one of the
first Romantic poets of the New World because of his
intensity of emotion and intimacy with nature, despite
the fact that much of his poetry is classical in form. He
was also one of the first to describe the American scene.
His "En el Teocalli de Cholula" (On the Temple Pyra-
mid of Cholula, 1820), written during his visit to Mexico when he was seventeen, antedated Spain's Romanticism by thirteen years. Nature provided the material for
"En una tempestad" (In a Hurricane, 1822), while his
visit to Niagara Falls in 1824 inspired "Ode to Niagara,"
the epitome of Romanticism in its awe of nature's violent grandeur and in its melancholy, induced by the poet's having just been refused by his Cuban sweetheart.

In his way of life, Heredia was also romantic. He was
sentenced to perpetual exile for his political activities
against Spain, and after living briefly in the United
States, eventually became a Mexican citizen.

ODE TO NIAGARA

My lyre! Give me my lyre! My bosom finds
The glow of inspiration. Oh, how long
Have I been left in darkness, since this light
Last visited my brow! Niagara!
Thou with thy rushing waters dost restore
The heavenly gift that sorrow took away.
Tremendous torrent! for an instant hush

The terrors of thy voice, and cast aside
Those wide-involving shadows, that my eyes
May see the fearful beauty of thy face!
I am not all unworthy of thy sight,
For from my very boyhood have I loved,
Shunning the meaner track of common minds,
To look on Nature in her loftier moods.
At the fierce rushing of the hurricane,
At the near bursting of the thunderbolt,
I have been touched with joy; and when the sea
Lashed by the wind hath rocked my bark, and showed
Its yawning caves beneath me, I have loved
Its dangers and the wrath of elements.
But never yet the madness of the sea
Hath moved me as thy grandeur moves me now . . .
The hoarse and rapid whirlpools there! My brain
Grows wild, my senses wander, as I gaze
Upon the hurrying waters, and my sight
Vainly would follow, as toward the verge
Sweeps the wide torrent. Waves innumerable
Meet there and madden,—waves innumerable
Urge on and overtake the waves before,
And disappear in thunder and in foam . . .
What seeks thy restless eye? Why are not here,
About the jaws of this abyss, the palms—
Ah, the delicious palms—that on the plains
Of my own native Cuba spring and spread
Their thickly foliaged summits to the sun . . . ?
But no, Niagara,—thy forest pines
Are fitter coronal for thee. The palm,
The effeminate myrtle and frail rose may grow
In gardens, and give out their fragrance there,
Unmanning him who breathes it. Thine it is
To do a nobler office. Generous minds
Behold thee, and are moved, and learn to rise
Above earth's frivolous pleasures; they partake
Thy grandeur, at the utterance of thy name.

God of all truth! in other lands I've seen
Lying philosophers, blaspheming men,
Questioners of thy mysteries, that draw
Their fellows deep into impiety;
And therefore doth my spirit seek thy face
In earth's majestic solitudes. Even here
My heart doth open all itself to thee . . .
I see thy never-resting waters run
And I bethink me how the tide of Time
Sweeps by eternity. So pass, of man,—
Pass, like a noonday dream—the blossoming days,
And he awakes to sorrow. I, alas!—
Feel that my youth is withered, and my brow
Ploughed early with the lines of grief and care.
Never have I so deeply felt as now
The hopeless solitude, the abandonment,
The anguish of a loveless life. Alas!
How can the impassioned, the unfrozen heart
Be happy without love? I would that one
Beautiful, worthy to be loved and joined
In love with me, now shared my lonely walk
On this tremendous brink. 'Twere sweet to see
Her sweet face touched with paleness, and become
More beautiful from fear, and overspread
With a faint smile, while clinging to my side.
Dreams,—dreams! I am an exile, and for me
There is no country and there is no love.
Hear, dread Niagara, my latest voice!
Yet a few years, and the cold earth shall close
Over the bones of him who sings thee now
Thus feelingly. Would that this, my humble verse,
Might be, like thee, immortal! I, meanwhile,
Cheerfully passing to the appointed rest,
Might raise my radiant forehead in the clouds
To listen to the echoes of my fame.

William Cullen Bryant (1827)

GERTRUDIS GÓMEZ DE AVELLANEDA
1814-1873   Cuba

Avellaneda was one of Latin America's authentic lyric
voices. She began as a poet, then wrote at least three
memorable plays, as well as a couple of novels. The two
sonnets translated here rank with the best of the form
in Spanish America: "Al Partir" (On Leaving), written
upon leaving Cuba for Spain in 1836, and "A Washington" (To Washington), composed later.

ON LEAVING

Pearl of the sea! Star of the Occident!
Beautiful Cuba! Now thy brilliant sky
Is, by the night, veiled from my searching eye,
Just as my heart by deepest gloom is rent.
Now must I leave. The crew so diligent
Labors to tear me from the land where I
Was born. Quickly the sails are bent,
Filled by warm winds that from your hot zone fly.

Farewell, my native land, my Eden dear;
Wherever furious Fate my lot shall cast,
Thy sweet name always will delight my ear.
Farewell! The sail is billowing in the blast.
The anchor rises, and as if in fear
The bark slices the waves in silence vast.

                                                    W.K.J.

TO WASHINGTON

History affords no model in the past
For your great life, nor shall the years to be

Produce a copy in your memory
   That equals you, throughout the ages vast.
   Europe beheld its soil besmirched with blood
By him they call the genius of war,
But America has glory greater far,
   Whom Heaven sent the Genius of Good.

Let the bold conqueror in his selfmade Hell
   Boast of the folks made slaves, bound by his thong,
      Rejoice in lands left waste and desolate:
The peoples of the world know all too well
   That he who rules them free alone is strong,
      That he who makes them great alone is great.

Chesley M. Hutchings

SALVADOR SANFUENTES
1817-1860   Chile

A student of Andrés Bello, who made him Secretary of
the University of Chile which he founded in 1843, Sanfuentes occupied many official and political positions in
Chile during his short life. But he also found time to
write narrative and dramatic poetry, of which the legend
"El campanario" (The Bell Tower, 1842) was the most
famous. It was inspired by J. J. Mora's *Leyendas es-
pañolas* (Spanish Legends, 1840), and is quoted in
many anthologies.

THE BELL TOWER

Canto I *describes an eighteenth century Chilean Marquis
who, after a wild youth, has turned pious. He lives a regulated
life, which the poet describes as follows:*

Free of all duties, he'd roll out of bed
And slowly dress when eight o'clock had passed.
Then to the chapel. After prayers were said,
He'd drink some chocolate to break his fast.
His dinner came at twelve, with meat and bread;
A long siesta, and high tea at last.
After all this, lest life should prove a bore,
He'd take a long ride in his coach and four.

At dusk on holy days he heard the bell
Of the cathedral by the sexton tolled.
The Marquis and his family as well
Would go to worship with the vicar's fold.
On other days, his rosary he'd tell
And with his household, family prayers would hold.
Since he in politics was diligent,
He'd then go out to see the president.

And every night, close on the stroke of ten
He'd plan to be at home, for at that hour,
The servants set out tasty food, so then
His evening snack the Marquis would devour.
With stomach satisfied, he'd yawn again,
Then as eleven strokes rang in the tower,
Stretched in his massive bed he'd seek his rest
And very soon be snoring with the best.

*The Marquis has a son and a daughter, Leonor; she lives a
sheltered life, meeting only the aristocracy and the clergy. Sanfuentes describes her life:*

There Leonor lived calm and satisfied
In such a tranquil, mystic life for years
Although she'd reached the age of many a bride,—
The age when dawning love brings sighs and tears
Even to virtuous girls with hearts untried.

While warned of man's deceit and filled with fears,
She now decides to throw off all pretence
And for herself seek love's experience.

When reaching such an age, each woman feels
A vague uncertainty when rests her eyes
On any dove that in the heavens wheels
And to his mate, swiftly descending, flies.
So she loves boys, yet naught of love reveals,
Surrendering to their charms only in sighs.
Yet at her mirror, blushes will confess
She has discovered her own loveliness.

Now she takes special care to see each shoe
So neatly fits her foot; and that her shawl
Drapes from her shoulder, giving lovely view.
Her fan she flips and shuts in sight of all.
When wearing hat that's pretty and that's new,
She notes that smoothly from it her curls fall.
Yet after all this lively agitation
Come pensive moments and preoccupation.

But Leonor loved no one. Reader, dream
Not so, or you will be deceived! Although
Of Counts, Lords, Marquises she'd met the cream,
She'd found them all uninteresting, slow.
And should she see plebian youths, she'd deem
Them utterly beneath her rank, and low.
Brought up with such ideas and estimation,
Like mud would she regard those of that station.

Yet she was sure something was lacking quite:
With happiness her heart could never beat.
On what she missed, she could not set her sight,
For like tough bronze, she thought herself complete.
At thought of such perfection, in great fright

Her priest confessor often would repeat:
"I've never seen girl holier than this one.
She's missed her calling if she's not a nun."

As far as I'm concerned, I must reveal,
Dear Reader, I see things in other light.
A Frenchman wise who knew how women feel
Made this remark that experience proves is right.
La Bruyère was his name; his words I steal
Which in my Spanish verse I thus indite:
"A woman's claim of coldness naught implies
Save that no man has caused her temperature to rise."

The father brings an old soldier, Antonio Gonzaga, to the house. On his staff is young Captain Eulogio, of humble origin, with whom Leonor falls in love after he has sung to the accompaniment of his guitar and they have danced together.

The remaining cantos tells the story of their ill-starred love. After their secret marriage is discovered, the plebian captain is imprisoned, while the aristocratic Leonor is forced to stay in a convent. She hangs herself by a bell rope and the mournfull tolling of the bell brings the nuns to discover her dead body.

                                                    W.K.J.

MARIANO RAMALLO
1817-1865   Bolivia

Ramallo combined the professions of lawyer, journalist, teacher and politician, while writing Romantic poetry on the side, and translating Byron and some of the French Romanticists. He was banished from La Paz following the publication of his "Elegía" (Elegy) to the exiled General Ballivián. Besides such long poems as "A mi hiji Natalia" (To My Daughter Natalia) and "Epitalamio de los bardos" (The Poets' Wedding Song), he is remembered for his "Una impresión al pie de Illimani" (Impressions at the Foot of Illimani), referring to the snow-capped cone outside La Paz.

IMPRESSIONS AT THE FOOT OF ILLIMANI

Long our winding track has led
By fair Chuquiapu's bed.
But though beautiful the scene,
   This can never be our way;
What we sought, we have not seen;
   We have lost another day,
For our path grows dark and steep,
And the river still and deep.

Still press onward, up the stream,
Where our road may plainer seem,
Round the column of grey rock
As we turn with breathless shock,
Flashes on us, lone and high
Illimani in the sky.
His eternal icy crest
   Centuries of snow have driven,
Upward toward the zenith pressed
   Seems the stairway unto Heaven.
But of mortal feet the trace
Never marred that sacred place,
Not the royal eagle's flight
Ever dared to touch that height.

Here is where we longed to tread,
   Here we hail the Andes' King.
Yet the heart recoils in dread,
   And in wild imagining.
Can it be that here we are

Near our goal and yet so far?
Where his brow so radiant glows,
   All illumined with life and joy
Lie unmelted depths of snows
   Rash invaders to destroy;
Wither with an arctic breath,
Clasp in an embrace of death.

No—not such our thoughts shall be.
Not so will we gaze on thee.
Blessing shalt thou be and blessed,
Mightiest giant of the west.
Down thy peak in rock-lined beds
Glide a thousand silvery threads;
Meet and part and meet once more
Till a hundred cataracts pour
All along each lofty wall.
   By their hidden mingling streams,
Bright and nameless flowers fall,
   Such as we behold in dreams.
But what climber from beneath
Dares to pluck the tempting wreath?

Dearer on the slopes below,
   Soars the palm-tree's slender frame;
Brighter the familiar glow
   Pomegranates all in flame.
While the song of forest bird
   Rings upon the perfumed air;
Never yet so gladly heard,
   Or so thrilling sweet as there.

Onward yet—a blissful start
Of fresh gladness in the heart.
Here is something in the scene
Shows where hand of man has been.
Sure some little rustic farm

Nestles in the valley warm.
Here the olives' measured line
Speaks the prompting of design;
And the lemon's silvery bloom
  Clustering near her fruit of gold,
Shows that Art has here found room
  To improve on Nature's mould.

Shall we stroll along the edge
Of this sheltering cedar hedge
  There to find the peasant's cot?
Better fancy who may dwell
In this fair, sequestered cell
  Than perhaps to find them not;
And some crumbling wall to trace
Like a ghost in this bright place.

Day is waning and we may
Here no more in safety stay.
Even as we turn to go,
Night is gathering below,
And his creeping shadow falls
All along the forest walls.
High above, the King of Day
Sheds as yet his lingering ray,
But we would not have the spark
  That our devious path has shown,
Leave us wandering in the dark,
  Haunt of terrors yet unknown.

Just a moment pause to raise
One last lingering wistful gaze
Where on Illimani's height
Blazes yet unfaded light,
Brighter than the glow of noon
Brighter that it fades so soon.
'Tis enough that we have trod

Near the secret haunt of God.
In the infancy of man
So his simple thoughts began.
Older, wiser, yet we will
Keep the heavenly vision still.

Agnes Blake Poor

RAFAEL POMBO
1833-1912   Colombia

One of Colombia's great Romanticists, Rafael Pombo
was noted for his love of nature and melancholic spirit.
He was passionately involved in politics, and traveled on
diplomatic missions to the United States where he
learned English so well that he first wrote the sonnet
"Our Madonna at Home" in that language. His best
known poems are "A Bolívar" (To Bolívar) and "Niágara" (At Niagara), part of which is translated here.

AT NIAGARA

Again I see thee!—once again I know
Mine oldtime witchery as in years gone by,
Titan of grace, white, fascinating, vast,
Sultan of torrents, calm in matchless power;
Eternally the same, Niagara!
Eternal in thine ecstasy, awake
In thy tremendous sway,—unwearying
Ever of thyself, as man untired
Of gazing upon thee.—How couldst thou tire?
Beauty, alive forever, acts and lives
In purity and cannot fail!—O thou,
The perfect daughter without human touch
Of His high Fiat, that perpetuates
The laws inviolable in their course,—

Fond sister of the skies, the light, the air!—
Guest unexpelled of Eden that we lost
Thy beauty is creation's constant work,
Transcending even its high Creator's breath.
Here, something tells us, here is God! . . .

From the globe's confines ultimate, men come
To visit thee, to raise themselves on high
With contemplation of thy matchless charms.
A thousand tongues along thy banks acclaim
In Thee the grandeur of their God, the boast
Of nature's purest triumph over all.
Heredia came and paid his tribute here,
Hailing Niagara in his soul, in dread
More of himself than thee, for all thy floods!
The Anglo-Saxon cyclops quick to prove
Unto the world that he is lord of thee,
Spans thy great gorges with his airy bridge,
Embracing thee as with an iron hand,
In sign that man (the insect of the hour,
The dizzying hour!) proclaims his reign abroad!
'Tis heaven herself laid down beneath thy feet
These angel pillows colored for the spheres;
And for one bridge, hers are a thousand round,—
To art of man opposing that of heaven,
Hangs tremulous here, as though the smile of peace
Amid the heavy breathings about death,
Her tranquil bow amidst the wild abyss!

Sufficing glory is thy ceaseless spring
Of beauties, thou art shrine perpetual
Of man's deep wonder. What can I for thee,
Save but to add my little name to thine?
I am the trifling shadow at the gates,
A day to hover silent, a light breath
In silence moving through thine icy mist—
If to the surge volcanic of thy breast

The earth, thy trembling cradle, hears the wind
Groan through its stony hollows in reply,—
I know not, for my heart is hushed, nor stirs
Within my soul the ardent flame of song.
But what is this to thee, who, changelessly
Assert'st thy majesty and pomp,—while I
In years of exile stand, and weariness
Of soul? Today I gaze on thee with eyes
Of sadness, Amphitheatre divine!—
Where 'mid thy gusts and mists, eternal strifes
Of crags and whirlpools rage. In me there stirs
No combat; nay, thy presence, rather than
Thy lofty beauty wakes my wonderment,
Inspires prostration,—yea, and chills my soul!
Thy waters seem like the beginning world
That leaps from out the hand of the Divine,
Inaugurating its eternal course
Throughout the ether deeps! Thou art like heaven
That bends upon the earth amid thy clouds
Half-veiling here the majesty of God.
Forever new and brilliant in thy sweep;
Forever fertile, and magnificent,
The vital spring of Mother Nature's breasts
Shining with healthful savors,—thou dost show
Thy grandeur in thy fall, and raisest high
From thine abyss the hymn of praise and life.
But oh! to me life is a sarcasm now;
My world has finished, and my soul is dead;
In my desire to sing speaks but the rime
Of hate, or De profundis as of death.
It is to lighten weary days,
    Niagara, my steps I hither press;
To turn indifferent shoulders to thy ways,
My brows immersed amid thine icy sprays,
    Rendering back to thee—forgetfulness.

                                        Thomas Walsh

"PLÁCIDO"
1809-1844   Cuba

Third among the great poets of Cuba, after Heredia and
Milanés, was Diego Gabriel de la Concepción Valdés,
the self-taught son of a Spanish dancer and a mulatto
hairdresser. The reading of Martínez de la Rosa's poetry was a revelation to him; he started writing eight-
eenth-century-style verse under the pen name of "Plácido," which he got from a druggist who encouraged his
literary ambitions. Classical poetry like his sonnet to
Greece was followed by pictures of native life and love
lyrics.

Suspected by the Spanish authorities when the slaves
planned an uprising in 1844, he was jailed and sentenced to be shot. On the eve of his execution, Plácido
composed a number of moving poems, "Plegaria a Dios"
(A Prayer to God), famous for its form and its deep
feeling, and "Adiós, Mamá" (Farewell to My Mother).
He was reciting "Himno a la Libertad" (Hymn to Liberty) on his way to execution. Though suppressed by
the Governor, these poems were widely circulated among
his fellow citizens.

GREECE

Like waves upon the ocean's fitful deep
Is Liberty, rolling her billows o'er
One favored land, while from another shore
Her ebbing waters backward slowly creep.
Greece once held wisdom to her fostering breast;
Her Alexander died; a feebler race
Saw the fierce Turk her arts and laws efface,—
The land of gods by godless men oppressed!
She comes again to fill the historian's page.

But while from Navarino's sands her eyes
See, eddying round the Othman navies, rise
The flames symbolic of her glorious age,
If Greece renews her old triumphant strains,
Unhappy Poland waits to wear her broken chains.

H. W. Hurlbut

FAREWELL TO MY MOTHER

The appointed lot has come upon me, mother,
The mournful ending of my years of strife;
The changing world I leave, and to another,
In blood and terror goes my spirit's life.
But thou, grief-stricken, cease thy mortal weeping,
And let thy soul her wonted peace regain;
I fall for right, and thoughts of thee are sweeping
Across my lyre, to wake its dying strain,—
A strain of joy and gladness, free, unfailing,
All-glorious and holy, pure, divine,
And innocent, unconscious as the wailing
I uttered at my birth; and I resign,
Even now, my life; even now, descending slowly,
Faith's mantle folds me to my slumbers holy.
Mother, farewell! God keep thee, and forever!

H. W. Hurlbut

HYMN TO LIBERTY

Oh, Liberty! I wait for thee
    To break this chain and dungeon bar;
    I hear thy spirit calling me
        Deep in the frozen North, afar,
With voice like God's, and visage like a star.

Long cradled by the mountain wind,
  Thy mates the eagle and the storm,
Arise! and from thy brow unbind
  The wreath that gives its starry form,
And smite the strength that would thy grace deform!

Yes, Liberty! thy dawning light,
  Obscured by dungeon bars, shall cast
Its splendor on the breaking night,
  And tyrants, flying pale and fast,
Shall tremble at thy gaze and stand aghast!

Anonymous, from the New York Tribune, *1844*

JOSÉ JACINTO MILANÉS Y FUENTES
1814-1863   Cuba

Milanés' career as a poet, begun at the age of twenty-three, lasted only seven years before he became insane. During that brief period, he was especially popular with women because of his sentimental melancholy and his praise of feminine capabilities, as in "A mi esposa" (To My Wife). By setting his poems within the tropical beauty of the Cuban landscape, he demonstrated the poetic value of local color to later writers. His failing was that he attempted to preach morality through his poems, as in "El Expósito" (The Foundling), in which he implied that illegitimate children grow up to be cruel and vicious. Milanés also wrote a Romantic drama, *El conde Alarcos* (Count Alarcos, 1838). In addition to his lyrical gift, he had the imagination that Plácido lacked.

TO MY WIFE

Not with mere frenzied, self-devouring passion
    Doest thou, beloved, thy lover bard inspire;
Love sweet is virtue, and as the skies serene,
    Draws me on to thee with heavenly desire.

Love that is peace, and pleasure, and salvation,
    Leaving brows unfurrowed, and a heart at rest
Only with sweet cares and amorous complaints
    Stirring the calm rapture of my happy breast.

Rich in priceless memories and in hopes divine
    With smiles for every cradle, tears for every tomb,
Joyful adorations in the early morn,
    Blessed thoughts when moonbeams break the twilight gloom.

Love that seeks the conquest of the great and true,
    Gazing on the artist, turning from the gold,
Seeing life's truest riches by the crowd foregone,
    While they vainly grasp at what the few withhold.

This wondrous love, all sweetness and all patience,
    Sister of pure Shame, twin-child of Modesty,
The cold world, sense-fettered, mocks at and denies,
    As a sick enthusiast's idle fantasy.

But thou knowest, darling, in thy heart serene,
    Holy tears are truer than the scoffing smile;
Be thy love my glory, my poetry thy truth,
    Let the sneering crowd my lofty faith revile!

Well I know how fatal, when the doubting soul
    Leaves Love's Eden home to dwell alone with grief;
For in woman's heart the pure heaven lingers,
    Bearing fruit of Loving, Feeling, and Belief.

H. W. Hurlbut

JOAQUÍN LORENZO LUACES
1827-1867   Cuba

Luaces ranked high among Cuban revolutionists and
poets. Many of his poems appeared in *Revista de la
Habana*, including his "Oda a Fields" (Ode to Fields,
1859), honoring the engineer who promoted the first
submarine cable between America and Europe. His
most highly praised poem, however, was "La salida
del cafetal" (Leaving the Coffee Plantation, 1855),
which is considered one of Cuba's best sonnets.

LEAVING THE COFFEE
PLANTATION

The fiery saddle horse of Camaguey
  Froths and champs on the silver bridle bit;
  Full of noble ardor and the strength of it,
His muscled mouth flings forth a ringing neigh;
His arching neck, his stamping hoofs, betray
  His fervent zeal; his rolling eye is lit
  With fire; his nostrils flare, eager to quit
The quiet spot and gallop far away.

At last my darling mounts the mettled steed,
  Into the stirrup puts her dainty shoe,
Raises the snapping whip—of which no need,
  For he, bow-taut, with straining thew
And flying tail, gallops with rushing speed
  And bears his haughty burden out of view.

Read Bain and W.K.J.

JUAN GUALBERTO PADILLA
1829-1896   Puerto Rico

Dr. Padilla, besides practicing medicine, wrote many
kinds and styles of poetry, frequently under the pen
name of "El Caribe." He was noted for the purity of
his Castilian, whether in humor and satire or in his Romantic poems of the East, which were influenced by
Victor Hugo's *Les Orientales*. Padilla was a member of
a group of writers who met to criticize each other's
work. When one of the members, José Gautier Benítez,
died of tuberculosis at the age of thirty, Padilla wrote a
funeral dirge for him that was to be one of his greatest
poems. Part of the dirge is translated here.

FUNERAL DIRGE FOR GAUTIER BENÍTEZ

Here beside your funeral bier
    Where all that's left of you still lies,
    Tears on tears fall from my eyes;
Tears from my lute, too, fall clear.
I weep for your youth so dear,
    For your life so fleeting, brief;
    Your song's accent strange—my grief
Perished echoes past avail,
Poor inspired, lost nightingale,
    Fate-doomed at your song's debut.

Superb your too early dawn
    There where lofty summits glow,
    Announcing that we soon should know
That a radiant sun was born—
Borincano's Song-God you
More pathetic than we knew—
Luminary swung to view.

Now you're gone just as suns go
Amid red clouds' most gorgeous glow
     They drop, gigantic down the deep.

A noble woman yesterday
     Who cradled you and faithfully
     Crowned this heroic head we see
With crown the genius wears alway.
Her sobbing here proclaims today
Her grief by this, your burial place
     While bitterly she thinks a space
That what devoured this brow's glad hour
Was inspiration's burning power,
     Its incandescent flame that kills.

Proud Poet of my Fatherland
     Who from soul deeps and chastity
Brought to us a world and grand
     Of enchanted poesie,
When within your sombre tomb
     You hear your lovely songs of old—
     In echoing concerts manifold
     By your own people voiced and free—
You will never die, you'll learn
While our island hearth-fires burn.

Murmuring sonorously
     They'll be messengers and true
Bringing laurels ceaselessly
     With our tears that fall like dew
May they shelter you from cold;
     May they lull your long, long sleep;
History will rich enfold
Eternal, glorious, we know
You singer of Puerto Rico.

Anonymous

JOSÉ GAUTIER BENÍTEZ
1851-1880   Puerto Rico

The most popular Puerto Rican poet of the nineteenth
century was Gautier Benítez who, under the influence
of the Spanish poet Bécquer, interpreted the soul of the
women of his island. He was the poet of the heart
whose verses gave full expression to his emotions and
inspired many followers. He showed his patriotism in
many subjective poems about Puerto Rico's beauty and
customs, but he disregarded its political aspects. With
his death, Puerto Rico's Romantic period came to an
end.

PUERTO RICO

Boriquen, name so pleasant to the mind,
Like some sweet memory of a love profound!
Garden of beauty, where can mortals find
Its equal even where lovely spots abound?

Pearl that the sea from deep shellpile has snatched
Amid the pounding of its pleasant waves,
By sleepy heron in white spume unmatched,
You doze as foamy tide your shoreline laves.
Island bedecked by palm fronds, in the breeze
Tossing a kiss afar across the seas.

You seem to one arriving on your soil
A lovely mystic city made of foam,
Fantastic haven far removed from toil
That mermaids sporting near regard as home.

A garden of enchantment, fountains playing
Above the azure sea that round you swirls,

A vase of many colored flowers swaying
Amid the foam and coral, scents and pearls.

You who at dusk, spilling your colors, came
In all the hues of brilliant sunset dressed,
Filling the ocean full of floating flame
Till the last rays of sun died in the west.
You who supply the air I breathe each day
Inspiring my spontaneous song of praise,
Accept the adoring tribute of my lay
That as your inspired poet to you I raise!

Some lovely bit of earth, hurled high in air
By fearful cataclysm from the western shore
Fell to the sea to make this island fair.

But from yon continent so vast, came naught
Of pomp or terror to your lovely land,—
Only its bounteous beauty has been brought.

Yet from those mountains no blood-thirsty beast
Like hungry tiger, lion, or jaguar
Or coiling boa came to your calm east,

Upon your hill tops to maintain their lair;
Nor yet within your limpid rivers swim
Grim alligators for us to beware.

Nor do your mountains fill with sudden roar
And, shaken to their deep foundations, creak,
With such hoarse breathing as from distant shore
From Cotopaxi and Orizaba's peak.

No fierce Niagara's torrent breaks your hush
With cataracts that heavenward toss their mist
While Iris, magic painter, by her brush,
Its shining flanks of gleaming silver kissed

With gold and carmine, purple and topaze.
Within your realm the condor, king of space,
To watch his flight no crystal mirror has.

However, many treasures you possess:
Fertile savannahs grow the sugar cane,
A lake of honey that your people bless,
Waving like blowing feathers or like grain

And the tall palm trees, swaying in the air
Within its hanging jar holds treasure trove,
Pure liquid, like an aerial fountain there.

Upon the broad slopes of your rising hills,
Home of the cedar and the pendola,
Your sturdy farmer, coffee bushes tills,
Where green and crimson berries bend each bow
Till on the ground its precious crop it spills.

But Ah, what pure delight each night discloses
In which the happy heart its passion sings
Amid a garden of lilies and of roses,
Urged into bloom by murmuring silver springs!
Your turtle doves so softly make complaint
With sorrowing sighs that can be heard at times;
The voice of toupicals and doves sound faint
From their shy nests amid the flowering limes.
My Island, what delights within your arms
Where peaceful, tender, happy folks abide,
And your whole inner world receives its charms
From the sweet influence of your world outside.

                                                      W.K.J.

MANUEL ACUÑA
1849-1873   Mexico

Acuña, a follower of the Spanish Romantic poets Es-
pronceda and Campoamor, actually studied medicine,
thus acquiring a scientific and skeptical viewpoint that
clashed with his early Roman Catholic training. In philosophy he was a Positivist, and in politics he practiced
his ideas of liberalism. However, it was for his lyric
power and Romantic temperament, tending at times
toward morbid emotionalism, that he was beloved by
his contemporaries. His "Ante un cadáver" (Before a
Corpse) is a mixture of Romanticism and scientific materialism. His famous "Nocturno a Rosario" (Nocturn
to Rosario), written shortly before his suicide, was inspired by his love for Rosario de la Peña (1847–1924), a
Romantic figure in Mexican literature; however, they
were not engaged, as is implied in the poem, and his
friends acquitted her of blame for his suicide.

NOCTURN TO ROSARIO

Well, then, I must tell thee
How much I adore thee,
Tell thee that I love thee
With all of my heart;
That I suffer so deeply
And often deplore thee.
I can wait thee no longer,
And with tears I implore thee.
Oh, let not my dreams, dear,
Forever depart!

I would that thou knowest
How long I have suffered;
I languish and weaken,

Deprived thus of sleep.
The hopes that I cherished
Alas, have all perished;
My long nights are gloomy,
So dark and so sombre
That I know not my future
Save that I must weep.

At night on my pillow
I place my sad forehead
In hopes I may journey
To some place less drear.
Long and far do I travel;
At the end of the journey
Does my Mother's face greet me,
Then to nothingness fades;
And there in her place
Does thy dear self appear.

I know that thy kisses
Are not mine to cherish.
I know that thy vision
Finds no place for me.
Yet I love thee with frenzy,
And ardent delirium;
I bless thy disdain and
Adore thy indifference.
The more thou dost scorn me,
The more I love thee.

At times I am tempted
To bid thee forever
Farewell, and erase thee
And thy form from my soul.
But since this would be futile
And my heart can't forget thee,
What wilt thou, since never

Can I blot out thy charm?
Should I smother my heart, then,
Or tear it out whole?

I had built thee a temple,
A shrine for thy presence,
A candle I'd lighted
To burn at thy shrine.
The sun would be gleaming
Behind the far belfry;
The torches would sparkle
With the incense smoke rising,
A welcoming dwelling
For your heart and mine.

What could be more charming
Than such life together,
United forever,
And loving each other?
You would love me so deeply,
I satisfied, too,
One soul shared between us,
And one body would do;
And in our midst, living
Like God, my dear Mother.

Imagine the beauty
And radiant hours!
How sweet would the journey
Across the world be!
That was my ambition,
My promised one, holy,
And I wandered in madness
With my soul full of flowers,
With my thoughts fixed on goodness,
For thee, just for thee.

God knows how my dream world
Was filled by this fancy,
My hopes and my longings,
My bliss and delight.
God knows that to nothing
Was my effort extended
Excepting to love thee
In that home of my mind,
The one that I knew best,
Where I first saw the light.

Such was my aspiration,
But to its attainment
A chasm opposes,
Whose depth none can tell.
So goodbye, dear, forever,
Oh, love, of my loving,
Oh, light of my darkness,
Perfume of my flowers,
Of my verse, inspiration,
To my youth, this farewell!

W.K.J.

JUAN ZORRILLA DE SAN MARTÍN
1855-1931   Uruguay

Zorrilla spent his long life in the service of his country
as a lawyer and a diplomat. Also a poet, he determined
to write an epic, *Tabaré* (1888), recording the struggle
of Uruguay's original inhabitants, the fierce Charrúas,
against the Spanish. As a devout Catholic, he saw God
on the side of the Spanish. Instead of the traditional
epic meter of Ercilla's *La Araucana*, Zorrilla used Bécquer's lyric stanza of seven and eleven syllables for much
of his poem. Vigor and emotion characterize this story
about a mestizo torn between his Indian heritage and

his Christian feelings, and further disturbed by his love
for Blanca, the sister of Governor Gonzalo de Orgaz.
The Indian cacique Yamandic takes her away during a
raid. Tabaré rescues her, but while returning her to the
white man's settlement, he is seen by the uncompre-
hending Spaniards who kill him.

TABARÉ

Canto 6

VIII

"An Indian!" one cries.
"Where?" shouts Gonzalo as with rage are riven
His eyes. "Look there! He's entering the woods!"
" 'Tis he! And Blanca, too, I swear to Heaven!"

IX

Dimly between the trees
The form of Tabaré
And in his arms the missing Spanish girl
Is for a moment seen, to fade away.

Weakly are heard her cries
As on his shoulder born,
Then girl and the Charrúa disappear.
Silent the sobs that from her breast were torn.

Noiselessly through the bush
Like ghost pursued by fates
As if driven by some impelling force
That his whole rigid body animates,

Weary and in a daze,
Still for the town he heads,
Leaving behind on the unfeeling ground
A bloody foot print every time he treads.

Gonzalo screams with rage
At glimpse of Tabaré,
And swiftly as an arrow from the bow
He darts with angry joy after his prey.

The clatterings of his armor and his arms
A fearful noise against the tree trunks make;
The echoes seem to leap from bush to bush,
The slumbering forest aisles awake.

After the captain dash
The priest and soldiers, taking up the chase.
Then as the distance stills their swift pursuit,
A heavy, hushed suspense pervades the place.

Suddenly to their ears
There comes a sharp, smothered cry,
And then a moan of pain and anguish breaks
That tense funereal hush of earth and sky . . .

XI

When priests and soldiers came
Upon Gonzalo, in the woods, they found
There, Tabaré, his breast pierced by a sword;
By his own blood enshrouded, on the ground.

And from the grandee's blade
The falling drops were reddening every leaf;
But Tabaré no longer heard the sound
Of Blanca's sobbing moans of bitter grief.

His life was ebbing now,
One shuddering sigh that seemed to be his last,
Then he lay motionless, his limbs outstretched.
Over the Spaniard's face no expression passed.

Silent and motionless,
Gripping his sword, oblivious to the rest

He stared at Blanca's face awash with tears;
He watched as, broken-hearted, to her breast

She clasped the Charrúa's corpse,
And on his dusky features fixed her eyes,—
Lips stilled, lids closed forever now,
Unheeding of her bitter, tremulous cries.

Perhaps before he crossed
The threshold of eternity where he'd abide,
His ears heard Blanca from the distant earth
As softly through her sobs his name she cried.

Never can Tabaré
His dying dream relate
To men of his lost race. Like them, he's gone,
Silent forever, for such is his fate.

They're silent, too.
For them the stretching desert mute shall be,
Still as a tomb abandoned by the dead,
Mouth without tongue, hopeless eternity.

Enveloped in night's shades
The day is dying too, and vague lament
From the far-off horizon comes to us,
Sounds that among the wind-blown trees are spent . . .

As when the shower ends
And winds of tempest cease,
The dripping of the raindrops can be heard,
The only sounds that break the evening peace;
So from that group of men
No single noise was heard,
Save an occasional metallic ring,
When one of those steel-armored soldiers stirred.

But now a moan from Blanca, who still held
In her enfolding arms dead Tabaré,
And then, raising his hand above the two,
The priest in solemn tones began to pray.

W.K.J.

III

DRAMA

ANONYMOUS: RABINAL ACHÍ

Guatemala

The only unquestionably authentic pre-Columbian play still in existence is an anonymous drama-dance from Guatemala, which was dictated in 1859 to Father Carlos Brasseur by an Indian, Bartolo Ziz, who had performed it several years before. Many of its elements are so typically Indian and so foreign to Spanish culture, such as the lengthy repetitions and the pagan sacrifice at the end, that there can be no doubt as to its authenticity. It was published in Spanish in 1862, and performed in Rabinal (Guatemala) to the music of a drum and two trumpets.

The play consists of four parts; in the first three parts, the Champion of the Queché Indians attacks a Rabinal war party and is captured. He is questioned about his reasons for waging war, and he replies that the Rabinal tribe attacked and captured tribute bearers, bringing chocolate. Still he is sentenced to death unless he enlists in the Rabinal army. In the first part, translated here, he is brought to the court of Chief Hobtoh (Five Showers).

THE RABINAL CHAMPION

Chief Five Showers
The Queen (*who does not speak*)
The Rabinal Achí or Champion
Ixok-Mun, servant of Rabinal Achí
The Queché champion
Mother of Feathers, Mother of the Green Birds, fiancée of
    Rabinal Achí
Twelve Yellow Eagles, Twelve Yellow Jaguars, Rabinal warrior
    leaders

Scene: The court of Chief Five Showers

QUECHÉ: I salute you, Chief. I am he who has just reached the entrance of the vast walls of the vast fortress, over which you extend your hands, your shadow. They brought the news of my presence to you. I am a warrior, a champion. Your warrior, your champion, outstanding among champions, Rabinal Achí, came to launch his challenge, his shout in my lips, in my face.

He told me, "I took news of your presence to my governor, my commander within the vast walls, the vast fortress, and the voice of my governor spoke thus: 'Bring this warrior, this champion before me that I may see in his face what a warrior he is, what a champion he is. Warn this warrior, this champion, not to cause uproar or scandal, but to humble himself when he enters these vast walls, this vast fortress.'"

Well, I am a warrior, a champion, and if I must humble myself, here I humble myself. Here is my arrow, here my shield, with which I shall conquer your fate, your lucky day. I shall smite your lower lips and your upper lip, and you will resent it, Oh, Chief. (*He threatens the Chief with his weapons.*)

IXOK-MUN: Warrior, Champion, Man of the Cavek-Queché tribe, do not kill my governor, my commander, Chief Five Showers, in the vast walls, the vast fortress where he is shut in.

QUECHÉ: Have them prepare my bench, my seat, for in my mountains, in my valleys, thus did they honor my fate and my lucky day. There I have my bench, my seat. Shall I remain here in this place exposed to the cold, exposed to the chill? Thus speaks my voice before Heaven and Earth. Heaven and Earth be with you, Chief Five Showers!

CHIEF FIVE SHOWERS: Warrior, Champion, Man of the Cavek-Queché tribe, thanks be to Heaven, thanks be to Earth that you have come to the vast walls, the vast fortress over which I extend my hands, my shadow, I, the Ancient One, Chief Five Shadows. (*From here on, for the sake of brevity, much of this repetition is omitted.*)

Tell us and reveal why you imitated the cry of the Coyote, the wolf, the weasel, beyond the vast walls, to lure out my servants with hopes of receiving rewards of yellow honey for providing food for me, Chief Five Showers? You also captured ten of my followers and would have taken them to the hills and valleys of Queché and there cut their roots, their trunks, if my bravery had not been alert. You seized me, too, and shut me up in a mountain cave and would have cut me down, had not my warrior, my Champion, rescued me by his arrow and his shield. When will you conquer your mad ambitions? Did you not plan to bury us? For that you will pay, I swear. You have said farewell to your mountains, to your valleys and you shall die here under Heaven, on the Earth. Heaven and Earth be with you, man of the Cavek Queché!

QUECHÉ: Chief Five Showers, in truth you have spoken truly. I have done wrong. But despite the ambition of my heart, I have not been able to conquer these beautiful mountains, those beautiful valleys. You spoke thus: "Say farewell to your mountains and your valleys." But I disobeyed, due to the desires of my heart.

If I must die here, then this is what my voice declares: "Now that you are well established within this vast fortress, give me drink, the twelve intoxicating, sweet, refreshing liquors that are drunk before sleeping, within these vast walls. Let me drink them as symbol of my death." So does my voice declare.

FIVE SHOWERS: Warrior, Champion. I hear your voice. I grant your request. Servants, bring my food and my drink as symbols of the death of this Man of Cavek Queché.

SERVANT: It is well, my governor, my commander. I shall give them to this warrior, this Champion.

(*Servants bring in a table loaded with food and drink. The Queché champion samples them disdainfully. He dances before the court. Then he returns and speaks.*)

QUECHÉ: Oh, Chief Five Showers, is this your food and drink? I find nothing to recommend them to my lips. If you could only taste the delicious, refreshing drinks that I enjoy in my mountains, in my valleys! Is this the cup from which you drink? I see here the skull of my ancient father. May you likewise use of the bones of my head. So when my sons come to trade loads of chocolate from my mountains, my valleys, they will say: "Here is the head of my ancient father." And from the bone of my arm, may you make the handle of the calabash of precious metals that will resound through these vast walls. And from my leg bone, may you make a beater for the big drum to shake Heaven in this vast fortress. This also would I have you say: "I shall lend you a wonderful handi-work of my lady so that you may be decorated with it as a supreme symbol of your death."

FIVE SHOWERS: So be it! Servants, bring the labor of my lady to this warrior!

(*A servant gives Queché a kind of cloak in which he wraps himself. He dances before the court, and at each corner, he utters his war cry.*)

QUECHÉ: Now grant me the Mother of Feathers, the Mother of the Green Birds, whose lips have never been desecrated, that I may dance with her, as a supreme symbol of my death under Heaven and on Earth.

FIVE SHOWERS: What do you desire, Man of Cavek Queché? Nevertheless, I grant your request. Servants, bring hither the Mother of the Green Birds.

IXOK-MUN: As you command, my governor (*He brings the Mother of the Green Birds to Queché.*) Here she is, Warrior, Champion. But dare not harm her. Dance with her only in this vast fortress.

(*The warrior greets the Maiden, who remains aloof from him in the dance, with her face toward him, as he moves before her with the shawl. So they circle the court and again pause before the Chief.*)

QUECHÉ: Chief Five Showers, grant me your approval. Here is she whom you gave me as companion. Keep her safely in the vast fortress. Now my voice requests that you lend me your twelve Yellow Eagles, your twelve Yellow Jaguars, armed and with their darts in their hands. Let me have practice in arms with them in the four corners of this vast fortress, as symbol of my death.

FIVE SHOWERS: So says your voice. Very well. I lend you my twelve Yellow Eagles, my twelve Jaguars. Chiefs, go and practice fencing with this warrior.

(The Eagles and Jaguars come out and perform with him a war dance about the court. Then he returns to the throne of the Chief and his family.)

QUECHÉ: Chief, you have granted my wish. Are these your Eagles and your Jaguars? Boast not of them before me. Some can see, some cannot. They have no teeth; they have no claws. If you shall come to see those of my mountains and my valleys, they see clearly. They fight with teeth and claws.

FIVE SHOWERS: We have seen the teeth of the Eagles and the Jaguars of your land. What have you to say of their sight?

QUECHÉ: This have I to say: Grant me three times twenty days that I may bid farewell to my mountains and my valleys; and to find tasty food.

(No one replies to him. He dances and disappears for a moment, then returns and faces the Eagles and Jaguars who stand in the middle of the court around a sort of altar.)

QUECHÉ: Oh, Eagles, Oh, Jaguars! You said: "He has departed." But I did not depart. I only went to say farewell to my mountains and my valleys. Ah, Heaven, Ah, Earth! My will and my bravery have not availed me. Vainly I sought my path under Heaven, on Earth. Oh, my gold, my silver! Alas, my arrows and my shield! Alas my Yaqui mace and axe! Alas, my wreaths and my sandals! Return to my mountains, my valleys! Now is my death necessary. Would I could change with the squirrel, the bird that die on the branch of the tree in their homeland where they see their food.

Oh, Eagles, Oh, Jaguars, come to conclude your duty. May

your teeth, your claws slay me quickly, for I am a champion
come from my mountains, my valleys. May Heaven and Earth
be with you, Oh, Eagles, Oh, Jaguars!

(*The Eagles and the Jaguars surround the Queché Champion. They lay him on the stone of sacrifice to open his breast and take out his heart, as the others dance in a round.*)

End.

W.K.J.

ANONYMOUS: PASSION PLAY OF TZINTZUNTZÁN

Seventeenth Century   Mexico

Typical of the plays written by priests all over the Spanish-speaking New World is this Passion Play of Tzintzuntzán, found on the shores of Lake Patzcuaro early in the twentieth century, but identified as a product of the seventeenth century. Borrowing from the Gospel of St. Luke, it dramatizes the bribery of Judas and the trial of Jesus. Several scenes are translated here.

PASSION PLAY

Act I. Scene 2

The Grand Sanhedrin

AN USHER: Illustrious Sanhedrin, in the outer halls awaits a
man who begs permission to enter. He says his name is Judas
and he claims to be a disciple of the false prophet who has
disturbed the peace of the Holy City.

ANNAS: Conduct the man hither! (*Exit the usher. He returns
with Judas.*)

ANNAS: Disciple of Jesus, what brings you to the Sanhedrin?
Speak, and be not afraid.

JUDAS: My name is Judas. I've never been afraid of anything, I'll have you know! Not of anything! But I learned you were meeting to consider a matter of great importance, so I said to myself: "That's the place to go!" The judges will be wanting to arrest Jesus, but won't dare. All right then, I'll dare, if they pay me enough money." That's why I'm here. I've come to tell you this: "If you want Jesus arrested I'll turn him over to you."

VARIOUS: This poor fellow must be out of his head!

JUDAS: Not me! I'm no more out of my head than any of you. I don't see where my proposition is anything out of the ordinary. Am I the first person who ever betrayed somebody? Certainly not! History will provide you with a thousand examples. Very well, then. Let's see your money and I'll bring you Jesus.

ANNAS: And what security do you offer?

JUDAS: I give you my word of honor.

ANNAS: Your word of honor isn't enough to satisfy us.

JUDAS: You insult me by doubting me.

ANNAS: I wouldn't argue the point. But you are His disciple, and His disciples would let themselves be crucified before they betrayed Him.

JUDAS: The others, maybe, but not me! That's why I'm here, to say to you: "You give and I'll give." Isn't that enough to prove that instead of being His disciple, I'm His enemy?

ANNAS: Perhaps! What's your price? What do you demand?

JUDAS: Thirty pieces of silver.

ANNAS: Thirty?

JUDAS: Do you think my price is high? Does that sound expensive? You have no cause to complain. I ask the price of a slave and I give you a prophet. Read the twenty-first chapter of Exodus and you'll find it says: "If thy ox gore a man servant or a maid servant, thou shalt give unto their master thirty shekels of silver." I'm offering you a bargain. You're going to get Jesus, but instead of a slave, He's a descendant of King David—so He claims. Therefore my price is very reasonable. I tell you, you're getting a bargain.

ANNAS: It's a deal.

JUDAS: When will you give me my money?
ANNAS: When will you deliver Jesus to us?
JUDAS: Tonight.
ANNAS: At what time?
JUDAS: Before the second watch.
ANNAS: Where?
JUDAS: I'll come back here and tell you where you can find Him.
ANNAS: Very well. You may then expect to receive your money.
JUDAS: But no counterfeit coins, mind you!
ANNAS: That comment was unnecessary.
JUDAS: Well—Maybe—but—
ANNAS: Don't you trust us?
JUDAS: I know men.
ANNAS: Enough of discussion! Fulfill your promise and we'll fulfill ours, but woe to you if you deceive us! (*Exit Annas. Judas starts out.*)
CAIAPHAS: Wait! You! How many soldiers do you need to capture your master?
JUDAS: Jesus will not defend Himself.
CAIAPHAS: But what about the disciples?
JUDAS: The disciples will obey the Master. But a few soldiers might come in handy.
CAIAPHAS: It will be arranged.

Act II. Scene II. The Grand Sanhedrin

ONE PRIEST: Let us chastise Him so that henceforth He will not preach against us.
ANOTHER: What does the law say about punishment of rebels?
THIRD: No one may be condemned without being heard.
ONE: We have a law, and according to that law, He must die.
A PRIEST: Away with Him!
THIRD: If He is innocent, let us hear Him. If He is guilty, away with Him! . . .
A PRIEST: Throw Him into jail for life!
THIRD: How can we condemn this just man?

ANOTHER: Kill Him! Away with Him!

NICODEMUS: An injustice is about to be committed here.

ARIMATHEA: That's my opinion, too.

NICODEMUS: I have a mind to defend Him myself.

ARIMATHEA: O my friend! I fear it will be in vain.

CAIAPHAS: Where is that humbug? Listen, false prophet, and reply without evasion. Speak as you did in the synagogue and in Galilee. I detest hypocrites.

NICODEMUS: Caiaphas, this man is accused, but not found guilty. Order your followers to respect Him, to untie Him, to give Him the free right to defend Himself. Otherwise the laws of our Elders will this night be trampled by these lawless people.

ARIMATHEA: I second the request of my friend Nicodemus.

CAIAPHAS: Let us hear the witnesses.

NICODEMUS: Caiaphas, lend a deaf ear to those men. Consider rather whether Jesus, instead of being a false prophet, may not be one sent by God, the voice of the Holy of Holies.

CAIAPHAS: Nothing good will come out of Galilee. So said the Scriptures, and Jesus is from Galilee.

NICODEMUS: Ah, but Jesus was born in Bethlehem, and the Scriptures declare: "From the race of David and from the City of David will come a prophet."

CAIAPHAS: Are you a defender of this man?

NICODEMUS: I am a Pharisee. I respect the Law. If Jesus is to be tried, judge Him by the same judgment as other men. The law must be straight as the Tower of David, firm as the Rock of Sinai.

CAIAPHAS: I asked you, are you His defender, Nicodemus?

NICODEMUS: I neither accuse nor defend. My only wish is that the law may be observed.

CAIAPHAS (to a Witness): Speak! What do you know about this trouble maker?

WITNESS: We have heard him say: "I will destroy the temple made by hand, and in three days I shall build another not made by hand."

CAIAPHAS: Jesus, have you no reply to the charge made against you?

VARIOUS: Yes, let Him speak! Let him defend Himself!

CAIAPHAS: Are you the Christ, the son of the Living God?

JESUS: I am. And you will see the Son of Man seated at the right hand of God and appearing in the clouds of Heaven.

CAIAPHAS: Blasphemy! He blasphemes. What need have we for witnesses? He is a blasphemer!

ALL: He is guilty! Let Him be sentenced to death. Death on the cross! The Cross for him! We have all heard His blasphemy.

ONE PRIEST: Now what have you to say, Nicodemus?

NICODEMUS: Let us flee from this place where the law clutches an assassin's dagger, and where the judges have all the appearances of executioners.

ARIMATHEA: Jesus is lost!

CAIAPHAS: Soldiers, I deliver the culprit over to you. Treat Him as he deserves.

Act III. Scene 1

Home of Pontius Pilate

PILATE: What have you seen, Flavius, that you come so strangely stirred?

FLAVIUS: My lord Pilate, I have seen a man whom all the Olympic gods of Homer cannot equal in majesty.

PILATE: Ha ha ha!

FLAVIUS: You would not laugh if you could have seen Him, if you could have heard Him as I did.

PILATE: Who was this man to whom you give the attributes of . . . God?

FLAVIUS: Jesus of Nazareth.

PILATE: Oh, the Galilean! He who cures man's ills, who gives life to the dead, sight to the blind, and agility to the cripples. By Aesculapius, He is a wonder! After all they tell of Him, provided it isn't a lie, He deserves to have His countrymen

put Him on the horns of the altar! But tell me, Flavius, tell
me what you have seen.

(End of the Mss.)

W.K.J.

ANONYMOUS: OLLANTA

Peru

Early students of New World drama accepted *Ollanta*
as an authentic pre-Columbian play, preserved by oral
tradition, until a Spanish priest, Antonio Valdés, wrote
it down and performed it in Sicuani, near Cuzco, in
1779. Padre Valdés himself made no claims as to its an-
tiquity; his nephew declared it to be the work of his
uncle. Though Indian legends do mention some of the
characters, later scholars found many evidences of Spanish influence, if not of Spanish origin. The mention of
beheading, among a people that punished its malefac-
tors by garrotting, is one. Even its opening lines contradict Garcilaso de la Vega's assertion that frivolous matters had no place in the drama of his people. Also, it
includes a gracioso typical of Spain's Golden Age in the
character Piqui-Chaqui (Flea Foot). Finally, its division
into three acts and its use of the *redondilla* verse form
are unquestionably European. The drama is now believed to be a rewriting of Inca history by an eighteenth-
century European who was not thoroughly familiar with
Inca customs.

OLLANTA

Ollanta, the low-born Inca war leader
Piqui-Chaqui, his servant
Cusi-Coyllur ("Joy Star"), daughter of the Inca

Pachacutic, Emperor of the Incas
Ccoya, his wife
Yma-Sumac ("Very Beautiful") daughter of Cusi and Ollanta

OLLANTA: Piqui-Chaqui, did you see the charming Cusi-Coyllur
at her home?

PIQUI: May the Sun God forbid my going there! Are you not
frightened at the thought that she is the Emperor's daughter?

OLLANTA: Even if she is, I shall love this tender dove. It is my
desire to shelter her alone in my heart.

PIQUI: The Devil has made you mad, or you are losing your
head. There are girls everywhere. You are too much involved
now. Some day the Inca will hear of your plans; he will have
your head cut off and he will throw you into the fire.

OLLANTA: Do not discourage me, or I shall choke you on the
spot. Do not speak to me about it again or I shall tear you to
pieces.

PIQUI: Well, drag me along like a dead dog, but do not say to
me every day and night and year: "Go, Piqui-Chaqui, look for
her!"

*Later grieving for Ollanta, the princess is entertained by a
dancing group of young people. The boys sing to her.*

SONG OF THE BOYS: Tuya, little bird,
                           Do not eat.
                           In my Princess' garden
                           Do not consume
                           The delicious maize.
                           White are the grains;
                           The ears are tender,
                           Of good taste within;
                           Soft are the leaves,
                           The snare for the greedy.
                           In the bird-lime thou shalt stick.
                           I shall cut off thy claws,
                           And thou shalt be caught.
                           Ask of the Piscaca bird

Hanging as a scarecrow.
You see it has been strangled.
Ask for its heart;
Seek its feathers;
You see it has been torn to pieces.
It picked only one little grain.
The same will befall you
If only one grain is missing.

The girls try to comfort the Princess by a deeply melan-cholic yarahui, an authentic Indian verse form.

CHORUS OF GIRLS: Two loving doves mourn and grieve
Sigh and coo on an old, dry tree trunk;
A cruel fate has separated them.
One, it is told, lost its beloved companion
In a stony field; it has never left it alone
    before.
And the dove weeps and laments
When it sees its companion already dead.
And it sings in these words:
"Where are thy eyes, oh, dove,
And where is thy lovely breast,
Thy heart so dear to me,
Thy softly caressing mouth?"
And the abandoned dove, wandering from
    rock to rock,
Calling out in tears, flies hither and thither,
Ever asking: "My heart, where art thou?"
Thus speaking, it flutters,
And one morning it sinks down dead.

Finally Ollanta asks the Inca for permission to marry the Princess. Angry at such presumption from a commoner, the Inca scornfully refuses his requests. In the most powerful scene of the drama, Ollanta turns his back on his emperor, who declared him a rebel.

OLLANTA: Oh, Ollanta, Ollanta, thus does the Emperor expose thee to the scorn of all the land in return for the many services that thou hast rendered! O Cusi-Coyllur, my love, today have I lost thee. I have brought thee to destruction, O princess. O my dove! O Cuzco, O beautiful city, from today on, in the future, I shall be an enemy, an enemy who will cruelly tear open thy bosom, to cast to the vultures thy heart, this tyrant, thy Inca. Persuading the tribe of the Antis, and seducing my countrymen, I shall bring many, many thousands, armed with shields. On the hill of Sacsahuamán thou wilt perceive my warriors like a cloud. Then the flames will rise; thou wilt sleep in blood and thy Inca at my feet. Then shall he learn whether the valleys will fail me, whether thou still hast a voice. "By no means can I give her to thee," he said to me, speaking of his daughter. And then this word also escaped him: "But she could not be for thee," he said, terribly enraged, as I besought him on my knees. He is Emperor because I am here; everyone knows that. Now let happen what may!

In the last act, the rebel Ollanta is at first successful. Then he is betrayed and captured. However, to provide a happy ending, Ollanta is pardoned by the new Inca. Cusi-Coyllur, imprisoned because she broke her vows as a Virgin of the Sun, is freed along with her daughter, and the chief characters are married.

Translation adapted from Elijah C. Hills

JUANA INÉS DE LA CRUZ
1648-1695   Mexico

The greatest woman writer of the Spanish-speaking New World was the Mexican "Tenth Muse," Sister Juana, of Jerónimo. While best known as a poet of the Baroque period, she also wrote plays, both by herself and in collaboration with the priest Juan de Guevara. One play entirely her own, done at the request of her patroness,

the wife of New Spain's Viceroy, was the mystic *Divino
Narciso* (The Divine Narcissus), written around 1680
and based on the Greek myth. This one-act play was
preceded, as usual, by a *loa*, one of the sixteen that she
wrote. These curtain raisers were usually brief and addressed to the audience. In this case, the subject is the
conversion of the Indians and the characters are allegor-
ical figures. Christian precepts are set forth, not only in
the versified *loa* translated here in prose and partly ab-
breviated, but also in the *auto* that followed. Humor is
provided through Occidente, the *galán* or juvenile, by
his ignorance of the Christian religion.

LOA TO THE DIVINE NARCISSUS

Characters

The West, a young Indian prince
America, an Indian princess
Religion, a Spanish lady
Christian Zeal, a Spanish governor
Indians, musicians, Spanish soldiers, etc.

Enter West, wearing a crown, and beside him, America, an
attractive Indian girl, wearing native costume. Before them
some Indian men and women dance the *Tocotín*, in their
feathers and with drums and jangles. Others provide the
music.

MEN MUSICIANS: Mexican nobles, whose ancient race originated
from the clear light of the sun, since this is the happy day in
which your greatest relic is venerated, come dressed in your
noblest garb, and combining joy and devotion, in festive
pomp worship the great god of Harvest.

WOMEN MUSICIANS: Since the abundance of the fields is due to
him who makes them fertile, it is fitting to bring the first
fruits of the new crops to him who made them possible. From
your veins offer the best blood that it may mingle in his honor

and in festive pomp worship the great god of Harvest. (*West and America take their seats and the music ends.*)

WEST: Of all the gods we worship, whose number in our famous city of Mexico exceeds two thousand, the greatest in my opinion is the great god of Harvest.

AMERICA: You are right, since he is the subsistence of our monarchy through the bounty of his fruits. Since from him comes the basis of our living, we consider him greatest. What good would it do for America to be rich in the gold of the mines, if the ground were too sterile for abundant harvests? However his gifts are not limited to our bodily sustenance. Making spiritual food of his flesh, purified of corporeal imperfection, he cleanses the stains of our souls. And so, faithfully worshipping him, let all repeat with me:

THEY AND THE MUSICIANS: In festive pomp worship the great god of Harvest.

(*The Indians exit, dancing. Enter Christian Religion, in the guise of a Spanish Lady, and Christian Zeal, as a Captain General in armor, followed by Spanish soldiers. They pause almost in the wings.*)

RELIGION: Since you are Christian Zeal, how can you control your wrath seeing Idolatry, in ignorance of Christian religion, worshiping a heathengod, with all her superstitious rites?

ZEAL: Religion, be not so swift to complain at my failure or grumble at my delay. My arm is already raised with the naked sword that I wear to avenge you. Step to one side until I make amends for the slight toward you. (*West and America dance onto the stage with the Musicians.*)

MUSICIANS: In festive pomp worship the great god of Harvest.

ZEAL: Here they come! Now I shall face them.

RELIGION: I'll accompany you because pity impels me to reach them before your fury overtakes them. I shall first invite them peaceably to accept my worship.

ZEAL: Then let's draw nearer, since they are engrossed in their stupid rites.

MUSICIANS: In festive pomp worship the great god of Harvest.

(Zeal and Religion step out onto the stage.)

RELIGION: O powerful West and beautiful and rich America, who live so miserably among those very riches, abandon your profane worship to which the devil incites you. Open your eyes. Open your eyes. Follow the true doctrine that my love offers you.

WEST: What unknown people are these I look upon, O Heavens, who want to interrupt the course of my joy?

AMERICA: What never-before-seen nation seeks to oppose the privileges of my ancient power?

WEST: O strange beauty, O foreign woman, tell me who you are who comes to interfere with my delights!

RELIGION: I am the Christian Religion and I intend that your lands and your people shall worship me.

WEST: You ask a strange favor.

AMERICA: What you seek is madness.

WEST: You would achieve an impossibility.

AMERICA: No doubt she's crazy. Let her alone, and on with our worship!

MUSICIANS: In festive pomp worship the great god of Harvest.

ZEAL: What's this, barbaric West? And you, blind Idolatry? Do you so scorn my beloved wife, Religion? Then realize that you have reached the limits of your evil. God will not permit you to persist in your sins. He sends me to punish you.

WEST: Who are you whose sight strikes terror in me?

ZEAL: I am Christian Zeal. Are you amazed that when your excesses bring scorn on Religion, Heaven will move to avenge her and punish your daring? I am God's minister. Observing that your tyranny has gone beyond bounds and weary of seeing you so long in error, God sends me to punish you. And this armed host with arrows and glittering steel are ministers of His anger and instruments of His wrath.

WEST: What god, what error, what punishment are you talking about? I do not understand your words, nor have I any idea who you are, who dares with such insistence to prevent my people from their proper worship as they proclaim:

MUSICIANS: In festive pomp worship the great god of Harvest.

AMERICA: Barbarian, madman, who blindly and with incomprehensible words seeks to disturb the calm that in serene peace we are enjoying, cease your efforts, unless you wish to be reduced to ashes that even the winds will be unable to find. And you, my husband, (*To West.*) and you, my subjects, close ears and eyes and give no heed to their fantasy. Let us continue our worship without permitting proud upstart nations to intrude or interrupt.

MUSICIANS: In festive pomp worship the great god of Harvest.

ZEAL: Since haughtily you scorn our first peaceful proposal, you shall suffer the second, frightful war. (*Drums and trumpets sound.*)

WEST: What abortion is this that Heaven sends against me? What weapons that my eyes have never before held? Ho, guards! Soldiers, discharge your arrows always kept ready!

AMERICA: What thunderbolts does Heaven direct against me? What fierce balls of burning lead fall like hail? What monstrous centaurs battle against my people?

VOICES: To arms! To arms! Fight! (*Trumpets blow. Shouts.*) Long live Spain! Long live her king! (*The battle is joined with Indians and Spanish soldiers entering and leaving, till finally the Indians retreat, pursued by the Spaniards, with West retreating from Religion, and America fleeing from Zeal.*)

RELIGION: Surrender, haughty West!

WEST: I must! But I am conquered by your force and not your words.

ZEAL: Die! Die, intrepid America!

RELIGION: Wait! Do not kill her; I need her alive.

ZEAL: Would you defend her when she offended you?

RELIGION: It was your duty to conquer her; my pity compels me to spare her life. You conquered her by force; but with soft persuasion I must appeal to her reason.

ZEAL: Surely you saw how stubbornly and blindly they denied your worship. Is it not just that all of them should die?

RELIGION: Speak not of justice, Zeal. Spare them! My gentle nature does not seek their death. I'd rather that they be converted and live.

AMERICA: If you beg him not to kill me and you show your compassion only because you hope to conquer my pride, with intellectual weapons, as earlier you used force, I tell you that you will fail. Though as a captive I may lament my lost liberty, yet my will, still free, will even more fervently worship my gods.

WEST: I told you that I was subdued by force, but now I say there is no force nor violence that can prevent the free operations of my will. Though I lament as a captive, you cannot prevent my saying from the bottom of my heart that I adore the god of Harvest.

RELIGION: I do not use force, but rather affection. Who is this god that you adore?

WEST: The god that gives fertility to the fruit-producing fields. The one to whom the heavens bow and whom the rains obey. In short, the god that cleanses us of sins and gives us food. Could there be a more benigned deity that provides more blessings than those I named?

RELIGION: God help me! What copies and caricatures of our sacred truth these lies are! (Aside.) O crafty serpent, how far will your trickery imitate the holy marvels of God! Well, with your own deceit, if God instructs my tongue, I shall convince her.

AMERICA: No wonder you are silenced! You see there is no other god than ours who reveals his works to benefit mankind.

RELIGION: Listen, blind Idolatry! And you, haughty West, hear what my voice proclaims. Your happiness depends on how well you heed my words. These miracles that you relate, these prodigies you mention, attributing them to your false deity, are the works of the true God and the fruits of His wisdom. If the flowering fields are fertile, if the seeds grow, and the rains fall, that is the work of His right hand.

AMERICA: Well, tell me, is yours a god of rare and exquisite material? And was he offered a sacrifice of blood? Is he the seed that provides our sustenance?

RELIGION: I say His infinite Majesty is not material. But His blessed humanity, placed bloodless on the Holy Sacrament of the Mass in showy splendor uses the seed of the wheat which is converted into his flesh and his blood; and this blood that, within the chalice, is the blood offered before the cross, innocent, pure and clear, was the world's redemption.

AMERICA: Since I yearn to believe this unheard-of thing, tell me: Will this deity that you so lovingly describe, be willing to give me food like that which I adore?

RELIGION: Yes, his wisdom dwells for this purpose among men.

AMERICA: And may I see this god to be convinced?

WEST: And so that once and for all she will desist from this theme?

RELIGION: Yes, you will see, once you are washed in the crystal fountain of baptism.

WEST: I know that before I approach a bountiful table I must wash. That has been my ancient custom.

ZEAL: That is not the sort of washing your stains require.

WEST: What, then?

RELIGION: That of a sacrament by virtue of whose living water you shall be cleansed of sin.

AMERICA: Since you give me so many details so fast, I cannot understand. I'd like to hear them more extensively, since divine inspiration moves me to want to learn them.

WEST: Me, too. And I'd like to know of the life and death of that great god that you affirm is in the bread.

RELIGION: Come on, then, and in a metaphoric idea, garbed in rhetorical colors, visible to the eye, I'll show it all to you, because I realize that you incline to visible objects, rather than to those that faith reveals through the ear. And so it is necessary that you make use of eyes so that through them you may receive the faith.

WEST: That's right. I'd rather see than have you tell me.

RELIGION: Come, then!

ZEAL: Religion, tell me, in what form did you decide to represent these mysteries?

RELIGION: In the allegory of a one act play do I intend to make them visible, so that by means of that *auto* she may be influenced and West may learn all he seeks to know.

ZEAL: And what will you call this *auto* that embodies your allegories?

RELIGION: *The Divine Narcissus*, because if that unfortunate youth had an idol that he adored in so strange a way, in which the devil feigned the mighty mystery of the Holy Eucharist, know that here also amid these heathen are there signs of a mighty marvel.

ZEAL: Where will it be performed?

RELIGION: In the royal city of Madrid, which is the center of Faith and the regal seat of the Catholic Monarchs to whom the Indies are indebted for the light of Evangelism that burns in the west.

ZEAL: Does it not seem inappropriate to write in Mexico for a performance in Madrid?

RELIGION: It is not unusual to produce something in one place for use elsewhere. Besides, this was not the whim of the one who wrote it, but rather an act of obedience, though a noble lady's request may not be completely carried out. And so this play, rustic perhaps and unpolished, is the result of an order and not the product of daring.

ZEAL: Then tell me, Religion, since you brought it up, how can you answer the objection that you introduce the Indies and want to transport them to Madrid?

RELIGION: Since it is only for the clarification of a religious precept, and since those persons introduced are only abstractions to paint what one tries to say, there is nothing objectionable even though one takes them to Madrid, because when performed there before intellectual people, neither distances nor oceans are upsetting.

ZEAL: Since that is so, prostrated at the royal feet esteemed in two worlds, let us ask the king's pardon.

AMERICA: And pardon from his famous queen, as well.

RELIGION: Whose sovereign feet the Indies humbly kiss.

ZEAL: And from his Supreme Council.

RELIGION: And from the ladies who bring glory to the hemisphere.

AMERICA: And from his literary men of whom I humbly beg

forgiveness for my attempt in these crude lines to describe so
great a mystery.

WEST: Come, because I am eager to see of what sort this god is
that I am to receive in food.

AMERICA AND WEST SING:　Now let our hearts rejoice;
　　　　　　　　　　　　We shall be blind no more,
　　　　　　　　　　　　Nor shall we raise our voice
　　　　　　　　　　　　To him we praised before,
　　　　　　　　　　　　For now we know the true
　　　　　　　　　　　　God of the Harvest, he
　　　　　　　　　　　　To whom all praise is due,
　　　　　　　　　　　　For gifts to such as we.
　　　　　　　　　　　　Redeemed from error and from
　　　　　　　　　　　　　　wrong,
　　　　　　　　　　　　With joyful voice we raise our song:

ALL: In festive pomp worship the great God of Harvest!

(*Singing and dancing they withdraw.*)

END OF THE LOA

W.K.J.

JERÓNIMO DE MONFORTE Y VERA
1680?-1740?　　　　　　　　　　　　　　　　　　Peru

On February 9, 1725, to celebrate the coronation of the
short-lived Luis I of Spain, Peru's Viceroy, Marqués de
Castelfuerte, invited nearly a thousand people to his
palace to watch the performance of *Amar es saber ven-
cer* (Love Finds a Way) by Antonio de Zamora, a
Spanish playwright. To give a local touch to the fes-
tivity, his friend the Peruvian dramatist Pedro de Peralta (1664-1743) contributed the introductory *loa*;
General Monforte wrote the *sainete, El amor duende*

(The Love Elf) to play between the acts; and Fernández de Castro (1689-1737), who recorded a description
of all the festivities, contributed the *fin de fiesta*, the
final sketch.

Little is known of Monforte. Though born in Ara-
gon, he spent most of his life in Peru. Between 1711 and
1715, he governed the district of Huánuco. In 1726 he
was appointed Corregidor of Huamalíes. This, his only
surviving play, is described in the original printed version of 1725, and in Lohmann Villena's *El arte drama-
tico en Lima* (Madrid, 1945), as "a between-acts sainete
written for a play performed in the palace for the happy
acclaim of the King, our Lord."

THE LOVE ELF

Characters

Love, an elf
Maran of Madrid, the First Man
González, a criollo, Second Man
First Tapada or Veiled Lady
Second Tapada, with face covered by her mantle
An elderly duenna or chaperone
A Negress

*Enter Love, singing. He wears an elfin costume with close-
fitting tunic and ridiculous hat. A bow hangs from his shoulder.*

LOVE (singing):   I'm a lively little elf.
                   I am love, the old folks say,
                   And if I was big one time,
                   I am very small today.

                   Look at me, just look at me
                   Though, My Lords and Ladies, you
                   May not have me in your view.

Elves, like love, no one can see.
Ay, ay, ay, you look at me
But nobody can you see. (*He masks his face
with his elfin hood.*)

From My Lord the Viceroy, I
Got a summons to a play.
Loyal subjects of his realm
Know to hear is to obey.
Look at me, just look at me, etc.

When I wear costume like this,
Let no critic show surprise.
You should know that Love may dress
In quaint styles and strange disguise.
Look at me, just look at me, etc.

Wool and iron lend mighty aid
To build beauty. That is plain.
Many a fool's wool-gathering;
What's more iron-like than disdain?
Look at me, just look at me, etc.

(*Enter two men wearing capes and swords, and with such
hats as are worn at night.*)

MARAN: González, since you've been in Lima longer than I,
you must know it better. And since you're a man-about-town,
tell me, what is your opinion of these veiled women called
Tapadas who, I hear, cover their faces and mouths with mantles?

GONZALEZ: Are you mentioning Tapadas? Beware! Don't you
realize, my dear Maran, that they are the forbidden fruit of
this garden spot?

MARAN: Lent brings special dispensations, and anyway, His Excellency, the Viceroy, isn't around to hear us.

GONZALEZ: Well, since he isn't listening and since your question springs from idle curiosity, I'll tell you what I know

about them. Every Tapada is beautiful. Since you can't see her face behind her veil, your optimistic judgment, that plays tricks on you, is sure of their loveliness; in moments of doubt, the brush of fantasy is likely to paint in brilliant colors. It makes no difference that your better judgment, when you listen to them, casts doubts on the beauty you imagine and makes it seem unlikely. Their wit is so far-fetched that it is without sense, yet their charm will make even the most circumspect judge laugh at what they say. If we sum them up in a phrase, these ladies of Lima with veils and long skirts are a sculpturing without a head and a poem without feet.

MARAN: To hear you talk, it will be better for a man to keep away from their witchery.

GONZALEZ: At least, they're not for me. I've reason to be sure that they can strip a treasure house in a single night.

MARAN: Then woe to the man who loves them! Anybody who falls for them must be a complete fool.

GONZALEZ: Yes, you don't catch me sipping at that fountain!

MARAN: And I also curse and deny love!

GONZALEZ: I abhor anything connected with love.

LOVE: Such infamous scorn! To think that they dare scoff like that at my power!

GONZALEZ: What a fine ending to a trip from Madrid it would be to toss away my purse after enduring risks and the ocean to make my fortune in this valley. They're quite a dish, these ladies of Lima, but every coin that falls into my hands is going to have a Genoese burial, down deep in a casket!

LOVE: Love is something to be felt, not seen, and the blindness of this pair makes my power all the stronger. They'll pay well for their scorn of me! I'll contrive such a trap that if they escape from the lips of affection, they'll fall into the hands of self-interest. (*Love sings*)

> I shall still my triumph have;
> Man cannot protect himself.
> If he should unstring my bow,
> Love has hands, since he's an elf!

312 SPANISH-AMERICAN LITERATURE

(From each side of the stage enters a Tapada, her face concealed by her mantle.)

GONZALEZ: Here come a couple of your veiled beauties.

MARAN: This will be a good chance to find out if people are telling the truth about them.

GONZALEZ: What about your determination to protect your money from their claws?

MARAN: Don't worry! Didn't Salazar the singer advocate wounding Fortune and attacking Courage? Besides, I'm not taking any chances. I've tied knots in the strings of my purse.

GONZALEZ: I'm very much afraid we're tottering, and if we stumble, it will mean a bad fall.

FIRST TAPADA: If they're performing a play tonight in the palace to celebrate the oath of allegiance to the new King, I want to be there.

SECOND TAPADA: That's true. We mustn't miss a play, with the royal family and all, there. I don't know of anybody who can get me a ticket, but since when have the rights of the mantle and the craft of a woman failed to bestow special privileges?

MARAN (approaching her): My Queen!

FIRST: Señor Foreigner.

MARAN: How do you know I've just come from Madrid?

FIRST: Because you said "Queen." Around here they say "Lovely Girl." But what do you want?

MARAN: To talk, if you'll allow me.

FIRST: Talking in what parrots do, but since you're a new arrival, go ahead. (They talk together.)

GONZALEZ: My dear Lady, if you will reward my humility by honoring me as your servant, you'll find in me an example of one who has just achieved happiness.

SECOND: The way you rambled on made me think you were running a Marathon, but be it as you desire, because when it comes to running, I can't distinguish the colors of the runners if they're any distance away.

LOVE: So they have contacted the Veiled Ladies? Now my triumph will be assured.

(*sings*)   In a lovely woman's conquest,
                Mantles play a part.
                They disguise her thoughts and let her
                Enter a man's heart.

(*Speaking*) Since this second fellow didn't speak quite so disrespectfully of me, I won't be quite so hard with him. (*Love hits González gently.*)

GONZALEZ: Who's that? There's somebody here. Even if I don't see anybody, I certainly hear footsteps.

LOVE: Since he admits hearing me, I'll convert his hearing into suffering. (*Sings*)

                Cast your eyes upon her beauty.
                After you have seen
                The reality before you,
                Senses are more keen.

(*Love steps behind the Second Tapada and pulls down her mantle, revealing her face.*)

SECOND: Hey! What's this? Who's pulling off my veil?

GONZALEZ: Somebody who wants to prove that bright dawn follows the darkness of night. May God bless your loveliness!

SECOND: Forever and forever, amen!

GONZALEZ (*aside*): She's stupid, but what difference? What I know about her will make up for that.

LOVE: Well, he's hooked. Now I'll see about the other fine gentleman, and let him have it. (*Love hits Maran hard.*)

MARAN: Who slapped me so hard? Who's giving me what I didn't ask for?

FIRST: If you're talking about giving, I wish you'd give me a hundred pesos that I need for an underskirt.

MARAN: Ouch! That really hurt.

LOVE: I'm glad you felt it, cruel miser. Love will make the blood flow because a begging mouth shoots arrows.

FIRST: Why don't you answer me?

MARAN: A blow of a hundred would leave anybody speechless.

FIRST: Bah, señor! Don't be stingy. Don't you know that closed lips go along with closed hands?

MARAN: Don't get mad, my dear lady, because even if I don't give you a hundred, you'll receive something. Here's my month's income in this purse that I'll turn over to you. If that isn't enough, I'll go to work as a day laborer.

FIRST: If that's all you've got, what else can we do?

MARAN: Now since you've condemned me to a month of fasting, let me see your face.

FIRST: What's this? Is that all you want to see?

MARAN: What's this? Have you more to offer?

FIRST: I'll draw aside my veil. Look and perish! (*She pulls back her shawl.*)

MARAN: What a lovely face! Pity you have such a demanding mouth.

FIRST: Now let's have the purse! I love its jingle.

MARAN: You're getting my soul along with it.

LOVE: To reveal what sort of soul he has, I'm going to switch purses. (*Love takes the purse and replaces it with one containing coal. Love sings.*)

> In a woman's plans and plots
> As she would beguile,
> Truth may play a lesser part
> Than a mocking smile.

SECOND: I'm getting thirsty, sir, with so much talking. How about getting me some sweets and a sherbet?

GONZALEZ: I'll get you anything you like. Wait and I'll be right back. (*Exit González.*)

LOVE: Here's my chance for trickery! I'm going to punish his ill treatment of me by changing her form. Everybody knows how easy it is to change a woman.

(*Sings*):   To call woman "fickle maid"
                  Is a commonplace,
                  For her love is changeable,
                  And likewise her face.

(*Love leads away the Second Tapada and replaces her with an elderly duenna, veiled in her mantle.*)

FIRST: With all this talk about giving and receiving, just so there can't be any trickery, it would be nice to see the money.

MARAN: My purse is full of good silver coins, my dear. (*Enter González with a napkin full of sweets. To each of his remarks, the duenna replies only by gestures.*)

GONZALEZ: Here are your refreshments. Since you're burning with anxiety, come and get them.

FIRST: I'll decorate my underskirt with wonderful lace.

GONZALEZ: Shall I get you some more? Are you saying yes?

LOVE (*to spectators*): Now you'll see some unhappy people!

FIRST: What's this I see? Scoundrel! This is coal! (*She shakes the purse and pours out lumps of coal.*)

MARAN: I tell you it can't be! My purse was full of white silver.

FIRST: Wait till I get my hands on you!

MARAN: Your hands haven't a chance as long as I have my feet. (*Maran runs out followed by the First Tapada.*)

LOVE (*sings*):   Every time that loveliness
                  Vaunts itself a bit,
                  All the coins that look so fine
                  Turn out counterfeit.

GONZALEZ: Now that your mouth has been sweetened, shouldn't I get rewarded by a view of my heaven? (*From the direction in which the First Tapada disappeared appears a Negress, veiled, and with Maran in pursuit.*)

MARAN: Hey! Wait! Even though you're wearing shoes, Lovely Tapada, you're running so fast that you'll end up barefoot, unless Jacinto Polo is completely wrong.

GONZALEZ: If polite request isn't enough to conquer your

aloofness, it's time to use force. (*He lifts the duenna's mantle.*) Heavens, I must be seeing things!

DUENNA: Darling Rodrigo, are there any more sweets? Because if you have nothing more to feed me and tempt my sweet tooth, don't ever think you'll conquer my coldness.

MARAN: Since you won't say anything, I'll have to get my own replies by looking at you. (*He takes off the Negress's veil and sees her black face.*) Heaven help me! What a dark night!

NEGRESS: Is Massa huntin' fo' a black diamond, too?

MARAN: Go and let some fish find the ink where you were spawned.

DUENNA: Sebastian, honey, aren't there any more sweets for me to swallow?

GONZALEZ: Beat it! Let a greyhound swallow you, because to be free of an old woman, I'd go looking for the hunting equipment. (*He runs off.*)

DUENNA: Honey, not even in the abyss will you be free of me. (*She follows him.*)

MARAN: What a bad time I have ahead of me without any money and with your complexion to look at! (*Exit.*)

NEGRESS: On 'count o' yo' black sins, wherever you go, Massa, Ah'll be right 'long aside you. (*She follows.*)

LOVE: Through the tricks of an elf, you've seen how you can't trust a mantle or love, so I'm right when I say:

(*sings*):   Look at me, just look at me,
                 Though, My Lords and Ladies, you
                 May find nothing in your view.
                 Elves, like Love, no one can see.
                 Ay, ay, ay, you look at me,
                 Yet nobody can you see.

(*As he sings, the entremés ends.*)

W.K.J.

ANONYMOUS: EL AMOR DE LA ESTANCIERA
Late Eighteenth Century   River Plate region

The anonymous *El amor de la Estanciera* (The Ranch Girl's Love), written about 1790, was the first play of the River Plate region to have local color. It tells of the courtship of the ranch girl Chepa by the gaucho Juancho Perucho and the Brazilian peddler Marcos Figueira. In doggerel verse, generally in lines of seven syllables, it extols the glories of pampas life and the virtues of the triumphant local suitor. Marcos, with his gifts and excessive courtesy is preferred by Mama Pancha and her daughter, but Papa Cancho decides in favor of Juancho, with the explanation:

> "At foreigners you'd best not look
> For you'll find everyone a crook!
> No, give me my own countrymen,
> Honest and upright, though they lack
> That foreign gloss, and even when
> They've only tatters on their back."

The disappointed Marcos resorts to threats and violence to get his bride, but the family closes ranks against him. The one-act play continues:

MARCOS: You'll never get me on the run,
                  For here I stand, and here's my gun!

                  (*He raises his gun.*)

PANCHA: He's crazy quite to want to fight.
                  Just give me room and with my broom
                  I'll sweep him out and clean the place.
                  Drop your gun or I'll scratch your face!
MARCOS: Let me alone or else I vow
                  That I shall kill her, anyhow.

(Cancho seizes a lasso. Juancho holds a bola, three stones tied to strings. Chepa is armed with an ox goad and Pancha grabs a branding iron, and they all attack Marcos.)

CANCHO:	Beat that man unmercifully!
JUANCHO:	Hang him from an ombú tree.
PANCHA:	Break his ribs before he's hung.
CHEPA:	Jab this stick right through his tongue.
MARCOS:	Help! Preserve me! Go away,
	In the name of God I pray.
	None of this do I deserve.
	Spare me and I'll gladly serve
	All of you at the wedding feast.
	That will make amends, at least.
CHEPA:	Spare him, Dad, for he's contrite.
CANCHO:	Let him cook, to serve him right.
	It will be what he's deserved,
	A meal well seasoned and well served,
	Tasty meat and tasty stew.
PANCHA:	He can kill a fat calf, too.
	We'll have a delicious meal.
CHEPA:	Think how good Juancho will feel.
JUANCHO:	If I get calf's head and wine,
	That's a banquet I'd call fine.
CANCHO:	So you shall, with wine like water,
	When you wed my Pancha's daughter.
JUANCHO:	Nothing else that I'd like better.
	Love's a horse without a fetter.
	I can't stop it; I can't rein it.
CHEPA:	Like my love, I can't restrain it.
	I'm filled with a fearful itch,
	Love or hunger, I don't know which.
CANCHO:	Join your hands then, lovers two.
	God rain down His gifts on you!
	May He send a son along
	To guard your flocks and keep them strong.

PANCHA: And pleased be God to send the bride
               A lovely little girl beside.

MARCOS: My heart is sad. I burn like fire,
               Though no tobacco's in my poke,
               For Chepa was my deep desire.
               To lose her is a sorry joke.

PANCHA: Well, son-in-law, you have a task.
               Look after her is what I ask.
               And may you pass long years of joy
               With many a healthy girl and boy!

JUANCHO: I'll treat her well. On that rely.
               For I shall never make her cry.
               No man could have a better wife,
               And I shall love her more than life.

CANCHO: Hey, Marcos, get the fire red.
               I'll skin the calf.

PANCHA: I'll bring the bread.

CANCHO: I'll grind the chile. (*Exeunt Marcos and
               Cancho.*)

CHEPA: As you said,
               I love you, Juan, as you love me.
               Dad said to treat you tenderly.

PANCHA: Juancho, you know there's one thing
                  more.
               You're got to ride down to the store
               To buy some blankets; and for mass
               Shoes and some clothes for her to wear,
               For she will be a useful lass.

CHEPA: In all the work I'll do my share. (*Enter
               Cancho.*)

CANCHO: The fire's hot and Marcos able.
               The food is done. Go set the table.
               (*Enter Marcos.*)

MARCOS: Everything's cooked and seasoned fine,
               And tender, too. It's time to dine.

CHEPA: What's on the menu for tonight?
               My Juancho has an appetite.

MARCOS: I've made corn soup and chicken stew,
                       And roasted calf, and partridge, too.

   (*The women set the table. Marcos brings the food. They
all sit down.*)

However each sweetheart first has to compose a poem about
the other one. Then Cancho suggests that they dance to Marcos'
guitar music.

                       "Play a fandango, a jig or a tango,
                       And we'll pair off for a regular spree
                       Chepa and Juancho, and Pancha and
                           me."

And they finish with a round of songs, ending with an appeal to
the audience:

                       "Here ends in marriage
                       Our dance and our play.
                       May you all be content
                       And go gaily away."

END

                                                              W.K.J.

CAMILO HENRÍQUEZ
1769-1825   Chile

The literature of independent Chile began with a priest
who was born in Valdivia, educated in Lima, and familiar with the writings of Rousseau, Montesquieu and
Voltaire. Padre Henríquez founded Chile's first newspaper, *Aurora*, in 1812. Following the defeat of the patriots at Rancagua in 1814, he fled to Buenos Aires.
There he wrote two plays, one of which was *La Camila
o la patriota de Sud América* (Camila or the South
American Patriot, 1817). The play is set in Ecuador,
and the main character, Diego, is looking for his wife
who disappeared after the patriots were slaughtered by

the Spanish soldiers. He finds her in an Indian camp
where she has taken refuge; the chief is a cultured man
who has been educated in the United States.

In the following scene from the final act, the cacique
and his wife engage in undramatic conversation through
which the playwright voices his ideas on interesting
drama. Although Henríquez was the first Chilean critic,
he could not understand why this play was a failure. He
had anticipated its performance all over the world.

CAMILA OR THE
SOUTH AMERICAN PATRIOT

(Enter the Cacique and his Wife from different sides.)

WIFE: Companion, what did you say to those poor people who
left here so dejected? they say the girl dissolved in tears. Do I
go to visit them or is it forbidden to see them, by your orders?

CACIQUE: They deserve no sympathy: They are rebels, the kind
that are called "patriots," when they are really insurgents.

WIFE: How can a man educated in the United States of North
America pronounce such words? Is this what you learned in a
college of that great Republic? Is that why McMonson took
you there? Is this the fruit of his kindnesses?

CACIQUE: You know that Jeveros is the capitol of the Spanish
settlement in Mainas. Its governor demands these strangers
and I must surrender them.

WIFE: Never! Better for our land to be laid waste! The Oma-
guas have debased everything. These foreigners are defenders
of the most illustrious cause the world has ever seen. To
whom will you surrender them? To the Spaniards? The Spaniards!

CACIQUE: I've told you not to get involved in affairs of government. Are we here like the Spanish governors who, to please
their wives, commit the worst iniquities? In the administration of public negotiation, the voice of women should not be
heard. You have no head for this sort of thing.

WIFE: But I have a just and compassionate heart.

CACIQUE: You women are nothing but tears. On your accounts, we refrained from declaring war against the Ucayas. Since our custom grants a vote to mothers and wives of the chief warriors in decisions about peace and war, you women filled the assembly with your laments and won the decision. Now you see! Such power has Nature given to your tears and your rage. And each day the Ucayas grow bolder!

WIFE: Why should we permit Americans to make war against each other? Children of the same motherland, brothers, why should they cut each others' throats so frantically? This would be a crime abhorrent to Nature. Certainly the imprisonment of these strangers is scandalous. Here they should find protection, safety, and generosity.

CACIQUE: Listen, my dear! (*He whispers to her.*)

WIFE: I'm glad. But I'm the last to find out about things.

CACIQUE: Yes . . . our friend . . . your minister . . .

WIFE: So charming.

CACIQUE: Fortunately it happens in the festival of the heroines of the country. Since I'm so fond of surprises, there will be three days of events, and no one else in the town knows what kind they are. The chief of the Ucayas, who used to be my enemy, has been very eager to do as I ask, and he will send us actors to present a couple of delightful theatrical performances. Keep my secret. My heart wouldn't allow me to keep secrets from you.

WIFE: Tell me, what are the plays about?

CACIQUE: The play the first night is *La Basilia*. It deals with a beautiful and deserving girl who after many dangers reached America from Germany, only to have to flee from attacks of a raiding party. Her mother died of disappointment when she realized that where she had hoped to find freedom there were only persecutors.

WIFE: Were these the same raiders that burned the houses in Guayaquil?

CACIQUE: Heavens, no, Petronita! These raiders didn't just burn houses: They killed men and women. They burned anybody who didn't agree with their abstract ideas. The number of their victims in Holland, Italy, Spain, and Portugal are beyond reckoning. Not even the genius of English mathematics can figure the number of families reduced to beggary and misfortune.

WIFE: Why were they allowed to commit such misdeeds?

CACIQUE: They were backed by powerful interests and by those eager for power.

WIFE: Nobody enjoys seeing that sort of monster in the theatre. The women will want to hurl even their seats at them.

CACIQUE: I know. But it is an instructive play full of tender and pitiful scenes. And besides, it has a happy ending. The amiable Basilia is about to perish in the sea and suffer all sorts of calamities, but is rescued and taken to Philadelphia where she is received with generous and affectionate hospitality. There in a week she collects a dowry of seventy thousand pesos. So she marries and goes to live comfortably in South Carolina.

WIFE: Did you ever see the play performed?

CACIQUE: No. In the United States I never attended the theatre because the Quakers don't go to plays.

WIFE: What do they do if they are compelled to stay home every night?

CACIQUE: They work, read, write, praise God, play with their children and chat with their wives. They are excellent and charitable men. Nevertheless, the exterminators hate them and want to burn them all, even their pleasant wives. They forbid the reading of Eusebius who praised their virtues. In Havana, some friends took me to the theatre, because *Basilia* can be performed in Spanish territory.

WIFE: Why?

CACIQUE: Because wicked men have made the King of Spain believe that the exterminators and the friends of the exterminators are the support of his throne. Besides, superstitious people are corrupted and frivolous, and they like love plots and other things as frivolous as they are. Let's talk about the second night's entertainment. That will open with a beautiful symphony, the work of a lady of Buenos Aires.

WIFE: That's too bad!

CACIQUE: Confound it! Didn't I say you have no judgment? A person can't talk to you. A clever Englishman got this music for the Drury Lane Theatre, and I obtained a copy in Philadelphia. And now you come out with "Too bad."

WIFE: I meant—

CACIQUE: That's what all the stupid people say— Nothing good can come out of America. Since they never read, they aren't acquainted with the good productions of American pens that have received well-deserved applause in Europe. In my small library I have some excellent English translations of works by Chileans, Peruvians, and Mexicans.

WIFE: I guess we talk like that because we don't know anything about such things.

CACIQUE: The music reveals the Buenos Aires character as the English describe it. The andante part is sweet, like the delicate duets that the minister and I play on flutes. But the alegro, the presto, and the prestissimo movements contain the fire of the universe. It is like a cavalry charge with sabres brandished. Buenos Aires will soon make itself known. And how beautiful its composer is! The Englishman had a portrait of her, painted without flattering the subject. The artist made her very brunette. Brunettes are often the most interesting.

WIFE: When you start discussing those things, you never stop. We're too old for that. What entertainment follows the music?

CACIQUE: I don't remember.

WIFE: Don't quit there.

CACIQUE: It's as you say. We're old, and memory fails with the years.

WIFE: But I notice you don't forget the pretty composer!

CACIQUE: Well, after the music, comes a short sentimental drama called *Maternal Charity*. This is its plot. Some respectable South American women form a society presided over by the wife of the amiable governor of the nation, to educate orphans and protect poor girls, from cruel and unnatural seductors. And you see how the society is persecuted and the

women give up in disgust. The orphans lament their unhappy
state and inspire the deepest pity.

WIFE: Who persecutes the society?

CACIQUE: I'm not exactly sure.

WIFE: We'll find out, because the English will put it in their
sheets.

CACIQUE: Their newspapers, you mean, Petronita.

WIFE: Yes, that's it. Didn't you tell me that the English publish in their newspapers everything that happens in the world?

CACIQUE: Yes, just like North America. And it's a fine idea
when they tell the truth and aren't partial or careless as *The
Courier* is. But here comes the minister. Leave us alone and
we'll talk later. (*Exit the Wife.*)

END

W.K.J.

JOSÉ PEÓN CONTRERAS
1843-1907   Mexico

If literary tastes had not changed, Peón Contreras might
have been Mexico's most popular dramatist. But the Romantic movement that had lasted only fifteen years in
Spain (1833–1848) was declining in the New World
when he was born in Mérida, Yucatán. Although he
had a unique lyric gift and his plays followed the popular formula (mysterious characters doomed by fate,
moving in the foreboding gloom of night, and speaking
in exuberant language), Peón was born too late. Many
of his plays were neither performed nor published, and
he made his living as the director of an insane asylum in
Mexico City. His native Mérida, however, honored him
by giving his name to its major theatre.

Gil González de Ávila, a one-act play in verse, performed in 1876, might well have come either from
Spain's Golden Age or its Romantic period. It is set

in sixteenth-century Mexico. Two scenes from the middle of the play are translated here.

GIL GONZÁLEZ DE ÁVILA

Characters

Gil González, condemned to death for treason
The Supreme Judge of Mexico
Violante, his daughter, secretly married to Gil

Tristan, the servant of Violante, has just brought news that Gil and his brother have been sentenced to be hanged as conspirators for trying to make the son of Hernán Cortés Emperor of Mexico. As Violante laments in her room, Gil González suddenly enters.

GIL: Violante!

VIOLANTE: At last I'm happy. They've given you your freedom!

GIL: It's been a century. Those slow and mortal hours have seemed forever. But now, though I can hardly believe it, I'm here. Let me look into your eyes and see myself mirrored there. Let me forget my anger in the burning light of their gleam. What happiness!

VIOLANTE: Infinite! I must not lose you. My heart needs to look at you every day, Gil González, even though for only an instant.

GIL: Would that we could anticipate so happy a lot!

VIOLANTE: May our hopes come to life, and when I die may they die with me. How happy I am! None could describe it!

GIL: Violante, your heart must kill those hopes before they're born.

VIOLANTE: What do you mean?

GIL: Alas, my Violante, your woes have not ended.

VIOLANTE: Could Fate ordain a thing like that?

GIL: I'm still in the power of the executioner. I have not broken my chains.

VIOLANTE: You mean you are not free?

GIL: I'm not.

VIOLANTE: What happened? Tell me why the tyrant still holds
you in a gloomy jail. What right has he? What right? What
have you done? You, so noble and generous. Oh, pitying God,
my heart dies in my breast! Then how could you come here?

GIL: It was only for a moment.

VIOLANTE: I will not let you leave me.

GIL: Keep calm, Violante. Isn't it true that after this mortal life
comes another in which the soul takes care of those still left
on earth? And isn't it true, my love, that happiness un-
achieved here is hoped for there, and that all delights have
been promised to the thirsty soul, beyond the lovely blue of
the sky?

VIOLANTE: Yes, all that is true. But I'm amazed to hear you talk
like that. It's madness!

GIL: Then if that happiness is sure, Violante, do not mourn.
Calmly, like me, accept your cup of woe.

VIOLANTE: I don't understand.

GIL: Unhappy girl!

VIOLANTE: Are you out of your mind when you torture my soul
like this?

FIL: Look and understand. (*He takes her hand and leads her to
the balcony.*)

VIOLANTE: Horrors! A gallows! God help me!

GIL: Have courage!

VIOLANTE: I'm delirious! I feel a chilling terror. Don't leave me.
I'm afraid.

GIL: Violante!

VIOLANTE: I can't endure this martyrdom. You to die! It's inhuman. You to die!

GIL: Along with Alonso, my brother.

VIOLANTE: I cannot be. Why, you've done nothing. I can't be
so cruelly treated by Fate!

GIL: Control yourself, I beg of you. Let me look upon you,
brave and strong.

VIOLANTE: You're right. I must defend you. And if death still pursues you, despite my grief and breaking heart, I must stand up against death. Between it and yourself I'll build a barrier with the mighty torrent of my sorrow. I'll throw myself at the feet of the judges.

GIL: That's useless!

VIOLANTE: Why?

GIL: Your father!

VIOLANTE: Oh, Heavens!

GIL: They will deny their favor and pity, despite your grief. Your father is my enemy. His deep rancor cannot be overcome.

VIOLANTE: But if I tell him—

GIL: Never! That would make it worse. To reveal your love for me would be to sign my death sentence. It is impossible!

VIOLANTE: Is his hatred so deep? What is the terrible secret concealed between you two? Tell me!

GIL: (after a pause to provide the transition): Listen! One night a year ago, my ecstatic eyes first saw you in the Cathedral. All else around me ceased to exist. Only you were there. I heard and saw nothing more. I fell in love with you and you with me! There was I, calm and happy, your heart in my breast and mine in yours. Suddenly I felt a light touch of a hand on my shoulder. I turned astonished toward the man beside me. "Do you like her?" he asked in sombre voice. "Yes, I think so," I replied. I am still amazed at the insult, for hardly had I answered his impertinent question when I felt his glove against my face. Never, so help me, had anything happened like that before! We both left the church, he mute and scowling, I no less so. I followed him for blocks. He stopped, and our swords flashed out. There, like gentlemen, it was necessary to die or kill. My anger gave me force, or perhaps it was Fate. I killed my enemy and then, Oh God, I learned he was——

VIOLANTE: My brother!

GIL: Yes, your brother. I swear, Violante, I had not known. It was dark and his face was hidden during the fight. And that was how I earned your father's hatred.

VIOLANTE: Cruel Fortune!

GIL: Tell me, was I to blame, or your brother? Tell me!

VIOLANTE: Of course you weren't. His was the insult.

GIL: But that is why my love and yours have always flourished in the shadows. Who would have thought that the flower of our love would die, hidden from the light of day? Who would have thought, Beloved, that while I was still young, an unjust fate would tear me grimly from your side forever? Farewell!

VIOLANTE: Never! I fear the violence of your judges, Gil.

GIL: Knowing my innocence, perhaps they will free me.

VIOLANTE: Don't go, my Gil!

GIL: Violante, I must.

VIOLANTE: No, never! You shall not leave me!

GIL: Farewell! Oh, horrible moment! (*He starts to leave.*)

VIOLANTE: You mustn't go. By the memory of that bewitching afternoon that passed so soon because of our happiness, I beg you! Remember when you talked to me of love and swore you would be true! And I swore always to be yours.

GIL: Don't remind me of our fleeting happiness!

VIOLANTE: For the sake of your love—

GIL: You're driving me mad!

VIOLANTE: No! You must not leave, no matter what you think. (*Enter the judge, rear.*)

JUDGE: Heaven's wrath! What's this? Am I dreaming?

GIL: Your father!

VIOLANTE: Heavens, my father!

JUDGE: What fate has subjected me to this? An Avila here? What indignity!

GIL: What insult! Hold your tongue, or—

VIOLANTE (*in a whisper*): Control yourself!

JUDGE (*to Violante*): Get out! (*Exit Violante.*) And who opened the door of your prison? I swear that tomorrow I'll have the guard Sancho Bermudo hanged!

GIL: That would be an act very worthy of you!

JUDGE: Anyone so derelict to his duty—

GIL: He gave me only an instant of freedom, and I swore to return. I left under parole, and I've always been faithful to my word. Never fear that I mean to flee your cowardly cruelty, Judge of New Spain. I am a noble. I know how to die.

JUDGE: What brought you to my house? What were you seeking?

GIL: Don't you suspect?

JUDGE: I can't begin to understand. Could it be that, fearful and uncertain of your fate, you sought an intermediary in Violante, hoping futilely to interrupt the course of your destiny that is mapping out the path of your brief career?

GIL: It was not that, on my honor!

JUDGE: Then what?

GIL: I came, sir, to ask a favor.

JUDGE (aside): I fear this man!

GIL: I came to hear your lips declare my crime and that of my brother.

JUDGE: Such indignity!

GIL: Calm yourself! Don't get wrought up! As a whim, I'd like to change places with you briefly, I to be the judge and you the criminal.

JUDGE: Heaven's wrath! Begone!

GIL: No, wait! Don't call for help. I could stop that before you said a word.

JUDGE: Very well. Speak!

GIL: Why did the judges mock every law and order our arrest?

JUDGE: Because you are traitors to your country and your king.

GIL (in an outburst of rage): In God's name! Such base insults to a gentleman! Why don't my hand and sword rise in revenge? Alas, Violante, I did not know how great my love was! Even I could not conceive it until this horrible moment. Traitors? Oh, God! Don't repeat that ignominious word! Did you dare say—? (Controlling himself, he turns to the judge.)

JUDGE: You forced me to tell you—

GIL: You lie!

JUDGE: I?

GIL: Yes, you. And if you do not want— (Threateningly.)

JUDGE: No, no!

GIL: Then tell me: Who is the liar?

JUDGE: I am.
GIL: You confess?
JUDGE: Since you compel me.
GIL: Was there any conspiracy?
JUDGE: None!
GIL: Was it all your cowardly invention?
JUDGE: Yes! Yes!
GIL: So you could pretend you were punishing treason?
JUDGE: That's true.
GIL: But why, tell me this! Why do I deserve your cruelty?
JUDGE: Why? Because I hate you with all my soul.

Pretending to relent, the judge promises to pardon them, and sends Gil back to the prison to release his brother. Secretly, however, the Judge dispatches a note by his servant, Parafán, ordering the immediate hanging of the Ávilas. Violante's dueña Inés returns to announce the impending execution. Violante rushes to her father to tell him that she is expecting a child from the man he wants to murder. It is too late! The cathedral bells toll the knell.

W.K.J.

CARLOS BELLO
1815-1854   Chile

The first Chilean national drama—if one can so describe a play set in France and written by the son of a Venezuelan grammarian father and an English mother—was Bello's *Amores del poeta* (The Loves of a Poet, 1842). The first performance of the play inaugurated the University Theatre, now Santiago's Municipal Theatre. Society people, having heard that the play's characters were based on local personalities, filled the theatre.

Matilde de Monville, a beautiful widow, is the ward of a gruff old soldier, Colonel Fiercour, who loves her. Eugenio Gressey, a frail young man like Bello himself,

also loves her. To protect him, she agrees to marry the
colonel. Here, from the second scene of the last act, is
a sample of the play's exuberant Romanticism.

THE LOVES OF A POET

SCENE: *a room in Matilde's house. Matilde is alone when Gressey appears and stares at her.*

GRESSEY (*after a pause*): Señora!

MATILDE (*rising in agitation*): You here!

GRESSEY: After reading your letter, I am leaving at once.

MATILDE: Yes, at once.

GRESSEY: But before saying my final farewell, a farewell perhaps
eternal, I wanted to see you, to speak to you, to engrave in my
aching breast with one final look the image of a woman lovely
as few are lovely, as no sweethearts are lovely, but an image
of a woman, not an angel, as I thought.

MATILDE: Gressey!

GRESSEY: I want to hear the echo of your sweet, gentle voice,
the siren of my happiness: I want to dream a moment as I
once dreamed, and then depart, depart forever. Are you shed-
ding a tear for your friend? Oh, one who abandons his love, his
everything, one who sees a blasted future, dead before it blos-
somed, one who falls headlong, like Lucifer, from his heaven
of hope into the deep and gloomy cavern of disillusionment,
with nothing to blame but his evil fate, he does not weep. No,
he despairs. Grief knots within his heart like a writhing serpent. His eyes blaze, his breath chokes him, and the words
that come to his dry lips are curses and blasphemy.

MATILDE: Gressey, calm yourself! I beg you!

GRESSEY: You are right, Matilde. I should leave you, serenely,
calmly, as you see me now. Forgive me. The unfortunate man
is often importunate. But his misfortune is his excuse, Matilde. (*He extends a hand toward her that she takes.*) I did
not mean to depart with tears in my eyes, but I love you. I am
leaving you, and ahead of me lies a black perspective; days

without dawn or light, nights without dreams, endless torment. A long and loveless existence. I was wandering through the world with uncertain steps when my anxious gaze caught a glimpse of you. For a moment, I dreamed you were mine. I thought I might clasp you in my arms, but you were a shadow, a mirage of the desert for a lost, weary soul thirsty for love. Oh! I must go. My torments are unspeakable: they are the memories of heaven lost to those who moan in eternal night. Like them, I see Death as my only hope, and I feel my desires more keenly and bitterly Matilde. Receive the farewell of a dying man. (*He starts to leave.*)

MATILDE: What are you saying? Die? No, Gressey! Wait! (*She seizes his hand.*) A terrible doubt assails me. Listen. Fiercour dragged that letter out of me on condition that he would forgive you and spare your life, and . . .

GRESSEY: Forgive? Forgive the injured party? God forgives sinners but Colonel Fiercour is willing to forgive Eugenio de Gressey! His forgiveness would be a poison, a blow . . .

MATILDE: Yes. Yes, I know that. But tell me, do you intend to provoke him?

GRESSEY: Not now.

MATILDE: If you did, your own hand would cause your death. Swear you won't, I beg you! The life you would destroy is mine. I bought it at the cost of my own well-being. Don't be so cruel as to make useless such a sacrifice.

GRESSEY: Matilde!

MATILDE: Surely you would not want me to have as daily companion in the cell that will be my refuge, or to see at the altar beside the Redeemer, a bloody spectre, and only a spectre. Would you take from me my sad consolation of praying to God for your good fortune? And when I feel the cold hand of death, would you want me to doubt that we shall meet again in that happier world, where all is love?

GRESSEY: Matilde, listen! I swear that even if life is a weight I can hardly endure, I shall bear up. But if you love me, why did you conceal that love?

MATILDE: Could you ever doubt it? Impossible! Passion speaks through the eyes. It forces the voice of a sigh to publish a secret that our lips vainly try to conceal. I love you. Yes, I love you with all the strength of a first love, with all the tenderness of a woman. You are my whole world. You are my breath, my life! Without you, the universe is a desert. Beside you, prison would be paradise.

GRESSEY (*embracing her*): Angel of light, comfort of my sorrow, your words brighten my hated existence. I revive! I breathe again.

MATILDE: Yes, we can still be happy. Let us fly from that cruel man as from the genii of evil. In a far-away land, unknown, penniless, but together, our happiness will be complete. Let us flee!

GRESSEY: Flee, never! You suggest something infamous. What a horrible idea. Impossible! (*Six o'clock strikes.*) Matilde, do you love me? Then farewell! (*Exit hastily.*)

(*In the final brief scenes, Gressey rushes to the garden, kills the colonel in a duel: he is the only one to have a loaded revolver, and he shoots him. Then Matilde joins him. The play ends with:*

GRESSEY: Matilde, you are free.

MATILDE: No, I am yours (*Falls into his arms*).

CURTAIN

W.K.J.

GERTRUDIS GÓMEZ DE AVELLANEDA
1814-1873   Cuba

"La Avellaneda," an amateur actress in Cuba, did not write plays until she went to Spain at the age of twenty-two. Then the thirteen plays she wrote, in verse as well as prose, were so successful that critics called her the greatest woman dramatist writing in Spanish. Among her finest works are the twelfth-century tragedy *Alfonso Munio* (1844), the Biblical play *Saúl* (1846), and *Bal-*

tasar (Belshazzar, 1858). *Baltasar,* a four-act play written in excellent verse that sometimes rises to great lyrical heights, is the love story of two Hebrew captives in Babylon. It won such commendations as Juan Valera's, "one of the most excellent productions of which modern dramatic literature can boast."

Doña Gertrudis came back to Cuba in 1859 to receive honors in a theatre named after her, but the death of her husband caused her to return to Spain. In 1910, in an attempt to revive the theater in independent Cuba, her comedy *La hija de las flores* (The Daughter of the Flowers, 1852), one of the gems of Spanish poetic drama, was revived in Havana, and enthusiastically received.

BELSHAZZAR

Characters

Elda, niece of Daniel
Ruben, in love with her
Joaquín, former King of Judea and grandfather of Ruben
Belshazzar, King of Babylon
Queen Nitocris, his mother
Neregel, his Minister

Pampered and unopposed, the Babylonian king is surfeited with pleasures and scorns the people he is supposed to govern. He has lost faith in God and man. When two Hebrew lovers, Ruben and Elda, dare to stand up for their rights and oppose his wishes, the king is for a moment roused to a new desire. But Elda will not accept his love and his disillusionment is bitter.

Act III

NEREGEL (*stopping the king as he is about to enter the harem*):
  Your Majesty!
KING: What is it?

NEREGEL: Your frightened subjects are agitated.

KING: Why?

NEREGEL: They say that Cyrus, in alliance with the Medes and other nations of the Orient, is marching against Babylon.

KING: And so you come to me with such absurd tales?

NEREGEL: The captives are the cause of it all.

KING: The captives?

NEREGEL: They assert—though I'm ashamed to mention it—that there exist some books or other that they carefully preserve, which clearly foretell the destruction of your kingdom. The common people are upset at such announcements, and I suspect that the discontented satraps play on their fears and anger.

KING: They're dreaming. All you need to do, Neregel, is wake them up.

NEREGEL: How?

KING: Tonight in the palace let there be served a splendid banquet to make the troublesome satraps forget their intrigues. Then tomorrow impose on the people . . .

NEREGEL: What, Your Majesty?

KING: A new tax.

NEREGEL: Order also the punishment of those malevolent captives. I shall gladly obey you.

KING: Tell me, how many gods have temples in Babylon?

NEREGEL: There are so many! The most sumptuous is the one consecrated to Belus.

KING: Yes, it cost a fortune, if I remember correctly, a sum that a hundred provinces could scarcely provide.

NEREGEL: That is true.

KING: It would cost far less to raise a few altars to that God of the Hebrews, and that would satisfy them.

NEREGEL (stepping back, frightened): But, Your Majesty! Do you believe in that God of the foreigners?

KING (ironically): Oh, absolutely! As much as I believe in any of our own gods.

NEREGEL: Your Majesty! We already have at least a hundred gods.

KING: Then we could put up with a hundred and one.

NEREGEL: Your immortal ancestors swore eternal war against the God of the Hebrews.

KING: My immortal ancestors did a lot of silly things.

NEREGEL: But I beg of you . . .

KING: I order that from now on the God of my beautiful slave girl share worship with the Caldean gods. Go and issue my decree!

NEREGEL: How horrible! (*Exit Neregel.*)

KING: Here she comes. Now she will see how completely she has triumphed.

(*Enter Elda.*)

In the ensuing scene, Elda tries to beg for the life of her lover, Ruben. The King, not letting her speak, talks of his love for her and announces that she is now freed. After he leaves to prepare the document, the courtier Rabsares brings in Joaquín and Ruben.

ELDA: My father!

JOAQUÍN: Beloved daughter! Am I dreaming? Do I really touch your head again? My daughter!

ELDA: Yes, father, yes! And Ruben! (*Extending her arms and approaching sweetheart.*)

RUBEN: Stop! Can I still call you by the holy name of betrothed?

ELDA (*with dignity*): I am alive. That proves I am true to you.

RUBEN (*falling at her feet and kissing her hands*): Forgive me!

ELDA: Ruben!

JOAQUÍN: Don't keep me in suspense. Tell me everything.

RUBEN: I can guess. The King has a noble nature. He is merciful. Isn't that it?

ELDA: "I want you to enjoy your triumph," he said only a moment ago, "and achieve your happiness."

JOAQUÍN: Of course! If he calls us here and gives you into our arms, could he later snatch you away from us?

RUBEN: Where is he? I want to throw myself joyfully at his feet.

ELDA: I am sure he intended to give us our freedom. But listen! Here he comes now.

JOAQUÍN: Oh, God, bestow Thy blessings on him!

RUBEN: And you, proud heart, restrain your animosity!

(*Enter Belshazzar carrying a document. Ruben approaches and kneels before him. At the same time, the muttering of the discontented subjects can be heard from the square.*)

KING: If fate does not decree that the lamb humble itself before the lion, still it makes the fierce king of the forest generous. (*He raises Ruben.*)

RUBEN: My Lord, my gratitude . . .

KING: Let us forget the past. I want only to remember that among the slaves I found a man, and from today on I make him second in my kingdom and first in my court! (*Gives him a scroll.*)

RUBEN: Your Majesty!

KING: And you, Joaquín, find yourself some quiet dwelling where you may rest after so many years of cruel sorrows, and I shall see that you have everything in abundance.

JOAQUÍN: I want nothing in the world, provided you give me my children. With them, you give me happiness and my heart forgets the former sorrows . . . (*Enter Neregel.*)

NEREGEL: Your Majesty!

KING: Why do the people rage?

NEREGEL: My Lord, they worship their old gods and protest your decree about a new god.

KING: Do they dare?

NEREGEL: And their anger increases because they have learned that two audacious men are in the palace, the younger of whom has committed a terrible crime against you.

ELDA (*running to Ruben as if to protect him*): Ruben!

JOAQUÍN: Oh, God!

NEREGEL: You hear them. They demand his blood.

JOAQUÍN: His blood?

KING: Let the doors be opened.

NEREGEL: Do you order? . . .

KING: Let the people come in. (*Neregel opens the door and a crowd enters the vestibule.*)

ELDA: (*worried and approaching the King*): My Lord!

JOAQUÍN: Elda!

RUBEN (*aside*): What is he saying?

KING: Today, O slave girl, I want the mantle of Semiramis to adorn you with new splendor.

JOAQUÍN: Your Majesty, that is impossible!

RUBEN: Is that the reason for your favors? Do you think that with this scroll you can buy my wife?

KING (*astonished*): What? Wife?

RUBEN: There is your infamous bribe! (*He tears the document and hurls it at the king's feet.*)

KING You! You!

JOAQUÍN: I fear Your Majesty does not know that Elda is already betrothed.

RUBEN: Yes, to me! I have no glory, no fortune, no other possession in the world. Do not deprive me of that love that is my existence! You, who are master of all the treasures of heaven, would not deprive a poor man of his only possession.

KING (*in a choked voice*): Are you not brother and sister?

ELDA: In my fear, I was too terrified to tell you the truth, My Lord. In your compassion, forgive my weakness. I bathe your feet with my tears.

JOAQUÍN (*also falling at the King's feet*): Be noble, great Belshazzar! Do not go back on your promises!

RUBEN (*at his feet*): Let not anger displace justice. Let your instinct of a man conquer the instinct of a despot.

KING: You are not brother and sister! You lied! In my illusion, I thought I had discovered noble souls. I sought to find truth in man! (*He utters a convulsive laugh. The others rise.*)

RUBEN: O King!

KING (*sarcastically*): Now you ask me to crown your triumph and let a servant and a slave girl mock my weakness!

ELDA: All I ask is justice. I ask you for my husband in the name of justice, of your glory, and of my God.

KING (*throwing her into the arms of a soldier*): Back to prison,
you vile slave! Among those people may your neck be bowed
under the yoke. In your shame may my mad illusions find
revenge!

JOAQUÍN (*attempting to defend the girl as soldiers try to take her
away*): No, barbarian!

RUBEN: You will have to trample over my corpse before you
dare carry out your impious threat. (*At this moment the
crowd pushes forward, filling the stairs. Their muttering
grows louder.*)

ELDA (*struggling desperately to free herself*): My Lord, do not
shame yourself before your subjects who are watching you.

RUBEN (*between Elda and the King*): Do not exhaust the patience of an unfortunate man.

KING (*angrily*): My subjects, your rage demands a victim. Take
him! (*He hurls Ruben toward the crowd who seize him with
angry cries and take him quickly away.*)

ELDA: Heaven!

JOAQUÍN: Stop them!

RUBEN: Ferocious mob, let me go!

JOAQUÍN: My children!

ELDA: My beloved!

NEREGEL: Destroy that infamous man and hurl his bloody remains into the square!

VOICES OF THE CROWD (*who have seized Ruben and are dragging
him away*): Death!

RUBEN: Father!

JOAQUÍN (*trying to reach him, but falling*): Take me with him!
Take me! (*Enter Queen Nitocris, who vainly tries to defend
the victims.*)

QUEEN: Gods of our people!

CURTAIN

W.K.J.

ROMÁN VIAL Y URETA
1833-1896   Chile

After the end of Romanticism, a printer from Valparaiso became one of Chile's outstanding dramatists of customs. Uneducated, but gifted with a keen ear for the language of the lower classes, Vial y Ureta dealt with current problems, especially those arising from the swelling influx of foreigners to the country. Besides *Choche y Bachicha* (George and the Italian), one of his best works was his one-act *Una votación popular* (A Popular Election, 1869), his first play. He was imitated by many of the Chilean local-color dramatists, including Luis Rodríguez (1838–1919), Juan Rafael Allende (1850–1909), and Antonio Espineira (1855–1907), the only university-educated dramatist among them.

A POPULAR ELECTION

On stage, Sergeant Beltrán of the Police and Corporal Poblete, somewhat drunk and smoking a cigarette.

POBLETE: Anybody who laughs by himself, my sergeant, is remembering his evil deeds. That's not my opinion, Sergeant Beltrán. That's the way the saying goes. So a person just repeats the saying and wonders, sir.

BELTRAN: Well! I'm laughing by myself because unfortunately I'm alone, and not seeing double, like you. (*He gestures to indicate that the corporal is drunk.*) Understand?

POBLETE: Yes, I understand, Sergeant Beltrán. You always insult me indirectly. And don't do it! But what I want to know is, why you laugh to yourself.

BELTRAN: That's obvious, Poblete. Because I saw you come staggering around the corner, hardly able to stand.

POBLETE: There come your subtle insults, Mr. Beltrán. You woke up with a mean disposition today! Are you going to tell me, or aren't you, why you're laughing?

BELTRAN: But I've already told you, man! Don't be a nuisance! Go to bed and you'll be better off.

POBLETE: There you go again! That's a personal insult, but I'll forgive it if you'll tell me why you were laughing.

BELTRAN: Come on, come on! I was laughing because we are winning the election. Now are you satisfied?

POBLETE: How could I be, sir, since that's not true? You don't fool me. I'm not as dumb as you think, my Sergeant.

BELTRAN: You couldn't be!

POBLETE: At it again! Didn't I visit the voting booth. Ask the captain if you don't believe me. He's tearing his hair because there are only Colorado votes in the ballot box (*Excitedly.*) But almost everybody in the company is Colorado, and there's no use trying to change them. We're winning, and there's nothing to be done about it. We of the opposition are winning.

BELTRAN: What's that? Do you mean you are in the Opposition Party, Poblete?

POBLETE: Of course, Sergeant. I've been in opposition for a long time. Did you think, Beltrán, that this heart of mine doesn't love my country and liberty?

BELTRAN: Of course you do. Of course. But I thought you were on the government side. Being for the government doesn't mean you can't be patriotic and liberal.

POBLETE: That's what you think, sir, because you are good and honorable. But the rest of the party—Well, I don't need to say anything more.

BELTRAN: But tell me, Poblete, about the honor and patriotism of your party.

POBLETE: Oh, sir, that's what you don't understand. In the party, the big guns are upright.

BELTRAN: Maybe they are, but I know they're scattering their pesos around.

POBLETE: So what, my sergeant? It's fine to be patriotic, and I'd be the last to say otherwise; but is that any reason to die of hunger? Why should I? I ask you. Just so those fine fellows that call us friends, that hold out their hands, without any

handouts, and who promise us this world and the next—
Well, when the voting is over, if I've ever got anything from
them, I don't remember it. Tell that to somebody else, Sergeant Beltrán.

BELGRAN: Let's get it straight. You sold out, Poblete?

POBLETE: Wait a minute, sir! What do you mean, sold out? I
haven't sold out to anybody, because a respectable man like
me doesn't just sell out, like that. To get a mere ten pesos for
a vote, do you call that selling out?

BELTRAN: You don't think that means anything? Selling your
conscience?

POBLETE: That's enough! I didn't sell my conscience, Mr. Sergeant. Just a vote, just a vote, do you understand? Would I
sell my conscience? Thank God, I can still call my soul my
own.

BELTRAN: Well, you were certainly badly paid, because my
Captain was paying twenty pesos, (*With emphasis*) not for
one's conscience, of course, but for one vote.

POBLETE (*with interest*): Are you telling me the truth, sergeant?

BELTRAN: Of course!

POBLETE: So you tell me the Liberals cheated me?

BELTRAN: That's what it looks like.

POBLETE: The rats! They stole ten pesos from me! At a time like
this? How right you were, sir, that those people haven't a
shred of patriotism or feeling.

BELTRAN: There's still time. Take advantage of your opportunity. Maybe later you won't be able to vote.

POBLETE: You're right, Sergeant. I'm going to look him up right
away. Our Captain is so good and generous! He wouldn't take
advantage of anybody. (*Exit, shouting*) Hurray for Captain
Carrión! Long live the government! (*The Sergeant follows
him.*)

END.

W.K.J.

A READING LIST

Readers who want to become acquainted with other examples of Latin American literature before 1888 will find material of interest in the following publications:

BIBLIOGRAPHIES

Hulet, Claude L., *Latin American Prose in English Translation* (Pan American Union, 1964)
———, *Latin American Poetry in English Translation* (Pan American Union, 1965)
Parks, George B. and Temple, Ruth Z., *The Literatures of the World in English Translation, a Bibliography, Vol. I: The Greek, Latin, and Romance Literatures* (Frederick Ungar, 1966)

INDIAN LITERATURES

The Book of Chilam Balam, tr. by Ralph L. Roys (Washington: Carnegie Institution of Washington, No. 438, 1933); also tr. by Alfredo Barrera V. and Sylvanus Morley (Washington: Carnegie Institution No. 585, 1949)
The Güegüence; a comedy drama in the Nahúatl-Spanish Dialect of Nicaragua, tr. by Daniel G. Brinton (Philadelphia: D.G. Brinton, 1883)
The Popol Vuh, the Mythic and Heroic Sagas of the Kichés of Central America, tr. by Lewis Spence (London: D. Nutt, 1908); also tr. by Delia Goetz and Sylvanus Morley (Univ. of Oklahoma Press, 1950)

POETRY

ARGENTINA

Campo, Estanislao, *Faust,* tr. by Walter Owen (Buenos Aires: Owen, 1943)

Hernández, José, *The Gaucho Martín Fierro*, tr. by Walter Owen (Farrar and Rinehart, 1936); First 26 cantos, tr. by Joseph Auslander in *Hispanic Notes and Monographs Series* (1932); see also Holmes, Henry A., *Martin Fierro, The Argentine Gaucho Epic* (Hispanic Institute, 1948)

CHILE

Ercilla, Alonso de, *The Araucaniad*, tr. by P. T. Manchester and C. N. Lancaster (Vanderbilt Univ. Press, 1945); First canto tr. by Walter Owen (Buenos Aires: Owen, 1945)

Oña, Pedro de, *Arauco Tamed*, tr. by C. N. Lancaster and P. T. Manchester (Univ. of New Mexico Press, 1948)

CUBA

Heredia, José María, *Selections from the Poetry of Heredia with Translations into English Verse*, tr. by James Kennedy (Havana: J. M. Eleizegui, 1844; London: Longmans, 1852)

Martí, José, *The America of Martí, Selected Writings*, tr. by Juan de Onís (New York: Noonday Press, 1953); *Tuya and Other Verses*, tr. by Cecil Charles (New York: Richardson, 1898)

MEXICO

Asbaje y Ramírez de Santillana ("Sor Juana Inés de la Cruz"), *The Pathless Grove, Sonnets*, tr. by Pauline Cook (Prairie City, Ill.: Decker Press, 1958); *The Tenth Muse*, tr. by Fanchon Royer (Paterson, N.Y.: St. Anthony Guild Press, 1952)

PROSE

Cox, Edward G., *A Reference Guide to the Literature of Travel, including Voyages, Geographical Descriptions, Adventure, Shipwreck, and Expeditions*, Vol. II: *The New World* (The Univ. of Washington Press, 1938)

The Hakluyt Society of London, beginning in 1847, pub-

lished many translations of works by New World travel-
ers: Cristóval de Acuña, Alvares Cabral, Columbus,
Núñez Cabeza de Vaca, Vázquez de Coronado, etc.
These translations are available in microcards
See Hulet, *Latin American Prose*, pp. 40-53; 64-83.

Bolton, Herbert E., ed., *Spanish Exploration in the South-
west, 1542-1706* (Scribners, 1916; Barnes and Noble,
1959)

Hammond, George P. and Agapito Rey, *Obregon's History
of 16th century Exploration in Western America* (Los
Angeles: Wetzel Pub. Co., 1928)

Hodge, F. W. and Lewis, T. H., *Spanish Explorers in the
Southern United States, 1528-1543* (Scribners, 1907)

Purchas, Samuel, *Purchas his Pilgrimes* (London: W.
Stansby, 1625) 4 vol. collection of colonial material

Wagner, Henry R., ed., *Spanish Voyages to the Northwest
Coast of America in the 16th Century* (San Francisco:
California Historical Society, 1929)

Columbus. Curtis, W. Eleroy, ed., *The Authentic Letters
of Columbus* (Chicago: José I. Rodrigues, 1895); also tr.
by Donald B. Clark (San Francisco: E. Grabhorn, 1924);
tr. by R. H. Major (London: Hakluyt Society, 1847,
1870); Morison, Samuel E., *Journals and Other Documents on the Life and Voyages of Columbus* (Heritage
Press, 1964)

Las Casas, Bartolomé. MacNutt, Francis A., *Las Casas, His
Life, His Apostolates, His Writings* (Putnam, 1908)

Ulloa, Antonio. Leonard, Irving A., *A Voyage to South
America by Antonio Ulloa* (Knopf, 1964)

ARGENTINA

Mármol, José, *Amalia*, tr. by Mary J. Serrano (Dutton,
1919; 1944)

Samiento, Domingo Faustino, *Facundo: Life in the Argentine Republic (Civilization and Barbarism)*, tr. by Mrs.
Horace Mann (N.Y.: Hafner, 1960; Collier, 1961);
Grummon, Stuart S., *A Sarmiento Anthology* (Princeton Univ. Press, 1948)

CHILE

Alvarado, Pedro de. Kelly, John E., *Pedro de Alvarado, Conquistador of Chile* (Princeton Univ. Press, 1932)

Blest Gana, Alberto, *Martín Rivas*, tr. by Mrs. Charles Whitham (London: Chapman and Hall, 1916; Knopf, 1918)

COLOMBIA

Isaacs, Jorge, *María, a South American Romance*, tr. by Rollo Ogden (Harper, 1890; 1918; 1925)

CUBA

Villaverde, Cirilo, *The Quadroon or Cecilia Valdes*, tr. by Mariano J. Lorente (Boston: L. C. Page, 1935); tr. by Sydney G. Gest (Vantage Press, 1962)

DOMINICAN REPUBLIC

Galván, Manuel de Jesús, *The Cross and the Sword*, tr. from *Enriquillo* by Robert Graves (Univ. of Indiana Press, 1954)

MEXICO

Los Conquistadores: First Person Accounts of the Conquerors of Mexico, tr. by Patricia de Fuentes (Orion Press, 1963)

Altamirano, Ignacio Manuel, *Christmas in the Mountains*, tr. by Harvey L. Johnson (Gainesville: Univ. of Florida Press, 1961); *El Zarco the Bandit*, tr. by Mary Allt (New York: Duches; London: Folio Society, 1957)

Benavente, Fray Toribio de ("Motolinía"), *Motolinía's History of the Indians of New Spain*, tr. by Francis B. Steck (Washington: Academy of American Franciscan History, 1951)

Calderón de la Barca, Señora Frances E., *Life in Mexico During a Residence of Two Years in That Country*, tr. anon. (Boston: Little, Brown, 1843; London: Simms and McIntyre, 1953)

Cervantes de Salazar, Francisco, *Life in Mexico . . . as*

Described in the Dialogues, tr. by M. L. B. Shepard
(Univ. of Texas Press, 1953)

Cienza de León, Pedro, *The Seventeen Years of Travel by
Peter de Cienza Through the Mighty Kingdom of Peru*,
tr. by Capt. John Stevens (London, 1709; 1711); tr. by
Sir Clements R. Markham in *Hakluyt*, Series I, xxxiii
(London, 1864), and Series II, liv (London, 1913)

Clavijero, Francisco Javier, *The History of Lower California*, tr. by Sarah E. Lake and A. A. Gray (Stanford
Univ. Press, 1937)

Cortés, Hernán, *Five Letters of Relation*, tr. by Francis A.
MacNutt (Putnam, 1908; Glendale, Calif.: Clark, 1941;
Grosset and Dunlap, [Paperback], 1960)

Díaz del Castillo, Bernal, *The True History of the Conquest of New Spain*, 5 vols., tr. by Alfred P. Maudslay
(London: Hakluyt Society, 1908-1916); many other versions, including paperback (Grove, 1958)

Fernández de Lizardi, José Joaquín, *The Itching Parrot*, tr.
by Katherine A. Porter (Doubleday, 1942)

Landa, Diego de, *Yucatan Before and After the Conquest*,
tr. by W. Gates (Baltimore: Maya Society, 1937); also
tr. by Alfred M. Tozzer in *Peabody Museum of American
Archaeology and Ethnology*, vol. 18-19, No. 1 (Harvard
Univ. Press, 1941)

López de Gómara, Francisco (Cortés's secretary), *The Pleasant Historie of the Conquest of Weast India* (London:
Bynnerman, 1578; N.Y.: Scholars' Facsimiles, 1940);
also tr. by Lesley B. Simpson, *The Life of the Conqueror
of Mexico* (Univ. of California Press, 1963)

Sahagún, Fray Bernardino de, *Florentine Codex*, tr. by
Arthur Anderson and Charles Dibble (Univ. of Wash-
ington Press, 1950-59); *History of Ancient Mexico*, tr. by
Fanny Bandelier (Nashville: Fisk Univ. Press, 1932)

Serra, Padre Junípero. *Writings*, 4 vols., tr. by Antonine
Tibesar (Washington: Academy of American Franciscan
History, 1956-7)

Sigüenza y Góngora, Carlos de, *The Misfortunes of Alonso*

Ramírez, tr. by Edwin W. Pleasants (Long Branch, N.J.;
Monmouth College Press, 1962)

Solís y Rivadaneyra, Antonio de, *History of the Conquest
of Mexico by the Mexicans*, 3 vols., tr. by Thomas Town-
send (London: T. Woodward, 1724, 1738, 1753, etc.)

PERU

Acosta, José de, *The Naturall and Morall Historie of the
East and West Indies*, tr. by E. Grimestone (London,
1604)

Garcilaso de la Vega, El Inca, *The Florida of the Incas, a
history of Hernando de Soto*, tr. by John Grier Varner
and Jeannette J. Varner (Univ. of Texas Press, 1951);
First Part of the Royal Commentaries of the Yncas, 2
vols., tr. by Sir Clements R. Markham, in *Hakluyt*, Series
I, xli and xlv (London, 1869-71); also tr. by María Jolas
(Orion, 1961)

Palma, Ricardo, *The Knight of the Cape and Thirty-Seven
other Selections from the Tradiciones Peruanas*, tr. by
Harriet de Onís (Knopf, 1945)

Pizarro, Pedro, *History of the Discovery and Conquest of
Peru*, 2 vols., tr. by Philip A. Means (New York: Cortés
Society, 1921)

Sarmiento de Gamboa, Pedro. *History of the Incas*, tr. by
Sir Clements R. Markham, in *Hakluyt*, Series II, xxii
(London, 1907)

VENEZUELA

Bolívar, Simón. Lecuna, Vicente, *Selected Writings of
Bolívar* (New York: Colonial Press, 1951)

DRAMA

CUBA

Gómez de Avellaneda, Gertrudis, *Belshazzar*, tr. by W. E.
Burbank (London: Stevens and Brown; San Francisco:
Roberts, 1914); also in *Poet Lore*, XVII (Summer, 1906)

GUATEMALA

The Shepherds Play of the Prodigal Son, tr. by George C.
Barker (Univ. of California Press; Cambridge Univ.
Press, 1953)

MEXICO

Ruiz de Alarcón, Juan, *The Lying Lover or the Ladies'
Friendship,* adapted by Sir Richard Steele (London:
E. Lintott, 1704); also *Truth Suspected,* tr. by Julio del
Toro and Robert V. Finney, in *Poet Lore,* XXX, 4
(1927); also tr. by Robt. C. Ryan, in *Spanish Drama*
(Bantam Books, 1962)

INDEX

Authors and Major Works

Includes authors mentioned in the Introduction but whose works are not translated. Titles are given in Spanish (in addition to the English) only when the title begins with a different letter from that of the translation.